THE RANDOM HOUSE ACHIEVEMENT PROGRAM IN LITERATURE

READING AND LITERATURE CONSULTANTS

TOM WOLPERT · LEE BENNETT HOPKINS

REVIEWERS

MEI-LING SHIROISHI ● **JACKIE MATTHEWS**

Library-Media Specialist *Curriculum Supervisor*
Chehalem Elementary School *Hillsborough County Schools*
Beaverton, Oregon *Tampa, Florida*

Project Editor: Michael A. Ross
Senior Manufacturing Associate: Catherine Bokman
Design and Production: Dimensions and Directions, Ltd.
Composition: Grafacon, Inc.
Cover Photo: Larry Lefever, Grant Heilman, Inc.
Photo Research: Helena Frost

ART AND PHOTO CREDIT LIST:

2, Frost Publishing Group, Ltd.; **3,** Barry Runk, Grant Heilman, Inc.; **4,** Lynn McLaren, Photo Researchers, Inc.; **7, 11,** Jan Palmer; **13,** Bert Dodson; **27,** Sal Murdocca; **28,** G. Palmer, United Nations; **30,** Art Stein, Photo Researchers, Inc.; **31,** Andy Bernhaut, Photo Researchers, Inc.; **35, 39,** John Lawn; **44,** Bert Dodson; **54,** Dick Smolinski; **60,** Sandra Speidel; **67, 73,** Hal Frenck; **75,** Barbara Rios, Photo Researchers, Inc.; **76,** Michelle A. Noiset; **80, 83,** Simon Galkin; **101,** John Lawn; **103,** Simon Galkin; **104,** Helena Frost, Frost Publishing Group, Ltd.; **107,** Simon Galkin; **136,** Sal Murdocca; **140,** Photo Researchers, Inc.; **142–143,** Simon Galkin; **144, 146,** Bob Baxter; **149, 156, 164,** Simon Galkin; **170,** R. Grist, United Nations; **176,** Jan Palmer; **180,** Larry B. Jennings, Photo Researchers, Inc.; **184,** Toni Angermayer, Photo Reseachers, Inc.; **187,** John Dominis, Life Magazine; **191,** Robert Baxter; **197,** Ron Church, Photo Researchers, Inc.; **202,** Phyllis Stevens, Frost Publishing Group, Ltd.; **203,** Jan Palmer; **208–275,** Museum of Modern Art.

Manufactured in the United States of America   ISBN 676-39734-4   89HL543

ACKNOWLEDGMENTS

Grateful acknowledgment is made to the following authors, agents and publishers for permission to use copyrighted materials:

Atheneum Publishers, Inc. for Lilian Moore, "Sunset" from the collection SOMETHING NEW BEGINS. Copyright © 1982 by Lilian Moore. Reprinted with the permission of Atheneum Publishers, Inc. Myra Cohn Livingston, "74th Street" from THE MALIBU AND OTHER POEMS. Copyright © 1972 by Myra Cohn Livingston (A Margaret K. McElderry Book). Reprinted with permission of Atheneum Publishers, Inc.

BRIDGE MAGAZINE for "Grandfather" by James Lim. From BRIDGE MAGAZINE, v. 3, #4, February 1975. Reprinted by permission of the editor of BRIDGE MAGAZINE.

Hallie Burnett: © 1953 by STORY MAGAZINE, "Polar Night" by Norah Burke. Reprinted by permission of Hallie Burnett.

Edmund Carpenter for "Two Songs—Uvavnuk." Reprinted by permission of Edmund Carpenter.

Miriam Cox, "Pygmalion and Galatea" from THE MAGIC AND THE SWORD by Miriam Cox. Copyright © 1960, 1956 by Harper & Row, Publishers, Inc. "Urashima" from THE THREE TREASURES by Miriam Cox. Copyright © 1964 by Harper & Row, Publishers, Inc.

Discovery Books for "Pride of Lion" from URBAN RIVER by Margaret Tsuda. Discovery Books. Copyright 1976 by Margaret Tsuda.

Dodd, Mead and Company for "How Whirlwind Saved Her Cub" reprinted by permission of Dodd, Mead & Company from BUFFALO WOMAN by Dorothy M. Johnson. Copyright © 1977 by Dorothy M. Johnson.

Doubleday & Company for "The Birds" from KISS ME AGAIN, STRANGER by Daphne du Maurier. Copyright 1952 by Daphne du Maurier. Reprinted by permission of Doubleday & Company.

E. P. Dutton, Inc. for "A Special Jujitsu" from A PRECOCIOUS AUTOBIOGRAPHY by Yevgeny Yevtushenko, translated by Andrew R. MacAndrew. English translation copyright © 1963 by E. P. Dutton. Reprinted by permission of the publisher, E. P. Dutton, a division of New American Library.

Blanche C. Gregory, Inc.: "The Sin of Madame Phloi" by Lilian Jackson Braun reprinted by permission of the author and Blanche C. Gregory, Inc. Copyright 1962 by Davis Publications. First published in ELLERY QUEEN'S MYSTERY MAGAZINE.

Harcourt Brace Jovanovich, Inc. for "What Shall He Tell That Son?" from THE PEOPLE, YES by Carl Sandburg, copyright 1936 by Harcourt Brace Jovanovich, Inc., renewed 1964 by Carl Sandburg. Reprinted by permission of the publisher. "I Remember Mama" Copyright 1944, 1945 by John van Druten; renewed 1973 by Carter Lodge, Executor of the Estate of John van Druten. Reprinted by permission of Harcourt Brace Jovanovich, Inc.

Harper & Row, Publishers, Inc. for Chapter 2 from OLD YELLER by Fred Gipson. Copyright © 1956 by Fred Gipson. "How the World Was Made—Cheyenne" from AMERICAN INDIAN MYTHOLOGY by Alice Marriott and Carol K. Rachlin (Thomas Y. Crowell) Copyright © 1968 by Alice Marriott and Carol K. Rachlin. Chapter 11 from TO KILL A MOCKINGBIRD by Harper Lee. Copyright © 1960 by Harper Lee. Text of "The Man Who Disappeared . . . into Thin Air" from INTO THE UNKNOWN: Nine Astounding Stories by Stephen Mooser. (J. B. Lippincott) Copyright © 1980 by Stephen Mooser. Pp. 121–132 from FIFTH CHINESE DAUGHTER by Jade Snow Wong. Copyright 1945, 1948, 1950 by Jade Snow Wong. All reprinted by permission of Harper & Row, Publishers, Inc.

HARPER'S MAGAZINE for "The New Kid" by Murray Heyert. Copyright © 1944 by HARPER'S MAGAZINE. All rights reserved. Reprinted from the June 1944 issue by special permission.

Laurence Hill & Company for "Last Cover" from BEST NATURE STORIES by Jane and Paul Annixter © 1974. Published by Laurence Hill & Company, Inc., Westport, Ct.

Holt, Rinehart & Winston, Inc. for "Acquainted With the Night" from THE POETRY OF ROBERT FROST edited by Edward Connery Lathem. Copyright 1928, © 1969 by Holt, Rinehart & Winston. Copyright © 1956 by Robert Frost. Reprinted by permission of Holt, Rinehart & Winston, Publishers.

Houghton Mifflin Company and George Allen & Unwin, Ltd. for "An Unexpected Party" and "Thror's Map" from THE HOBBIT by J. R. R. Tolkien. Copyright © 1966 by J. R. R. Tolkien. Reprinted by permission of Houghton Mifflin Company and George Allen & Unwin (Publishers) Ltd.

TABLE OF CONTENTS

ONE WHO KNOWS NOTHING IS CONFIDENT IN EVERYTHING.

I AM PART OF ALL THAT I HAVE MET.

WHAT WE FRANKLY GIVE, FOREVER IS OUR OWN.

TO THE STUDENT

We are born into a world that we know nothing about. As we grow, we begin to learn about the immediate world that surrounds us and the world of ideas, experiences, and people that exists beyond our reach. Sometimes we are fortunate to meet a person who can share experiences with us. But what about those ideas and experiences that we cannot touch or hear about? How do we know about the worlds of the past and the dreams of the future? Literature is the answer. Literature opens the door to new worlds.

As you read this book many authors will begin to share their worlds with you. Not only what they say, but how they say it, is important. You will experience new ideas . . . new thoughts. You will find your emotions being excited as you cry or laugh at what others have to share.

The beauty of all this is that all you have to do is read. You don't have to leave your world to discover the excitement of living in new and different places. Between the pages of a book you can discover loneliness and happiness; young life and old life; frustration and inspiration; mystery and intrigue; the real and the make-believe. All of this is yours to explore by reading literature.

Sunset

Lilian Moore

There's dazzle
   in the western sky,
colors spill and
   run.
The pond mouth
lies open
   greedy
for the last drop
of
melting
sun.

A word to the wise is sufficient.

Driving to Town Late to Mail a Letter

Robert Bly

It is a cold and snowy night. The main street is deserted.
The only things moving are swirls of snow.
As I lift the mailbox door, I feel its cold iron.
There is a privacy I love in this snowy night.
Driving around, I will waste more time.

LOCKED IN

INGEMAR GUSTAFSON
translated by MAY SWENSON

All my life I lived in a cocoanut.
It was cramped and dark.
Especially in the morning when I had to shave.
But what pained me most was that I had no way
to get into touch with the outside world.
If no one out there happened to find the cocoanut,
if no one cracked it, then I was doomed
to live all my life in the nut, and maybe even die there.
I died in the cocoanut.
A couple of years later they found the cocoanut,
cracked it, and found me shrunk and crumpled inside.
"What an accident!"
"If only we had found it earlier . . ."
"Then maybe we could have saved him."
"Maybe there are more of them locked in like that . . ."
"Whom we might be able to save,"
they said, and started knocking to pieces
every cocoanut within reach.
No use! Meaningless! A waste of time!
A person who chooses to live in a cocoanut!
Such a nut is one in a million!
But I have a brother-in-law who
lives in an
acorn

ALONE

Edgar Allan Poe

From childhood's hour I have not been
As others were—I have not seen
As others saw—I could not bring
My passions from a common spring.
From the same source I have not taken
My sorrow; I could not awaken
My heart to joy at the same tone;
And all I lov'd, *I* lov'd alone.
Then—in my childhood—in the dawn
Of a most stormy life—was drawn
From ev'ry depth of good and ill
The mystery which binds me still:
From the torrent, or the fountain,
From the red cliff of the mountain,
From the sun that 'round me roll'd
In its autumn tint of gold—
From the lightning in the sky
As it pass'd me flying by—
From the thunder and the storm,
And the cloud that took the form
(When the rest of Heaven was blue)
Of a demon in my view.

Last Cover

Paul Annixter

I'm not sure I can tell you what you want to know about my brother; but everything about the pet fox is important, so I'll tell all that from the beginning.

It goes back to a winter afternoon after I'd hunted the woods all day for a sign of our lost pet. I remember the way my mother looked up as I came into the kitchen. Without my speaking, she knew what had happened. For six hours I had walked, reading signs, looking for a delicate print in the damp soil or even a hair that might have told of a red fox passing that way—but I had found nothing.

"Did you go up in the foothills?" Mom asked.

I nodded. My face was stiff from held-back tears. My brother, Colin, who was going on twelve, got it all from one look at me and went into a heartbroken, almost silent, crying.

Three weeks before, Bandit, the pet fox Colin and I had raised from a tiny kit, had disappeared, and not even a rumor had been heard of him since.

"He'd have had to go off soon anyway," Mom comforted. "A big, lolloping fellow like him, he's got to live his life same as us. But he may come back. That fox set a lot of store by you boys in spite of his wild ways."

"He set a lot of store by our food, anyway," Father said. He sat in a chair by the kitchen window, mending a piece of harness. "We'll be seeing a lot more of that fellow, never fear. That fox learned to pine for table scraps and young chickens. He was getting to be an egg thief, too, and he's not likely to forget that."

"That was only pranking when he was little," Colin said desperately.

From the first, the tame fox had made tension in the family. It was Father who said we'd better name him Bandit, after he'd made away with his first young chicken.

"Maybe you know," Father said shortly. "But when an animal turns to egg sucking, he's usually incurable. He'd better not come pranking around my chicken run again."

It was late February, and I remember the bleak, dead cold that had set in, cold that was a rare thing for our Carolina hills. Flocks of sparrows and snowbirds had appeared, to peck hungrily at all that the pigs and chickens didn't eat.

"This one's a killer," Father would say of a morning, looking out at the whitened barn roof. "This one will make the shoats squeal."

A fire snapped all day in our cookstove and another in the stone fireplace in the living room, but still

5

the farmhouse was never warm. The leafless woods were bleak and empty, and I spoke of that to Father when I came back from my search.

"It's always a sad time in the woods when the seven sleepers are under cover," he said.

"What sleepers are they?" I asked. Father was full of woods lore.

"Why, all the animals that have got sense enough to hole up and stay hid in weather like this. Let's see, how was it the old rhyme named them?

> Surly bear and sooty bat,
> Brown chuck and masked coon
> Chippy-munk and sly skunk,
> And all the mouses
> 'Cept in men's houses.

"And man would have joined them and made it eight, Granther Yeary always said, if he'd had a little more sense."

"I was wondering if the red fox mightn't make it eight," Mom said.

Father shook his head. "Late winter's a high time for foxes. Time when they're out deviling, not sleeping."

My chest felt hollow. I wanted to cry like Colin over our lost fox, but at fourteen a boy doesn't cry. Colin had squatted down on the floor and got out his small hammer and nails to start another new frame for a new picture. Maybe then he'd make a drawing for the frame and be able to forget his misery. It had been that way with him since he was five.

I thought of the new dress Mom had brought home a few days before in a heavy cardboard box. That box

cover would be fine for Colin to draw on. I spoke of it, and Mom's glance thanked me as she went to get it. She and I worried a lot about Colin. He was small for his age, delicate and blond, his hair much lighter and softer than mine, his eyes deep and wide and blue. He was often sick, and I knew the fear Mom had that he might be predestined. I'm just ordinary, like Father. I'm the sort of stuff that can take it—tough and strong—but Colin was always sort of special.

Mom lighted the lamp. Colin began cutting his white cardboard carefully, fitting it into his frame. Father's sharp glance turned on him now and again.

"There goes the boy making another frame before there's a picture for it," he said. "It's too much like cutting out a man's suit for a fellow that's say, twelve years old. Who knows whether he'll grow into it?"

Mom was into him then, quick. "Not a single frame of Colin's has ever gone to waste. The boy has real talent, Sumter, and it's time you realized it."

"Of course he has," Father said. "All kids have 'em. But they get over 'em."

"It isn't the pox we're talking of," Mom sniffed.

"In a way it is. Ever since you started talking up Colin's art, I've had an invalid for help around the place."

Father wasn't as hard as he made out, I knew, but he had to hold a balance against all Mom's frothing. For him the thing was the land and all that pertained to it. I was following in Father's footsteps, true to form, but Colin threatened to break the family tradition with his leaning toward art,

with Mom "aiding and abetting him," as Father liked to put it. For the past two years she had had dreams of my brother becoming a real artist and going away to the city to study.

It wasn't that Father had no understanding of such things. I could remember, through the years, Colin lying on his stomach in the front room making pencil sketches, and how a good drawing would catch Father's eye halfway across the room; and how he would sometimes gather up two or three of them to study, frowning and muttering, one hand in his beard, while a great pride rose in Colin, and in me too. Most of Colin's drawings were of the woods and wild things, and there Father was a master critic. He made out to scorn what seemed to him a passive "white-livered" interpretation of nature through brush and pencil instead of rod and rifle.

At supper that night, Colin could scarcely eat. Ever since he'd been able to walk, my brother had had a growing love of wild things; but Bandit had been like his very own, a gift of the woods. One afternoon a year and a half before, Father and Laban Small had been running a vixen through the hills with their dogs. With the last of her strength the she-fox had made for her den, not far from our house. The dogs had overtaken her and killed her just before she reached it. When Father and Laban came up, they'd found Colin crouched nearby holding her cub in his arms.

Father had been for killing the cub, which was still too young to shift for itself, but Colin's grief had brought Mom into it. We'd taken the young fox into the kitchen, all of us, except Father, gone a bit silly over the little thing. Colin had held it in his arms and fed it warm milk from a spoon.

"Watch out with all your soft ways," Father had warned, standing in the doorway. "You'll make too much of him. Remember, you can't make a dog out of a fox. Half of that little critter has to love, but the other half is a wild hunter. You boys will mean a whole lot to him while he's kit, but there'll come a day when you won't mean a thing to him, and he'll leave you shorn."

For two weeks after that, Colin had nursed the cub, weaning it from milk to bits of meat. For a year they were always together. The cub grew fast. It was soon following Colin and me about the barnyard. It turned out to be a patch fox, with a saddle of darker fur across its shoulders.

I haven't the words to tell you what the fox meant to us. It was far more wonderful owning him than owning any dog. There was something rare and secret, like the spirit of the woods about him; and back of his calm, straw-gold eyes was the sense of a brain the equal of a man's. The fox became Colin's whole life.

Each day, going and coming from school, Colin and I took long side trips through the woods, looking for Bandit. Wild things' memories were short, we knew; we'd have to find him soon, or the old bond would be broken.

Ever since I was ten I'd been allowed to hunt with Father, so I was good at reading signs. But, in a way, Colin knew more about the woods and wild things than Father or me. What came to me from long observation, Colin seemed to know by instinct.

It was Colin who felt out, like an Indian, the stretch of woods where Bandit had his den, who found the first slim, small fox-print in the damp earth. And then, on an afternoon in March, we saw him. I remember the day well, the racing clouds, the wind rattling the tops of the pine trees and swaying the Spanish moss. Bandit had just come out of a clump of laurel; in the maze of leaves behind him we caught a glimpse of a slim red vixen, so we knew he had found a mate. She melted from sight like a shadow, but Bandit turned to watch us, his mouth open, his tongue lolling as he smiled his old foxy smile. On his thin chops, I saw a telltale chicken feather.

Colin moved silently forward, his movements so quiet and casual he seemed to be standing still. He called Bandit's name, and the fox held his ground, drawn to us with all his senses. For a few moments he let Colin actually put an arm about him. It was then I knew that he loved us still, for all of Father's warnings. He really loved us back, with a fierce, secret love no tame thing ever gave. But the urge of his life just then was toward his new mate. Suddenly, he whirled about and disappeared in the laurels.

Colin looked at me with glowing eyes. "We haven't really lost him, Stan. When he gets through with his spring sparking he may come back. But we've got to show ourselves to him a lot, so he won't forget."

"It's a go," I said.

"Promise not to say a word to Father," Colin said, and I agreed. For I knew by the chicken feather that Bandit had been up to no good.

A week later the woods were budding, and the thickets were rustling with all manner of wild things scurrying on the love scent. Colin managed to get a glimpse of Bandit every few days. He couldn't get close though, for the spring running was a lot more important to a fox than any human beings were.

Every now and then Colin got out his framed box cover and looked at it, but he never drew anything on it; he never even picked up his pencil. I remember wondering if what Father had said about framing a picture before you had one had spoiled something for him.

I was helping Father with the planting now, but Colin managed to be in the woods every day. By degrees, he learned Bandit's range, where he drank and rested, and where he was likely to be according to the time of day. One day he told me how he had petted Bandit again, and how they had walked together a long way in the woods. All this time we had kept his secret from Father.

As summer came on, Bandit began to live up to the prediction Father had made. Accustomed to human beings he moved without fear about the scattered farms of the region, raiding barns and hen runs that other foxes wouldn't have dared go near. And he taught his wild mate to do the same. Almost every night they got into some poultry house, and by late June, Bandit was not only killing chickens and ducks but feeding on eggs and young chicks whenever he got the chance.

Stories of his doings came to us from many sources, for he was still easily recognized by the dark patch on his shoulders. Many a farmer took a shot at him as he fled, and some of them set out on his trail with dogs, but they always returned home without even sighting him. Bandit was familiar with all the dogs in the region, and he knew a hundred tricks to confound them. He got a reputation that year beyond that of any fox our

hills had known. His confidence grew, and he gave up wild hunting altogether and lived entirely off the poultry farmers. By September, the hill farmers banded together to hunt him down.

It was Father who brought home that news one night. All time-honored rules of the fox chase were to be broken in this hunt; if the dogs couldn't bring Bandit down, he was to be shot on sight. I was stricken and furious. I remember the misery of Colin's face in the lamplight. Father, who took pride in all the ritual of the hunt, had refused to be a party to such an affair, though in justice he could do nothing but sanction any sort of hunt; for Bandit, as old Sam Wetherwax put it, had been "purely getting in the Lord's hair."

The hunt began next morning, and it was the biggest turnout our hills had known. There were at least twenty mounted men in the party and as many dogs. Father and I were working in the lower field as they passed along the river road. Most of the hunters carried rifles, and they looked ugly.

Twice during the morning I went up to the house to find Colin, but he was nowhere around. As we worked, Father and I could follow the progress of the hunt by the distant hound music on the breeze. We could tell just where the hunters first caught sight of the fox and where Bandit was leading the dogs during the first hour. We knew as well as if we'd seen it how Bandit roused another fox along Turkey Branch and forced it to run for him, and how the dogs swept after it

9

for twenty minutes before they sensed their mistake.

Noon came, and Colin had not come in to eat. After dinner Father didn't go back to the field. He moped about, listening to the hound talk. He didn't like what was on any more than I did, and now and again I caught his smile of satisfaction when we heard the broken, angry notes of the hunting horn, telling that the dogs had lost the trail or had run another fox.

I was restless, and I went up into the hills in midafternoon. I ranged the woods for miles, thinking all the time of Colin. Time lost all meaning for me, and the short day was nearing an end, when I heard the horn talking again, telling that the fox had put over another trick. All day he had deviled the dogs and mocked the hunters. This new trick and the coming night would work to save him. I was wildly glad, as I moved down toward Turkey Branch and stood listening for a time by the deep, shaded pool where for years we boys had gone swimming, sailed boats, and dreamed summer dreams.

Suddenly, out of the corner of my eye, I saw the sharp ears and thin, pointed mask of a fox—in the water almost beneath me. It was Bandit, craftily submerged there, all but his head, resting in the cool water of the pool and the shadow of the two big beeches that spread above it. He must have run forty miles or more since morning. And he must have hidden in this place before. His knowing, crafty mask blended perfectly with the shadows and a mass of drift and branches that had collected by the

bank of the pool. He was so still that a pair of thrushes flew up from the spot as I came up, not knowing he was there.

Bandit's bright, harried eyes were looking right at me. But I did not look at him direct. Some woods instinct, swifter than thought, kept me from it. So he and I met as in another world, indirectly, with feeling but without sign or greeting.

Suddenly I saw that Colin was standing almost beside me. Silently as a water snake, he had come out of the bushes and stood there. Our eyes met, and a quick and secret smile passed between us. It was a rare moment in which I really "met" my brother, when something of his essence flowed into me, and I knew all of him. I've never lost it since.

My eyes still turned from the fox, my heart pounding, I moved quietly away, and Colin moved with me. We whistled softly as we went, pretending to busy ourselves along the bank of the stream. There was magic in it, as if by will we wove a web of protection about the fox, a ring-pass-not that none might penetrate. It was so, too, we felt, in the brain of Bandit, and that doubled the charm. To us he was still our little pet that we had carried about in our arms on countless summer afternoons.

Two hundred yards upstream, we stopped beside slim, fresh tracks in the mud where Bandit had entered the branch. The tracks angled upstream. But in the water the wily creature had turned down.

We climbed the far bank to wait, and Colin told me how Bandit's secret had been his secret ever since an afternoon three months before, when he'd watched the fox swim downstream to hide in the deep pool. Today he'd waited on the bank, feeling that Bandit, hard pressed by the dogs, might again seek the pool for sanctuary.

We looked back once as we turned homeward. He still had not moved. We didn't know until later that he was killed that same night by a chance hunter, as he crept out from his hiding place.

That evening Colin worked a long time on his framed box cover that had lain about the house untouched all summer. He kept at it all the next day too. I had never seen him work so hard. I seemed to sense in the air the feeling he was putting into it, how he was *believing* his picture into being. It was evening before he finished it. Without a word he handed it to Father. Mom and I went and looked over his shoulder.

It was a delicate and intricate pencil drawing of the deep branch pool; and there was Bandit's head and watching, fear-filled eyes hiding there amid the leaves and shadows, woven craftily into the maze of twigs and branches, as if by nature's art itself. Hardly a fox there at all, but the place where he was—or should have been. I recognized it instantly, but Mom gave a sort of incredulous sniff.

"I'll declare," she said, "it's mazy as a puzzle. It just looks like a lot of sticks and leaves to me."

Long minutes of study passed before Father's eye picked out the picture's secret, as few men's could have done. I laid that to Father's being a born hunter. That was a picture that might have been done especially for him. In fact, I guess it was.

Finally he turned to Colin with his deep, slow smile. "So that's how Bandit fooled them all," he said. He sat holding the picture with a sort of tenderness for a long time, while we glowed in the warmth of the shared secret. That was Colin's moment. Colin's art stopped being a pox to Father right there. And later, when the time came for Colin to go to art school, it was Father who was his solid backer.

OLD YELLER

Fred Gipson

The novel Old Yeller *is set in Texas in the 1860's. It tells the story of the friendship between 14-year-old Travis and his dog. When the selection below opens, Travis' father has just left home for several months to sell cattle in Kansas. Travis, as the "man of the house," is now responsible for taking care of his mother and five-year-old brother Arliss.*

It was the next morning when the big yeller dog came.

I found him at daylight when Mama told me to step out to the dog run and cut down a side of middling meat hanging to the pole rafters.

The minute I opened the door and looked up, I saw that the meat was gone. It had been tied to the rafter with bear-grass blades braided together for string. Now nothing was left hanging to the pole but the frazzled ends of the snapped blades.

I looked down then. At the same instant, a dog rose from where he'd been curled up on the ground beside the barrel that held our cornmeal. He was a big ugly slick-haired yeller dog. One short ear had been chewed clear off and his tail had been bobbed so close to his rump that there was hardly stub enough left to wag. But the most noticeable thing to me about him was how thin and starved looking he was, all but for his belly. His belly was swelled up as tight and round as a pumpkin.

It wasn't hard to tell how come that belly was so full. All I had to do was look at the piece of curled-up rind lying in the dirt beside him, with all the meat gnawed off. That side of meat had been a big one, but now there wasn't enough meat left on the rind to interest a pack rat.

Well, to lose the only meat we had left from last winter's hog butchering was bad enough. But what made me even madder was the way the dog acted. He didn't even have the manners to feel ashamed of what he'd done. He rose to his feet, stretched, yawned, then came romping toward me, wiggling that stub tail and yelling *Yow! Yow! Yow!* Just like he belonged there and I was his best friend.

"Why, you thieving rascal!" I shouted and kicked at him as hard as I could.

He ducked, just in time, so that I missed him by a hair. But nobody could have told I missed, after the way he fell over on the ground and lay there, with his belly up and his four feet in the air, squawling and bellering at the top of his voice. From the racket he made, you'd have thought I had a club and was breaking every bone in his body.

Mama came running to stick her head through the door and say, "What on earth, Travis?"

"Why, this old stray dog has come and eaten our middling meat clear up," I said.

I aimed another kick at him. He was quick and rolled out of reach again, just in time, then fell back to the ground and lay there, yelling louder than ever.

Then out came Little Arliss. He was naked, like he always slept in the summer. He was hollering "A dog! A dog!" He ran past me and fell on the dog and petted him till he quit howling, then turned on me, fighting mad.

"You quit kicking my dog!" he yelled fiercely. "You kick my dog, and I'll wear you to a frazzle!"

The battling stick that Mama used to beat the dirt out of clothes when she washed stood leaning against the wall. Now, Little Arliss grabbed it up in both hands and came at me, swinging.

It was such a surprise move, Little Arliss making fight at me that way, that I just stood there with my mouth open and let him clout me a good one before I thought to move. Then Mama stepped in and took the stick away from him.

Arliss turned on her, ready to fight with his bare fists. Then he decided against it and ran and put his arms around the big dog's neck. He began to yell: "He's my dog. You can't kick him. He's my dog!"

The big dog was back up on his feet now, wagging his stub tail again and licking the tears off Arliss's face with his pink tongue.

Mama laughed. "Well, Travis," she said, "it looks like we've got us a dog."

"But Mama," I said. "You don't mean we'd keep an old ugly dog like that. One that will come in and steal meat right out of the house."

"Well, maybe we can't keep him," Mama said. "Maybe he belongs to somebody around here who'll want him back."

"He doesn't belong to anybody in the settlement," I said. "I know every dog at Salt Licks."

"Well, then," Mama said. "If he's a stray, there's no reason why Little Arliss can't claim him. And you'll have to admit he's a smart dog. Mighty few dogs have sense enough to figure out a way to reach a side of meat hanging that high. He must have climbed up on top of that meal barrel and jumped from there."

I went over and looked at the wooden lid on top of the meal barrel. Sure enough, in the thin film of dust that had settled over it were dog tracks.

"Well, all right," I admitted. "He's a smart dog. But I still don't want him."

"Now, Travis," Mama said. "You're not being fair. You had you a dog when you were little, but Arliss has never had one. He's too little for you to play with, and he gets lonely."

I didn't say any more. When Mama got her mind set a certain way, there was no use in arguing with her. But I didn't want that meat-thieving dog on the place, and I didn't aim to have him. I might have to put up with him for a day or so, but sooner or later, I'd find a way to get rid of him.

Mama must have guessed what was going on in my mind, for she kept handing me sober looks all the time she was getting breakfast.

She fed us cornmeal mush cooked in a pot swung over the fireplace. She sweetened it with wild honey that Papa and I had cut out of a bee tree last fall, and added cream skimmed off last night's milk. It was good eating; but I'd had my appetite whetted for fried middling meat to go with it.

Mama waited till I was done, then said: "Now, Travis, as soon as you've milked the cows, I think you ought to get your gun and try to kill us a fat young doe for meat. And while you're gone, I want you to do some thinking on what I said about Little Arliss and this stray dog."

THE PRINCESS
&
THE TIN BOX

Written and illustrated by James Thurber

Once upon a time, in a far country, there lived a king whose daughter was the prettiest princess in the world. Her eyes were like the cornflower, her hair was sweeter than the hyacinth, and her throat made the swan look dusty.

From the time she was a year old, the princess had been showered with presents. Her nursery looked like Cartier's window. Her toys were all made of gold or platinum or diamonds or emeralds. She was not permitted to have wooden blocks or china dolls or rubber dogs or linen books, because such materials were considered cheap for the daughter of a king.

When she was seven, she was allowed to attend the wedding of her brother and throw real pearls at the bride instead of rice. Only the nightingale, with his lyre of gold, was permitted to sing for the princess. The common blackbird, with his boxwood flute, was kept out of the palace grounds. She walked in silver-and-samite slippers to a sapphire-and-topaz bathroom and slept in an ivory bed inlaid with rubies.

On the day the princess was eighteen, the king sent a royal ambassador to the courts of five neighboring kingdoms to announce that he would give his daughter's hand in marriage to the prince who brought her the gift she liked the most.

The first prince to arrive at the palace rode a swift white stallion and laid at the feet of the princess an enormous apple made of solid gold which he had taken from a dragon who had guarded it for a thousand years. It was placed on a long ebony table set up to hold the gifts of the princess's suitors. The second prince, who came on a gray charger, brought her a nightingale of a thousand diamonds, and it was placed beside the golden apple. The third prince, riding on a black horse, carried a great jewel box made of platinum and sapphires, and it was placed next to the diamond nightingale. The fourth prince, astride a fiery yellow horse, gave the princess a gigantic heart made of rubies and pierced by an emerald arrow. It was placed next to the platinum-and-sapphire jewel box.

Now the fifth prince was the strongest and handsomest of all the five suitors, but he was the son of a poor king whose realm had been overrun by mice and locusts and wizards and mining engineers so that there was nothing much of value left in it. He came plodding up to the palace of the princess on a plow horse and he brought her a small tin box filled with mica and feldspar and hornblende which he had picked up on the way.

The other princes roared with disdainful laughter when they saw the tawdry gift the fifth prince had brought to the princess. But she examined it with great interest and squealed with delight, for all her life she had been glutted with precious stones and priceless metals, but she had never seen tin before or mica or feldspar or hornblende. The tin box was placed next to the ruby heart pierced with an emerald arrow.

"Now," the king said to his daughter, "you must select the gift you like best and marry the prince that brought it."

The princess smiled and walked up to the table and picked up the present she liked the most. It was the platinum-and-sapphire jewel box, the gift of the third prince.

"The way I figure it," she said, "is this. It is a very large and expensive box, and when I am married, I will meet many admirers who will give me precious gems with which to fill it to the top. Therefore, it is the most valuable of all the gifts my suitors have brought me and I like it the best."

The princess married the third prince that very day in the midst of great merriment and high revelry. More than a hundred thousand pearls were thrown at her and she loved it.

Moral: All those who thought the princess was going to select the tin box filled with worthless stones instead of one of the other gifts will kindly stay after class and write one hundred times on the blackboard "I would rather have a hunk of aluminum silicate than a diamond necklace."

Sarah Cynthia Sylvia Stout Would Not Take the Garbage Out

Shel Silverstein

Sarah Cynthia Sylvia Stout
Would not take the garbage out!
She'd scour the pots and scrape the pans,
Candy the yams and spice the hams,
And though her daddy would scream and shout,
She simply would not take the garbage out.
And so it piled up to the ceilings:
Coffee grounds, potato peelings,
Brown bananas, rotten peas,
Chunks of sour cottage cheese.
It filled the can, it covered the floor,
It cracked the window and blocked the door
With bacon rinds and chicken bones,
Drippy ends of ice cream cones,
Prune pits, peach pits, orange peel,
Gloppy glumps of cold oatmeal,
Pizza crusts and withered greens,
Soggy beans and tangerines,
Crusts of black burned buttered toast,
Gristly bits of beefy roasts . . .

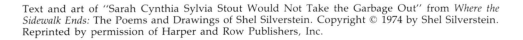

The garbage rolled on down the hall,
It raised the roof, it broke the wall . . .
Greasy napkins, cookie crumbs,
Globs of gooey bubble gum,
Cellophane from green baloney,
Rubbery blubbery macaroni,
Peanut butter, caked and dry,
Curdled milk and crusts of pie,
Moldy melons, dried-up mustard,
Eggshells mixed with lemon custard,
Cold french fries and rancid meat,
Yellow lumps of Cream of Wheat.
At last the garbage reached so high
That finally it touched the sky.
And all the neighbors moved away,
And none of her friends would come to play.
And finally Sarah Cynthia Stout said,
"OK, I'll take the garbage out!"
But then, of course, it was too late . . .
The garbage reached across the state,
From New York to the Golden Gate.
And there, in the garbage she did hate,
Poor Sarah met an awful fate,
That I cannot right now relate
Because the hour is much too late.
But children, remember Sarah Stout
And always take the garbage out!

ANOTHER APRIL

Jesse Stuart

"Now, Pap, you won't get cold," Mom said as she put a
heavy wool cap over his head.

"Huh, what did ye say?" Grandpa asked, holding his big
hand cupped over his ear to catch the sound.

"Wait until I get your gloves," Mom said, hollering real
loud in Grandpa's ear. Mom had forgotten about his gloves until
he raised his big bare hand above his ear to catch the sound of
Mom's voice.

"Don't get 'em," Grandpa said, "I won't ketch cold."

Mom didn't pay any attention to what Grandpa said. She
went on to get the gloves anyway. Grandpa turned toward me.
He saw that I was looking at him.

"Yer Ma's a-puttin' enough clothes on me to kill a man,"
Grandpa said, then he laughed a coarse laugh like March wind
among the pine tops at his own words. I started laughing but
not at Grandpa's words. He thought I was laughing at them and
we both laughed together. It pleased Grandpa to think that I
had laughed with him over something funny that he had said.
But I was laughing at the way he was dressed. He looked like a
picture of Santa Claus. But Grandpa's cheeks were not cherry-
red like Santa Claus' cheeks. They were covered with white thin
beard—and above his eyes were long white eyebrows almost as
white as percoon petals and very much longer.

Grandpa was wearing a heavy wool suit that hung loosely
about his big body but fitted him tightly round the waist where
he was as big and as round as a flour barrel. His pant legs were
as big 'round his pipestem legs as emptied meal sacks. And his
big shoes, with his heavy wool socks dropping down over their
tops, looked like sled runners. Grandpa wore a heavy wool shirt
and over his wool shirt he wore a heavy wool sweater and then
his coat over the top of all this. Over his coat he wore a heavy
overcoat and about his neck he wore a wool scarf.

The way Mom had dressed Grandpa you'd think there was
a heavy snow on the ground but there wasn't. April was here

instead and the sun was shining on the green hills where the wild plums and the wild crab apples were in bloom enough to make you think there were big snowdrifts sprinkled over the green hills. When I looked at Grandpa and then looked out the window at the sunshine and the green grass I laughed more. Grandpa laughed with me.

"I'm a-goin' to see my old friend," Grandpa said just as Mom came down the stairs with his gloves.

"Who is he, Grandpa?" I asked, but Grandpa just looked at my mouth working. He didn't know what I was saying. And he hated to ask me the second time.

Mom put the big wool gloves on Grandpa's hands. He stood there just like I had to do years ago, and let Mom put his gloves on. If Mom didn't get his fingers back in the glove-fingers exactly right Grandpa quarreled at Mom. And when Mom fixed his fingers exactly right in his gloves the way he wanted them Grandpa was pleased.

"I'll be a-goin' to see 'im," Grandpa said to Mom. "I know he'll still be there."

Mom opened our front door for Grandpa and he stepped out slowly, supporting himself with his big cane in one hand. With the other hand he held to the door facing. Mom let him out of the house just like she used to let me out in the spring. And when Grandpa left the house I wanted to go with him, but Mom wouldn't let me go. I wondered if he would get away from the house—get out of Mom's sight—and pull off his shoes and go barefooted and wade the creeks like I used to do when Mom let me out. Since Mom wouldn't let me go with Grandpa, I watched him as he walked slowly down the path in front of our house. Mom stood there watching Grandpa too. I think she was afraid that he would fall. But Mom was fooled; Grandpa toddled along the path better than my baby brother could.

"He used to be a powerful man," Mom said more to herself than she did to me. "He was a timber cutter. No man could cut more timber than my father; no man in the timber woods could sink an ax deeper into a log than my father. And no man could lift the end of a bigger saw log than Pop could."

"Who is Grandpa goin' to see, Mom?" I asked.

"He's not goin' to see anybody," Mom said.

"I heard 'im say that he was goin' to see an old friend," I told her.

"Oh, he was just a-talkin'," Mom said.

I watched Grandpa stop under the pine tree in our front yard. He set his cane against the pine tree trunk, pulled off his gloves and put them in his pocket. Then Grandpa stooped over slowly, as slowly as the wind bends down a sapling, and picked up a pine cone in his big soft fingers. Grandpa stood fondling the pine cone in his hand. Then, one by one, he pulled the little chips from the pine cone—tearing it to pieces like he was hunting for something in it—and after he had torn it to pieces he threw the pine-cone stem on the ground. Then he pulled pine needles from a low-hanging pine bough and he felt each pine needle between his fingers. He played with them a long time before he started down the path.

"What's Grandpa doin'?" I asked Mom.

But Mom didn't answer me.

"How long has Grandpa been with us?" I asked Mom.

"Before you's born," she said. "Pap has been with us eleven years. He was eighty when he quit cuttin' timber and farmin'; now he's ninety-one."

I had heard her say that when she was a girl he'd walk out on the snow and ice barefooted and carry wood in the house and put it on the fire. He had shoes but he wouldn't bother to put them on. And I heard her say that he would cut timber on the coldest days without socks on his feet but with his feet stuck down in cold brogan shoes and he worked stripped above the waist so his arms would have freedom when he swung his double-bitted ax. I had heard her tell how he'd sweat and how the sweat in his beard would be icicles by the time he got home from work on the cold winter days. Now Mom wouldn't let him get out of the house for she wanted him to live a long time.

As I watched Grandpa go down the path toward the hog pen he stopped to examine every little thing along his path. Once he waved his cane at a butterfly as it zigzagged over his head, its polka-dot wings fanning the blue April air. Grandpa would stand when a puff of wind came along, and hold his face against the wind and let the wind play with his white whiskers. I thought maybe his face was hot under his beard and he was letting the wind cool his face. When he reached the hog pen he called the hogs down to the fence. They came running and grunting to Grandpa just like they were talking to him. I knew that Grandpa couldn't hear them trying to talk to him but he could see their mouths working and he knew they were trying to say something. He leaned his cane against the hog pen, reached over the fence, and patted the hogs' heads. Grandpa didn't miss patting one of our seven hogs.

As he toddled up the little path alongside the hog pen he stopped under a blooming dogwood. He pulled a white blossom from a bough that swayed over the path above his head, and he leaned his big bundled body against the dogwood while he tore each petal from the blossom and examined it carefully. There wasn't anything his dim blue eyes missed. He stopped under a redbud tree before he reached the garden to break a tiny spray of redbud blossoms. He took each blossom from the spray and examined it carefully.

"Gee, it's funny to watch Grandpa," I said to Mom, then I laughed.

"Poor Pap," Mom said. "He's seen a lot of Aprils come and go. He's seen more Aprils than he will ever see again."

I don't think Grandpa missed a thing on the little circle he took before he reached the house. He played with a bumblebee that was bending a wildflower blossom that grew near our corncrib beside a big bluff. But Grandpa didn't try to catch the bumblebee in his big bare hand. I wondered if he would and if the bumblebee would sting him, and if he would holler. Grandpa even pulled a butterfly cocoon from a blackberry briar that grew beside his path. I saw him try to tear it into shreds but he couldn't. There wasn't any butterfly in it, for I'd seen it before. I wondered if the butterfly with the polka-dot wings, that Grandpa waved his cane at when he first left the house, had come from this cocoon. I laughed when Grandpa couldn't tear the cocoon apart.

"I'll bet I can tear that cocoon apart for Grandpa if you'd let me go help him," I said to Mom.

"You leave your Grandpa alone," Mom said. "Let 'im enjoy April."

Then I knew that this was the first time Mom had let Grandpa out of the house all winter. I knew that Grandpa loved the sunshine and the fresh April air that blew from the redbud and dogwood blossoms. He loved the bumblebees, the hogs, the pine cones, and pine needles. Grandpa didn't miss a thing along his walk. And every day from now on until just before frost Grandpa would take this little walk. He'd stop along and look at everything as he had done summers before. But each year he didn't take as long a walk as he had taken the year before. Now this spring he didn't go down to the lower end of the hog pen as he had done last year. And when I could first remember Grandpa going on his walks he used to go out of sight. He'd go all over the farm. And he'd come to the house and take me on his knee and tell me about all what he had seen. Now Grandpa wasn't getting out of sight. I could see him from the window along all of his walk.

Grandpa didn't come back into the house at the front door. He tottled around back of the house toward the smokehouse and I ran through the living room to the dining room so I could look out the window and watch him.

"Where's Grandpa goin'?" I asked Mom.

"Now never mind," Mom said. "Leave Grandpa alone. Don't go out there and disturb him."

"I won't bother 'im, Mom," I said. "I just want to watch 'im."

"All right," Mom said.

But Mom wanted to be sure that I didn't bother him so she followed me into the dining room. Maybe she wanted to see what Grandpa was going to do. She stood by the window and we watched Grandpa as he walked down beside our smokehouse where a tall sassafras tree's thin leaves fluttered in the blue April wind. Above the smokehouse and the tall sassafras was a blue April sky—so high you couldn't see the sky-roof. It was just blue space and little white clouds floated upon this blue.

When Grandpa reached the smokehouse he leaned his cane against the sassafras tree. He let himself down slowly to his knees as he looked carefully at the ground. Grandpa was looking at something and I wondered what it was. I just didn't think or I would have known.

"There you are, my good old friend," Grandpa said.

"Who is his friend, Mom?" I asked.

Mom didn't say anything. Then I saw.

"He's playin' with that old terrapin, Mom," I said.

"I know he is," Mom said.

"The terrapin doesn't mind if Grandpa strokes his head with his hand," I said.

"I know it," Mom said.

"But the old terrapin won't let me do it," I said. "Why does he let Grandpa?"

"The terrapin knows your Grandpa."

"He ought to know me," I said, "but when I try to stroke his head with my hand, he closes up in his shell."

Mom didn't say anything. She stood by the window watching Grandpa and listening to Grandpa talk to the terrapin.

"My old friend, how do you like the sunshine?" Grandpa asked the terrapin.

The terrapin turned his fleshless face to one side like a hen does when she looks at you in the sunlight. He was trying to talk to Grandpa; maybe the terrapin could understand what Grandpa was saying.

"Old fellow, it's been a hard winter," Grandpa said. "How have you fared under the smokehouse floor?"

"Does the terrapin know what Grandpa is sayin'?" I asked Mom.

"I don't know," she said.

"I'm awfully glad to see you, old fellow," Grandpa said.

He didn't offer to bite Grandpa's big soft hand as he stroked his head.

"Looks like the terrapin would bite Grandpa," I said.

"That terrapin has spent the winters under that smokehouse for fifteen years," Mom said. "Pap has been acquainted with him for eleven years. He's been talkin' to that terrapin every spring."

"How does Grandpa know the terrapin is old?" I asked Mom.

"It's got 1847 cut on its shell," Mom said. "We know he's ninety-five years old. He's older than that. We don't know how old he was when that date was cut on his back."

"Who cut 1847 on his back, Mom?"

"I don't know, child," she said, "but I'd say whoever cut that date on his back has long been under the ground."

Then I wondered how a terrapin could get that old and what kind of a looking person he was who cut the date on the terrapin's back. I wondered where it happened—if it happened near where our house stood. I wondered who lived here on this land then, what kind of a house they lived in, and if they had a sassafras with tiny thin April leaves on its top growing in their yard, and if the person that cut the date on the terrapin's back was buried at Plum Grove, if he had farmed these hills where we lived today and cut timber like Grandpa had—and if he had seen the Aprils pass like Grandpa had seen them and if he enjoyed them like Grandpa was enjoying this April. I wondered if he had looked at the dogwood blossoms, the redbud blossoms, and talked to this same terrapin.

"Are you well, old fellow?" Grandpa asked the terrapin.

The terrapin just looked at Grandpa.

"I'm well as common for a man of my age," Grandpa said.

"Did the terrapin ask Grandpa if he was well?" I asked Mom.

"I don't know," Mom said. "I can't talk to a terrapin."

"But Grandpa can."

"Yes."

"Wait until tomatoes get ripe and we'll go to the garden together," Grandpa said.

"Does the terrapin eat tomatoes?" I asked Mom.

"Yes, that terrapin has been eatin' tomatoes from our garden for fifteen years," Mom said. "When Mick was tossin'

the terrapins out of the tomato patch, he picked up this one and found the date cut on his back. He put him back in the patch and told him to help himself. He lives from our garden every year. We don't bother him and don't allow anybody else to bother him. He spends his winters under our smokehouse floor buried in the dry ground."

"Gee, Grandpa looks like the terrapin," I said.

Mom didn't say anything; tears came to her eyes. She wiped them from her eyes with the corner of her apron.

"I'll be back to see you," Grandpa said. "I'm a-gettin' a little chilly; I'll be gettin' back to the house."

The terrapin twisted his wrinkled neck without moving his big body, poking his head deeper into the April wind as Grandpa pulled his bundled body up by holding to the sassafras tree trunk.

"Good-by, old friend!"

The terrapin poked his head deeper into the wind, holding one eye on Grandpa, for I could see his eye shining in the sinking sunlight.

Grandpa got his cane that was leaned against the sassafras tree trunk and hobbled slowly toward the house. The terrapin looked at him with first one eye and then the other.

GRANDFATHER

James Lim

You sit cushioned from the world
in that chair;
you rest, and I watch.
The stillness of the room
settles lightly on the floor,
settles lightly like dust—
it streams
down to the earth,
is laden with sunlight.
You are old
like roots are old.
You have earthen eyes
made fertile with older days:
watery days without end, seemingly,
and days
with a stillness in the air
like a fog, thick and lonely.
You waited, always, for mountains,
but now you rest. The room is silent,
and you are old,
your roots are old.
Tell me a story
before the sun sets.

The noblest question
in the world is,
what good may I do in it?

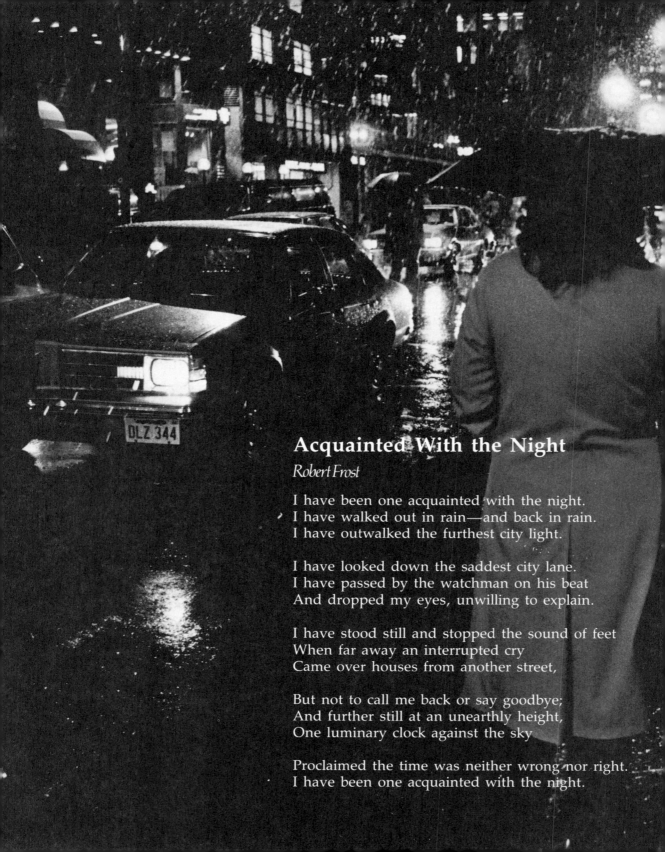

Acquainted With the Night

Robert Frost

I have been one acquainted with the night.
I have walked out in rain—and back in rain.
I have outwalked the furthest city light.

I have looked down the saddest city lane.
I have passed by the watchman on his beat
And dropped my eyes, unwilling to explain.

I have stood still and stopped the sound of feet
When far away an interrupted cry
Came over houses from another street,

But not to call me back or say goodbye;
And further still at an unearthly height,
One luminary clock against the sky

Proclaimed the time was neither wrong nor right.
I have been one acquainted with the night.

I Was Born Today

Amado Nervo

Every day that dawns, you must say
    to yourself,
''I was born today!
The world is new to me.
This light that I behold
Strikes my unclouded eyes for the
    first time;
The rain that scatters its crystal drops
Is my baptism!

''Then let us live a pure life,
A shining life!
Already, yesterday is lost. Was it bad?
    Was it beautiful?
. . . Let it be forgotten.
And of that yesterday let there remain
    only the essence,
The precious gold of what I loved
    and suffered
As I walked along the road . . .

"Today, every moment shall bring
      feelings of well being and cheer.
And the reason for my existence,
My most urgent resolve,
Will be to spread happiness all over the world,
To pour the wine of goodness into the
      eager mouths around me . . .

"My only peace will be the peace of others;
Their dreams, my dreams;
Their joy, my joy;
My crystal tear,
The tear that trembles on the eyelash of another;
My heartbeat,
The beat of every heart that throbs
Throughout worlds without end!"

Every day that dawns, you must say to yourself,
"I was born today!"

STAMPEDE

ALLAN BOSWORTH

Nobody ever found out how Ma Collins managed to locate the camp that night before we threw the herd out on the long trail. There had been a heavy fog in the evening when we bedded down on the prairie maybe fifteen miles from San Antone, and at two o'clock in the morning it was still so thick you couldn't see your horse's ears. I know, because from midnight until two I rode my very first night herd, singing to the longhorns in a voice that hadn't decided whether to be soprano or baritone.

But the fog must have lifted just before daylight. Ed Schuler got up then to rustle breakfast. He went around the chuck wagon to get some wood, and the first thing I heard was when he let out a surprised whistle and came over by my bed to shake McQuiston's shoulder and tell him we had company. Bat McQuiston was the Bar 9 trail boss.

I wish I could make you see how everything was. Maybe the mornings were younger, those days, and the earth hadn't been scarred so much by plows and fences and roads; maybe at fifteen you see with clearer eyes. I raised my head from the saddle and smelled the dew-fresh dawn and the trampled grass, and a little breeze bringing the clean, sweet scent of cattle; and then I caught a whiff of

mesquite-wood smoke and knew it was nearly breakfast time. Three or four big stars blazed overhead, but it was getting light in the east above the dark rim of prairie. I rubbed dreams out of my eyes and looked that way under the wagon, and saw Ma Collins.

She was like an old-fashioned cutout, one of those silhouette pictures done in black against a pale gold background. She was sitting in a buggy, just watching the camp. Her sunbonnet came up to a starched peak against the sky, and her gaunt, patient shoulders made angles. The reins were half-hitched around the whip socket, as if she had been there a long time, waiting with her hands folded in her lap and the team of little Spanish mules asleep. It wasn't until Ed Schuler went back to put wood on the fire that she moved at all, and by then McQuiston was stamping into his boots and going out to see what she wanted.

"Mornin', ma'am!" he called. "Get yourself lost in the fog?"

"No, don't reckon I did," she said. Her voice was soft and tired. "Ain't this the Bar 9 outfit?"

"Yes'm, it is."

"And you're trailing these cows all the way to Dodge City?"

"Yes'm, if we can hold 'em together that long."

She gathered up her skirts and got down out of the buggy. "Well," she said, "I'm Ma Collins, and I'm going up the trail with you."

Bat McQuiston's eyes kind of bugged out. The way she said that, you'd have thought she was talking about hitching up and driving to San Antone for a couple of yards of calico.

"Well, now, that's quite a ways," McQuiston said, laughing. "But we'd be proud to have you come into camp and have a cup of coffee."

Ma reached into the buggy and lifted out a rusty bucket with a little green shrub growing in it. "I'm going," she said. "If you don't think it's all right for me to go, you just ask Sam Murray."

Sam Murray owned the Bar 9 and a couple of other Texas brands, but he was already up the trail about ten days ahead of us, and there wasn't any way of asking him. McQuiston started getting uneasy.

"Sam ain't here, ma'am," he said. "But you just couldn't hardly go. It ain't no place for a lady. There's rivers to cross, and dry drives, and maybe Comanche trouble. Besides—"

"I know all about them things," Ma Collins told him, starting for the wagon. "Could you spare a little water for my rosebush? The sun was mighty hot on it yesterday."

Everybody was up by then, and maybe enjoying seeing Bat McQuiston run into something he couldn't boss around. I forget some of the names; we had nearly twenty-five hundred head of cattle, and there were about ten men besides the wrangler and the cook. The wrangler was Scotty Andrews, and I remember Curly

Spence and Bill Ike Parrish and Tennessee Jones. There were myself— Bud Rogers—and Dan Robie, who was a colored boy about nineteen and one of the best riders I ever saw. It was a long time ago.

Ma Collins was about forty; her hair was turning gray, and she had that dried-up, sun-and-wind look of the frontier woman. She didn't take much notice of anybody after the introductions. She watched the fire, not moving when the wind changed and smoke blew her way. But she picked up the bucket holding her little rosebush and put it behind the bedding roll out of the smoke.

Ed Schuler poured her a tin cup of coffee, and Bat McQuiston watched her and started walking up and down. It was nearly sunup, and the cattle were beginning to move out and graze. They were headed in the direction we wanted them to go, but they were spreading out too much.

"Now, Miz Collins," McQuiston said firmly, "we're just goin' to have to get movin'. I'm mighty sorry, but we can't take you along."

"I'll drive my own team," Ma Collins said, sipping the coffee. "I've got bedding, and a little tent to put up if the weather gets bad."

"I mean," McQuiston said, "we just can't—We—well, why do you want to go up the trail, anyway? Like I said, it ain't no place for a lady!"

"I reckon I can stand it," Ma said. "And you couldn't stop me if I just tagged along."

McQuiston poured himself a cup of coffee and choked on it. He got red in the face and told Curly and Dan Robie and me to saddle up and relieve

the last night herd and string the cattle
out. Ma Collins looked up at me as I
went by.

"How old are you, child?" she asked.

I could see Curly grinning, and
knew they'd all hooraw me about
being called that. I blushed and told
her I was going on sixteen.

"Does your mother know you're
going up the trail?"

"Yes'm," I said. "I had to do some
tall talking. She didn't want me to go
yet, but pa said I had to go
sometime."

"Yes," Ma Collins said. "Yes, they
all have to go, sooner or later. Seems
like it's in their blood."

Curly and Dan Robie and I went
out to the remuda to saddle up, and
McQuiston came that way, cussing
softly behind his hand.

"Be careful, Bat," Curly told him.
"This child will hear you!"

McQuiston didn't think he was
funny. "What can I do?" he asked.
"I'm bossin' this outfit, but she ain't
on the payroll, and she's bound and
determined to tag along. What could
anybody do?"

"You tell me," Curly grinned. "I
hear it's a free country."

He was right; it was mighty free
and wide and wild, and it belonged to
any man who could saddle a horse
and ride. But it wasn't a woman's
country for a thousand miles in the
direction we were headed. We didn't
expect to see another woman until we
hit Dodge City.

"What you suppose she wants to
go for?" I asked Dan Robie, when we
fell back in the drag.

Dan was pretty smart. He'd been
up the trail twice, and to New
Orleans, and all over. Like I said, he
was one of the best riders I ever saw,

35

and he went to a lot of trouble to teach me things about handling cattle. I know, now, that Dan turned to me out of loneliness; the others didn't have much to do with him. Sometimes I caught him watching their horseplay around camp with a wistful look.

"There's a man somewhere up there," Dan said. "A woman goes traipsin' off somewhere like this, there's always a man."

I thought about that awhile, and decided that whoever the man was, he just might as well give up. There was something about the set of Ma's shoulders that showed she was going to hang on till she found him. It wasn't spunk exactly, or even determination; it was just the kind of slow patience that wears mountains down.

Ma Collins was there that night when we made camp at Leon Springs, and there wasn't anything McQuiston could do except ask her to sit down and have supper with us. Then, later, he told Dan Robie to help her set up that little tent, because it looked like it might rain.

"She'll get tired," McQuiston predicted. "She'll get enough of it a long time before we get to Red River."

But she didn't show any signs of getting tired. I remember our watering places; we camped on the Cibolo, and at Boerne, and we hit the Guadalupe at Comfort, and went on up to the Llano and the San Saba. Ma Collins was always there when we bedded the herd down for the night.

It wasn't any kind of trick for a buggy and a team of mules to keep up with the outfit. Bat McQuiston aimed

to get the Bar 9's to Dodge City weighing more than they did when we slapped the trail brand on them, and we averaged about ten miles a day. It took a little while to get the herd trail-broke; after that a couple of big, powerful line-backed steers from the Nueces brush stepped out every morning and took the lead, and the others fell into accustomed places all down the line. I tell you, a big herd of Texas longhorns on the trail was something to see. It was like an army on the march, with dust clouds for banners and the gleam of proud, sun-tipped horns for bayonets. Sometimes the cattle would be strung out for a mile or more, threading the hill passes or winding through the post-oak country; sometimes, where the grass was good, we let them bunch and feed on a wide front.

In open country Ma Collins sometimes drove her buggy along at the side of the herd, and McQuiston worried for a while because none of those longhorns had ever seen a buggy before. But they got used to it, and we didn't have any trouble on that account. More often, she drove behind the drag, and I felt sorry for her then, because she got all the dust.

But when she drove there, I saw her more often. Dan Robie and I brought up the drag—Dan because he was a colored boy, and I because I was so green that Curly Spence was always asking McQuiston how many trading stamps he swapped for me. The drag was the orneriest spot in the herd; we not only had to eat dust but all the mean scalawag steers dropped back there and kept lagging or trying to break away into the brush.

But I wouldn't have traded jobs with President Rutherford B. Hayes. I was learning how to handle cattle; I was out in the open and riding a horse. And at night there was always the shine of firelight on a wind-flapped wagon tarp, and a million stars overhead, and sometimes another campfire away out on the prairie, as if one of the stars had fallen out of the sky. There was always somebody to tell a big windy in the evening before we turned in to our bedding rolls, although for the first few nights Ma Collins was with us the boys acted mighty bashful.

She didn't talk much. I thought it was because McQuiston was still letting her know that she wasn't exactly welcome, even if he did have to invite her to supper with us. Then, after the boys got used to having her around, and watching their talk and maybe even slicking up a little because she was there, she would sometimes act like she was a thousand miles away. The night we camped by the Colorado, Ed Schuler got out his old fiddle and played a few tunes, and The Parson, who had a good tenor voice, started singing. I remember that The Parson was singing When the Work's All Done This Fall when Ma got up all of a sudden and went to her tent.

McQuiston had stepped out of the firelight to look at the sky for weather signs, and he saw her go. He came back into the camp, pitching mad.

"One of you jaspers say somethin' you hadn't ought to say before a lady?" he demanded. "Talk up! The one that done it is fired!"

"Now, don't get ringy," Bill Ike Parrish told him. "We don't know

what made her leave, unless she couldn't stand The Parson's warbling."

McQuiston looked around and cooled off a little. He said, "Dan, you go out to her tent and ask her if she'd like a cup of coffee before she goes to bed. And here, take her some water for that rosebush. I didn't see her water it tonight."

I wasn't but fifteen, but I knew how it was with Bat McQuiston. He was a big man, and tough as whitleather, and they said he had killed a couple of men once in a saloon fight at Laredo. But under his hide he was soft as a baby.

Only he wasn't going to let anybody think he was soft. He unrolled his bed tarp, and said, "Of course we can't have her tagging along all through the Indian Nation, nursing that rosebush. I've seen the time on this trail when there ain't water enough to wet your tongue." He sat down, grunting as he pulled off his boots. "So I wrote a letter to Sam Murray, in care of Doan's store. Told him we're goin' to have to send her packin' back home."

He fixed his saddle for a pillow and slid into his tarp. I saw Dan Robie come back from Ma Collins' tent and put his bed down where he always slept, a little way out from everybody else. The lantern light winked out in her tent, and there wasn't anything but the dying fire and the stars; there was just the lonesome sound of the wind, and now and then a few notes of the night herders' song to the longhorn cattle.

Clear Fork—that was where they ran. It came up a thunder-and-lightning storm about one o'clock in the morning. Dan Robie and Tennessee Jones had the night herd, and they said one minute everything was peaceful, and the next there was a clap of thunder, and that just blew the lid off. It was my first stampede; I woke up to feel the whole earth shaking and to hear McQuiston yelling for us to hit the saddle.

I didn't have my boots on before the herd came right through the edge of the camp. It began to rain, and there was a zigzag streak of lightning flashing clear across the sky, mighty low, and I saw the cattle like a dark rolling wave, splitting into two streams past Ma Collins' buggy and her little tent. The tent was under a post-oak tree that night, and I reckon that helped; the leaders went around it all right but the press of the cattle behind and on both sides pushed some of the steers right into the tent and wrecked it.

You hear a lot about cowboys getting killed in stampedes, but nine times out of ten it was when horses fell and rolled on their riders, and not because of getting trampled by the steers. A longhorn would always try to jump over anything lying on the ground. McQuiston knew that, but he was scared to death until the cattle thinned out and another flash of lightning showed Ma Collins hugging the tree.

He ran out and grabbed her by the arm. "Get in the wagon and stay there till we get back!" he ordered.

"You wait a minute!" Ma said. She jerked her arm free and began digging around in what was left of the tent. "You wait till I find my rosebush!"

"The devil with your rosebush!" McQuiston yelled. But he couldn't boss her around. So he said, "Excuse me, ma'am. . . . Come on, boys!"

They ran for an hour, and it was nine o'clock in the morning before we rounded up all the scattered bunches and tallied them again. We got them pointed north, and went back to get the wagon. Ed Schuler was in the saddle like the rest of us, so nobody expected anything but coffee for breakfast.

But it was there. Hot biscuits and bacon and blackstrap sorghum molasses. And when Ma Collins learned nobody was hurt, I saw her smile for the first time.

What could you do with a woman like that? I think McQuiston was ready to give up trying to send her home, because he said if she wasn't with the Bar 9 she'd just tie onto some other outfit. But he swore he wasn't going to be bothered helping her cross the Red River. From what we heard, it was running bank full, and there would be trouble enough floating the chuck wagon over.

I remember our watering places, because in those days you measured progress up the trail by the rivers crossed and left behind—the shining rivers with the singing names. Elm Creek and Brazos, Pony Creek, Wichita and Beaver, Paradise and Pease—all running clear before plows broke the plains, all washing the dust from hooves and wheels. And I remember the Red, biggest of all, gleaming like a pink ribbon in the sunshine when we sighted it from away off.

We camped a couple of miles out from Doan's store, which was a kind of disappointment to me, because at that time it was made of buffalo hides and wagon tarps stretched over a frame of poles. There were three other herds waiting for the river to drop before they tried to cross, and one of them was Sam Murray's other northbound outfit.

He rode out to our camp that first evening. Dusk was gray, and it began to rain slowly, and you could smell wet hides and saddle leather, and wood smoke beaten down to earth. Sam Murray got down from his horse and came into the firelight, a big man wearing the same kind of flop-brimmed hat and ducking jumper and scuffed boots as anybody else, although I reckon he was worth a couple of hundred thousand dollars.

"Howdy, boys," he said, and tipped his hat to Ma Collins. "Howdy, Mary."

She spoke to him, and then there was a silence, and everybody felt awkward and maybe afraid he was going to tell Ma she had to go home.

It was somehow worse because of the rain; the Bar 9 camp was a good place to be, with its warmth and flickering light, and the music of the rain on the wagon tarp Ed Schuler had rigged as a fly.

"Well," Ma Collins said, "I haven't got so far to go now. You tell him I can go on with the outfit, Sam."

"Well, I sure wouldn't try to stop you, after what happened," Sam Murray said gently. "But you hadn't ought to have come, Mary. What good will it do?"

Ma Collins looked out beyond the shelter of the fly, where that rusty bucket was setting so the rosebush would get the rain.

"I want to see my boy's grave," she said. "I want to see it just once."

We heard her, and all of us were afraid to look at her. But she wasn't going to cry, because she was past all crying. We heard what she said, and then there was just the sound of the

rain on the wagon tarp for a minute, and the hiss and sputter of wet wood in the fire.

"It ain't right for him to be buried up there so far away from home," she went on in that tired voice. "In such a lonesome place. They told me it was out on the prairie, miles from anywhere."

"Yes'm," Sam Murray said.

"I brought a little rosebush along, Sam. From the yard at home. He used to like the roses there. He was a good boy."

Sam Murray cleared his throat. "A fine boy, Mary. But . . . well, it's been two years . . . nearly three. I ain't so sure you could find his—the place, I mean."

"It's just across the Cimarron, they said. Just on the other side of the Cimarron crossing."

"I know," Sam nodded. "But nesters have come into that country. The crossing ain't in the same place now. Every time you drive a herd up north the fences and the plowed fields have pushed the trail a little farther west."

Ma Collins folded her hands in her lap, and I couldn't see her face for the shadow of her sunbonnet. I looked at McQuiston, and knew he was sorry he had written that letter.

"I'll find it," Ma said patiently. "I've scrimped and saved for two years to make this trip, and I'll feel better when the rosebush is planted there. It's a hardy variety, and it'll grow."

Nobody on the trail knew how to handle cattle any better than Bat McQuiston. He let the other outfits throw their herds across the river first, and they lost some steers doing it.

McQuiston waited a week after the rain stopped, and we cut dry cottonwood timbers and lashed them to the running gear of the wagon and the buggy, so they could be rafted over. And then the day before the crossing he saw to it that the herd wasn't watered at all.

That way the longhorns came down to the river thirsty, and McQuiston timed it to get them there in the heat of the day. The water was down some, showing scarred red banks and the pale roots of undermined trees on both sides, but it was still mighty wide, with flecks of foam the size of wagon sheets riding along with the current. Dan Robie said that was because the snow was melting way up in New Mexico.

Dan and I didn't see the lead steers hit the river, but we kept the drag closing in, and everything seemed to be working out smoothly enough. By the time we got to the riverbank, there was the wagon already on the other side, and Ma Collins' buggy beside it; and the Bar 9's were swimming across in an almost unbroken stream that bent with the current and came out in Indian Territory a couple of hundred yards below.

Even the scalawags were thirsty enough to wade belly-deep into the water. Curly Spence and Tennessee Jones were there to help, and we crowded the steers in the shallows, slapping ropes' ends on their rumps. They tried to turn and couldn't. They began to swim.

Dan put his horse just downstream from mine, and I felt better because I knew he was keeping an eye on me. He said, "Give your horse his head, and slip your feet out of the stirrups. If you have to, you can slide back into the water and hold on to his tail."

The Red River spilled cold into my boots and I said good-bye to Texas.

"A couple more big ones to cross, Bud!" Curly called over to me. And then he yelled, "Look out for that tree, kid!"

I remember how it looked. It was all like a dream from then on—like a nightmare that won't end. It was a great big cottonwood, drifting down the current, trunk first, like a battering ram, and at the other end the branches fanned out, half of them submerged; and the whole tree was rolling a little. I didn't do a thing; I was too scared. But my horse got out of the way just by inches, and then the butt end of the trunk glanced against a swimming longhorn in a way that turned the whole tree. The current caught it, and it swung broadside and really started to roll.

Curly and Tennessee shouted a warning to Dan Robie, but there wasn't time for him to get clear. The nightmare was frozen now. I can still see Dan's face, and that pleading in his eyes, and then a submerged limb tangled with his horse's legs, throwing him on his side. We saw Dan spill out of the saddle, and a branch as thick as a man's leg swung over and slapped hard against the back of his neck.

He went under. Tennessee and Curly had their ropes out, and Curly made a throw, but the whole tree was in between and he only snagged a limb. I saw Dan's horse swimming toward the shore, and then Dan came

up a long way downriver, floating face down beside one of those big patches of foam. The nightmare broke and I began to cry like I was a baby.

There must have been hundreds of pitiful little buryings like that one, up and down the whole dusty, windswept reaches of the Texas cattle trail before the settlements came. So many things could happen to a man between the Nueces and Dodge City or Abilene; and when they did, there wasn't much anybody could do. We didn't have any lumber for a coffin; we wrapped Dan Robie in his bed tarp, like a sailor going to his last rest at sea, and we dug a shallow grave on the lonesome prairie.

The picture is still in my mind like it was yesterday: the longhorn cattle strung out and moving slowly with an undertone of complaining bawls and bellowings, and killdeers running along the bank of the Red River with shrill, mournful cries; and big Bat McQuiston standing in awkward embarrassment that amounted to shame as he tried to remember something out of the Bible. I remember the cloud shadows moving lazily across the grass, and the smell of freshly turned earth, and the way Tennessee and Curly put Dan down into the grave, wanting to be tender and wanting to get it over and done with.

The wind was whipping at the wagon tarp, slapping it against the bows; the wind was bending the prairie grass. And there was Ma Collins standing by McQuiston's side with the wind ruffling her calico dress and her sunbonnet framing her pinched face, and the old heartbreak hard and dry in her eyes. I knew then, and I know now, how many mothers of Texas boys went up the long trail without ever leaving home.

"Our Father—" It was McQuiston, and I had never heard his voice like that before. "Our Father, there ain't much we can say. You know what happened down here, and you know Dan was a mighty good hand. We're turning him into Your keeping, Amen."

Then there was just the murmur of the wind, and the first dry whisper of earth on Dan's bed tarp. And Ma Collins' tired voice asking, "Do you know where to write his folks?"

McQuiston shook his head. That was why he was ashamed; that was the reason all of us felt the same sense of guilt. We had lived with Dan Robie for a couple of months without ever knowing him, without ever asking where his home was.

"No, ma'am," McQuiston said. "I don't know whether Dan had any folks."

We stood there, and Ed Schuler went away and came back with the endgate of the wagon. He said, "This is the only thing we got for a marker. I can whittle his name on it."

"We got to get moving," McQuiston said. He shifted his weight restlessly and looked up at the cattle scattering across the prairie to the north. "Bud, you and Bill Ike—"

"Wait a minute," said Ma Collins. She walked over to her buggy, with its wheels washed yellow again by the Red River, and came back, carrying the rosebush. She got down on her knees by the mound of fresh earth and scooped a little hole there with her patient hands, and all at once she began to cry. She had needed to cry for a long, long time.

McQuiston was kind of choked up himself. He said, "Bud, you and Bill Ike ride down by the river and drag up some cottonwoods. We'll have to make a picket fence to keep the cattle off."

It was morning before we moved the Bar 9's out on the trail again, into Indian Territory, where spring ran like a tide over the rolling prairies. When we got to the Cimarron and crossed it, we saw what was happening to the land, changing it so that it would never be the same, and we knew that the old trail and the wild, free ways were dying. We spent two days looking around the old crossing for something that would mark the grave of Ma Collins' boy. There wasn't anything but bare, dun fields, with furrows running where the longhorns used to walk.

But I don't think it mattered as much to Ma Collins anymore. She had planted her Texas rose with loving hands, and watered it with a mother's tears. It was for her own boy, and for Dan Robie, and for every other gallant rider who ever went up the trail with the longhorn cattle. It would keep their memory green.

excerpt from

Buffalo Woman

Dorothy M. Johnson

How Whirlwind Saved Her Cub

The novel Buffalo Woman *tells the story of Whirlwind, a member of the Sioux tribe born in the early 1800's. This selection from the book tells of Whirlwind's bravery in risking her life to save her grandson from a grizzly bear.*

Whirlwind slung her baby grandson's cradleboard onto her back with the ease of long practice and went walking at a brisk pace, answering the baby when he made small sounds. She had two things hidden under her dress: her digging stick and a soft leather bag for carrying roots. She thought she knew where biscuit root would be growing—desert parsley. The roots were good to eat raw, or she might dry and grind them to make big flat cakes. The biscuit root made good mush with a wild onion cooked in it.

As a rule she liked company when she worked, but there was no point in inviting some other busy woman to come along to dig something that might not be there.

She did tell her destination to one person, her grandson Shoots, thirteen years old. She met him when he was returning on foot from his turn at guarding part of the vast pony herd.

"Your little brother is going to help me dig biscuit root over there," she said. "Don't tell anybody where we are. Let the other women be sharp-eyed and find their own roots."

Shoots smiled and promised. He patted his baby brother's cheek and said, "Ho, warrior, old man chief. Take care of Grandmother." The baby jumped in his buckskin wrappings and cooed.

The biscuit root was plentiful on flat ground under a cutbank, just out of sight of the lodges. Whirlwind carefully propped the baby's cradleboard against a rock so the sun wouldn't shine in the child's face. Then, talking to him quietly, she began to dig skillfully, filling her buckskin bag, stooping and kneeling and rising again like a young woman. She was not young, she had lived through fifty-six winters, but she was strong and happy and healthy.

Her back was toward the baby when she heard him shriek with glee. She turned instantly—and saw a dreadful thing. Between her and the baby was another kind of baby, an awkward little bear cub, the cub of the frightfully dangerous grizzly bear. The cub itself was harmless, but the old-woman bear, its mother, must be near, and she would protect her child.

Whirlwind did not even think of danger to herself. She ran to save *her* cub. She snatched up the baby on his cradleboard and threw him, with all her strength, above her head toward the level top of the cutbank.

At that moment the old-woman bear appeared. She snarled and came running, a shambling, awkward-looking run but very fast.

Whirlwind saw with horror the cradleboard with its precious burden sliding back down the cutbank. She had been too close when she threw the baby upward. The baby was screaming. Grandmother Whirlwind ran, picked up the cradleboard, ran back a few steps, and then threw hard again. This time the bundle stayed up there.

Whirlwind ran again toward the cutbank and climbed as fast as she could, digging into the dirt frantically with clutching fingers and digging toes.

The upper part of her body was on the flat ground and she was gripping a small tree as she tried to pull up her legs. Just then the old-woman grizzly reached up and tore at the legs with curved claws as long as a big man's middle finger.

Whirlwind thought, I am dead—but my cub is safe if the sow bear does not come up here. No, I am not dead yet. I have something more to do. She screamed as hard as she could.

And her scream was heard.

Shoots was an untried boy. He had never even asked to go along with a war party to do errands for men of proved courage, to watch how a man should act. He had only thought of going on the hill to starve and thirst and lament to the Powers, praying for a powerful spirit helper. He had not yet done this thing. He believed his heart was strong. That day he found out.

He was only playing when he heard the she-bear snarl. He was practicing a stealthy approach, intending to startle Grandmother Whirlwind. He was creeping quietly through thin brush, pretending that she was an enemy. He did not really expect to surprise her; she was usually very alert. She would scold when she discovered what he was up to, and then she would laugh at him because she had caught him.

He saw a bundle fly through the air and slide down the cutbank. It happened too fast for him to see that it was the cradleboard with his baby brother. He heard fast movement in the weeds as Whirlwind ran back and threw the cradleboard again. He stood up, mouth open, just as she scrambled up the bank. With horror he saw the old-woman bear's claws rake her struggling legs.

With his heart in his mouth he did the best thing he could think of. He dropped his bow and grabbed the cub with both hands, so that it squalled with fear and pain. Then he threw it hard—past its mother.

Hearing her child cry, the woman bear whirled away from the cutbank to protect her cub. Shoots snatched up his bow; it was a good one, as strong as he could pull, and in a quiver on his shoulder he had six hunting arrows tipped with sharpened iron. At his waist he had a good steel knife.

But his enemy was better armed, with twenty immensely long, curved, sharp, death-dealing claws and a mouthful of long, sharp teeth, and she weighed more than five times as much as he did. She was protected by thick fur. Shoots was almost naked.

He stood his ground and fired his arrows at her, fast but very carefully. Few grizzlies had ever been killed by one man alone; there were true tales of some bears killing men even after they should have been dead themselves. The woman bear yelled in pain and fury. She batted at the arrows deep in her flesh. She bit at them. But she kept coming.

Then Shoots did the last thing he could do, because it was too late to run. While the grizzly fought at the arrows, especially one that had gone into her left eye, he leaped on her back. With all his strength he sank his good steel knife into her throat, through the heavy fur and hide.

Then, as Grandmother Whirlwind had done, he clambered up the cutbank while the bear groped and swiped at him. He wondered why he could not see very well. He wondered who was screaming. He wondered if this was the day he was going to die.

Whirlwind, lying helpless with the calf of one leg torn away, screamed louder when she saw him with blood running down his face, but he did not even know blood was there.

She cried, "Take the baby and run!" in so commanding a voice that he never thought of doing otherwise. With the cradled baby under one arm, he ran toward camp, howling for help, but stumbling.

His yells were heard. Two men on horseback lashed their ponies and met him. One seized the squalling baby. The other pulled Shoots up behind him on the pony. They rode fast toward where Whirlwind lay.

They leaped off—the one with the baby hung the cradleboard on a tree branch—and Shoots tumbled off. He had just realized that there was something he ought to do to prove his valor. He did something that his people talked about for many years afterward. While the men knelt by Whirlwind, he slid down the cutbank, picked up his bow, and struck the bear with it. She was coughing and dying. He shouted, as warriors do, "I, Shoots, have killed her! I count the first coup!"

Whirlwind and the men above heard him say it. They shouted in wonder and admiration. For a man to kill a grizzly without help was a very great thing indeed, and he had actually gone back into danger to count coup and claim the credit that was due him. He had counted coup against an armed enemy, after he was wounded, although he had never gone to war before that day. Now he was entitled to wear an eagle feather upright in his hair for first coup, a feather tipped with red paint because he had been wounded in battle.

He was the one who rode toward camp for more help while the two men stayed with Whirlwind and did what they could to make her comfortable. A crowd of people came hurrying after he delivered his message. There were women on horseback with poles and hides to make a pony drag for Whirlwind, because a great chunk of the muscles in the calf of one leg had been torn out by the she-bear's claws. There were men riding and boys riding, leading horses. More women brought supplies to help the wounded, and a medicine woman came with them, carrying her bundle of magic things. Round Cloud Woman came riding, crying, and Morning Rider came at a hard gallop to see about his mother and his infant son.

Whirlwind fought them off, so keyed up and triumphant that she did not yet feel much pain. "Let me carry my grandchild!" she ordered when Round Cloud tried to take him away.

"I saved your cub," Whirlwind kept boasting, laughing and proud. "And Shoots saved us both. He is not a cub any more. He is a warrior!" She tried to make a victory trill in his honor, but as they lifted her gently onto the pony drag she fainted.

Morning Rider himself attended to the wound of his son Shoots, who did not even remember when the old-woman bear had slashed his forehead. The boy was able to laugh as he said, "She tried to scalp me!"

Morning Rider covered the wound with clotted blood from the bear and tied the flap of skin down with a strip of buckskin around the boy's head. He remarked fondly, "You will have a big scar there. The girls will keep asking you to tell how you got it. I am very proud of you."

Now maybe Grandmother Whirlwind would stop treating him like a little boy, to be ordered around.

He heard her shouting, laughing: "Behold Shoots—he is a warrior. He fought a grizzly bear and killed her."

Shoots shouted back, "Behold Whirlwind! She is a warrior. She was wounded in battle."

He began to sing a praise song for her, although he was feeling weak all of a sudden.

She laughed hysterically. "I am a warrior who was wounded while running away! Take the hide of the enemy—it belongs to Shoots."

Women were skinning out the dead, bloody bear and fighting with a horse that reared, not wanting to carry the hide on its back. The medicine woman filled a big dish with bear blood. She washed the great wound on Whirlwind's leg with

48

water, chanting prayers. She covered the wound with the bear's thickening blood and then cut a big piece of the bear's hide, covering the wound and the blood with the raw side of the fresh hide.

She said with pity, "My friend, I think you will have trouble walking—always, as long as you live. But nobody will ever forget how you saved your son's cub today."

They killed the great bear's cub and cut off its claws to make a necklace for the baby when he grew older. They cut off the immense claws of the woman bear; these were for Shoots. Not long afterward, when he went out to lament for a vision, his dream was a powerful one and when he made up his protective medicine bag, one of the claws was in it. The others he wore for a necklace when he dressed up.

That night the people had a victorious kill dance over the bloody hides of the great bear and the little one. Morning Rider rode around the camp circle leading a fine horse to give away, with Shoots riding beside him. Morning Rider sang:

"A bear killed a woman long ago.
A bear killed a mother long ago.
Now the woman's son has avenged her.
The warrior son has avenged his mother!"

Morning Rider gave the fine horse to a very brave old warrior, who gave Shoots a new name. The warrior shouted, "The boy Shoots counted first coup on a grizzly bear and killed her to save two people. So I give him an honorable name. Kills Grizzly is his name!"

Grandmother Whirlwind lay on her bed, smiling as she listened to the singing and the triumphant drumming of the kill dance in honor of Shoots—no, now she must remember to call him Kills Grizzly. Her daughter was with her, and the medicine woman, who used all her spells and prayers and medicines to try to ease the pain. No matter how Whirlwind lay, with her foot propped up, the pain was very great, but her pride was greater.

"It does not hurt," she said. "It is nothing." She pretended to sleep.

Brings Horses stayed, and Morning Rider's wives came back with their sleepy children. They spoke softly but were full of talk that Whirlwind wanted to hear: about how everyone was honoring Shoots for his courage and talking about how brave Whirlwind herself was.

"Everybody wants to see you," one of them remarked, smiling, "but we refused them all—all except one, who will come soon."

They were hurrying around, Whirlwind noticed, to tidy up the lodge—her work, but she could not do it now. It must be an important visitor or the women would not be so careful to have everything neat and nice this late at night, with the baby and the little girl, Reaches Far, asleep.

Men's voices came nearer, two men. One was Morning Rider; his mother did not recognize the other one. Morning Rider entered and ushered in his companion. He said, "This is Whirlwind Woman, my mother. She saved my baby son."

The other man stood looking down at her. He smiled a little and said, "I am Crazy Horse."

Whirlwind gasped. For once in her life, she had nothing to say. This was the great man, the quiet one, whose very presence made the hearts of his people big.

Morning Rider told her, "I have asked Crazy Horse to name the baby, and he agrees. When the boy is old enough, we will have the ear-piercing ceremony. But today Crazy Horse will give my youngest son a name."

Round Cloud Woman brought the sleeping infant. She was shaking with excitement.

Crazy Horse looked long at the sleeping little face. Then he touched the child's forehead and said, "I give you a name that you can make great in honor of your grandmother, who saved you, and your brother, who counted first coup on the bear. I name the child She Throws Him."

A murmur of delight went up among Morning Rider's family: "Thank you, friend, thank you!"

Round Cloud Woman said to her child, "Wake up, She Throws Him, so that sometime you can say you looked on the face of Crazy Horse the day he gave you your name." The baby opened his eyes, yawned, and went to sleep again.

Now Whirlwind thought of something to say: "My son has forgotten his manners. I did not raise him right. He has not asked our visitor to sit down in the place of honor beside him."

The two men chuckled, and Morning Rider explained, "I asked him before we came, but he thought he would not stay long enough. Will the visitor sit down and smoke?"

Crazy Horse would. Morning Rider filled and lighted the sacred pipe and smoked it to the Powers of the six directions. Then he passed it to Crazy Horse, who did the same and gave back the sacred pipe.

"I wish also to speak to the warrior woman," he said. "Grandmother, how is it with you in your pain?" He used the term "grandmother" in the sense of great respect.

"Not so bad," she replied stoutly, as a warrior should.

Crazy Horse stood up, then knelt beside her and looked into her face. "I give you a name, too, Grandmother. Your name is Saved Her Cub."

Then he nodded and left the lodge, leaving Whirlwind speechless for the second time that day.

When she got her wits back, she complained happily, "But I am too old to remember another name for myself!"

Morning Rider replied, "Others will remember."

●●

Ain't I a Woman?

Sojourner Truth

Isabella Baumfree was born into slavery in about 1797. When a law passed in 1828 gave her her freedom, she changed her name to Sojourner Truth. "Sojourner" means "traveler," and Sojourner Truth traveled around the United States making speeches that urged the abolition of slavery. She delivered the "Ain't I A Woman?" speech at a women's-rights convention in 1851.

Well, Children, where there is so much racket there must be something out of kilter. I think that between the Negroes of the South and the women at the North, all talking about rights, the white men will be in a fix pretty soon. But what's all this here talking about?

That man over there says that women need to be helped into carriages, and lifted over ditches, and to have the best place everywhere. Nobody ever helps me into carriages, or over mud puddles, or gives me any best place! And ain't I a woman? Look at me! Look at my arm! I have ploughed and planted. I have gathered into barns, and no man could head me! And ain't I a woman? I could work as much as a man—when I could get it— and bear the lash as well! And ain't I a woman? I have borne 13 children, and seen them most all sold off to slavery. When I cried out with my mother's grief, none but Jesus heard me! And ain't I a woman?

Then they talk about this thing in the head; what's this they call it? [Intellect, someone whispers.] That's it, honey. What's that got to do with women's rights or Negro's rights? If my cup won't hold but a pint, and yours holds a quart, wouldn't you be mean not to let me have my little half-measure full?

Then that little man in black there, he says women can't have as much rights as men, 'cause Christ wasn't a woman! Where did your Christ come from? Where did your Christ come from? From God and a woman! Man had nothing to do with Him.

If the first woman God ever made was strong enough to turn the world upside down all alone, these women together ought to be able to turn it back, and get it right side up again! And now they is asking to do it, the men better let them.

Obliged to you for hearing me, and now old Sojourner ain't got nothing more to say.

The Day the Sun Came Out

Dorothy M. Johnson

We left the home place behind mile by slow mile, heading for the mountains, across the prairie where the wind blew forever.

At first there were four of us with the one-horse wagon and its skimpy load. Pa and I walked, because I was a big boy of eleven. My two little sisters romped and trotted until they got tired and had to be boosted up into the wagon bed.

That was no covered Conestoga, like Pa's folks came west in, but just an old farm wagon, drawn by one weary horse, creaking and rumbling westward to the mountains, toward the little woods town where Pa thought he had an old uncle who owned a little two-bit sawmill.

Two weeks we had been moving when we picked up Mary, who had run away from somewhere that she wouldn't tell. Pa didn't want her along, but she stood up to him with no fear in her voice.

"I'd rather go with a family and look after kids," she said, "but I ain't going back. If you won't take me, I'll travel with any wagon that will."

Pa scowled at her, and wide blue eyes stared back.

"How old are you?" he demanded.

"Twenty," she said. "There's teamsters come this way sometimes. I'd rather go with you folks. But I won't go back."

"We're prid'near out of grub," my father told her. "We're clean out of money. I got all I can handle without taking anybody else." He turned away as if he hated the sight of her. "You'll have to walk," he said.

So she went along with us and looked after the little girls, but Pa wouldn't talk to her.

On the prairie, the wind blew. But in the mountains, there
was rain. When we stopped at little timber claims along the
way, the homesteaders said it had rained all summer. Crops
among the blackened stumps were rotted and spoiled. There
was no cheer anywhere, and little hospitality. The people we
talked to were beyond worrying. They were scared and
desperate.

So was Pa. He traveled twice as far each day as the wagon,
ranging through the woods with his rifle, but he never saw

game. He had been depending on venison, but we never got any except as a grudging gift from the homesteaders.

He brought in a porcupine once, and that was fat meat and good. Mary roasted it in chunks over the fire, half crying with the smoke. Pa and I rigged up the tarp sheet for a shelter to keep the rain from putting the fire clean out.

The porcupine was long gone, except for some of the dried-out fat that Mary had saved, when we came to an old, empty cabin. Pa said we'd have to stop. The horse was wore out, couldn't pull anymore up those grades on the deep-rutted roads through the mountains.

At the cabin, at least there was shelter. We had a few potatoes left and some corn meal. There was a creek that probably had fish in it, if a person could catch them. Pa tried it for half a day before he gave up. To this day I don't care for fishing. I remember my father's sunken eyes in his gaunt, grim face.

He took Mary and me outside the cabin to talk. Rain dripped on us from branches overhead.

"I think I know where we are," he said. "I calculate to get to old John's and back in about four days. There'll be grub in the town, and they'll let me have some whether old John's still there or not."

He looked at me. "You do like she tells you," he warned. It was the first time he had admitted Mary was on earth since we picked her up two weeks before.

"You're my pardner," he said to me, "but it might be she's got more brains. You mind what she says."

He burst out with bitterness. "There ain't anything good left in the world, or people to care if you live or die. But I'll get grub in the town and come back with it."

He took a deep breath and added, "If you get too all-fired hungry, butcher the horse. It'll be better than starvin'."

He kissed the little girls good-bye and plodded off through the woods with one blanket and the rifle.

The cabin was moldy and had no floor. We kept a fire going under a hole in the roof, so it was full of blinding smoke, but we had to keep the fire so as to dry out the wood.

The third night, we lost the horse. A bear scared him. We heard the racket, and Mary and I ran out, but we couldn't see anything in the dark.

In gray daylight I went looking for him, and must have walked fifteen miles. It seemed like I had to have that horse at the cabin when Pa came or he'd whip me. I got plumb lost two or three times and thought maybe I was going to die there alone and nobody would ever know it, but I found the way back to the clearing.

That was the fourth day, and Pa didn't come. That was the day we ate up the last of the grub.

The fifth day, Mary went looking for the horse. My sisters whimpered, huddled in a quilt by the fire, because they were scared and hungry.

I never did get dried out, always having to bring in more damp wood and going out to yell to see if Mary would hear me and not get lost. But I couldn't cry like the little girls did, because I was big, eleven years old.

It was near dark when there was an answer to my yelling, and Mary came into the clearing.

Mary didn't have the horse—we never saw hide nor hair of that old horse again—but she was carrying something big and white that looked like a pumpkin with no color to it.

She didn't say anything, just looked around and saw Pa wasn't there yet, at the end of the fifth day.

"What's that thing?" my sister Elizabeth demanded.

"Mushroom," Mary answered. "I bet it hefts ten pounds."

"What are you going to do with it now?" I sneered. "Play football here?"

"Eat it—maybe," she said, putting it in a corner. Her wet hair hung over her shoulders. She huddled by the fire.

My sister Sarah began to whimper again. "I'm hungry!" she kept saying.

"Mushrooms ain't good eating," I said. "They can kill you."

"Maybe," Mary answered. "Maybe they can. I don't set up to know all about everything, like some people."

"What's that mark on your shoulder?" I asked her. "You tore your dress on the brush."

"What do you think it is?" she said, her head bowed in the smoke.

"Looks like scars," I guessed.

" 'Tis scars. They whipped me. Now mind your own business. I want to think."

Elizabeth whimpered, "Why don't Pa come back?"

"He's coming," Mary promised. "Can't come in the dark. Your pa'll take care of you soon's he can."

She got up and rummaged around in the grub box.

"Nothing there but empty dishes," I growled. "If there was anything, we'd know it."

Mary stood up. She was holding the can with the porcupine grease.

"I'm going to have something to eat," she said coolly. "You kids can't have any yet. And I don't want any squalling, mind."

It was a cruel thing, what she did then. She sliced that big, solid mushroom and heated grease in a pan.

The smell of it brought the little girls out of their quilt, but she told them to go back in so fierce a voice that they obeyed. They cried to break your heart.

I didn't cry. I watched, hating her.

I endured the smell of the mushroom frying as long as I could. Then I said, "Give me some."

"Tomorrow," Mary answered. "Tomorrow, maybe. But not tonight." She turned to me with a sharp command: "Don't bother me! Just leave me be."

She knelt by the fire and finished frying the slice of mushroom.

If I'd had Pa's rifle, I would have been willing to kill her right then and there.

She didn't eat right away. She looked at the brown, fried slice for a while and said, "By tomorrow morning, I guess you can tell whether you want any."

The little girls stared at her as she ate. Sarah was chewing an old leather glove.

When Mary crawled into the quilts with them, they moved as close as they could get.

I was so scared that my stomach heaved, empty as it was.

Mary didn't stay in the quilts long. She took a drink out of the water bucket and sat down by the fire and looked through the smoke at me.

She said in a low voice, "I don't know how it will be if it's poison. Just do the best you can with the girls. Because your pa will come back, you know. . . . You better go to bed. I'm going to sit up."

And so would you sit up. If it might be your last night on earth and the pain of death might seize you at any moment, you would sit up by the smoky fire, wide-awake, remembering whatever you had to remember, savoring life.

We sat in silence after the girls had gone to sleep. Once I asked, "How long does it take?"

"I never heard," she answered. "Don't think about it."

I slept after a while, with my chin on my chest.

Mary's moving around brought me wide-awake. The blackness of night was fading.

"I guess it's all right," Mary said. "I would be able to tell by now, wouldn't I?"

I answered gruffly, "I don't know."

Mary stood in the doorway for a while, looking out at the dripping world as if she found it beautiful. Then she fried slices of the mushroom while the little girls danced with anxiety.

We feasted, we three, my sisters and I, until Mary ruled, "That'll hold you," and would not cook any more. She didn't touch any of the mushroom herself.

That was a strange day in the moldy cabin. Mary laughed and was gay; she told stories, and we played "Who's Got the Thimble?" with a pine cone.

In the afternoon we heard a shout, and my sisters screamed and I ran ahead of them across the clearing.

The rain had stopped. My father came plunging out of the woods leading a packhorse—and well I remember the treasures of food in that pack.

He glanced at us anxiously as he tore at the ropes that bound the pack.

"Where did the other one go?" he demanded.

Mary came out of the cabin then, walking sedately. As she came toward us, the sun began to shine.

My stepmother was a wonderful woman.

excerpt from I Know Why The Caged Bird Sings —

Maya Angelou

In this excerpt from her autobiography, Maya Angelou talks about her experiences obtaining and performing her job as a streetcar conductor in San Francisco during World War II.

Once I had settled on getting a job, all that remained was to decide which kind of job I was most fitted for. My intellectual pride had kept me from selecting typing, shorthand or filing as subjects in school, so office work was ruled out. War plants and shipyards demanded birth certificates, and mine would reveal me to be fifteen, and ineligible for work. So the well-paying defense jobs were also out. Women had replaced men on the streetcars as conductors and motormen, and the thought of sailing up and down the hills of San Francisco in a dark-blue uniform, with a money changer at my belt, caught my fancy.

Mother was as easy as I had anticipated. The world was moving so fast, so much money was being made, so many people were dying in Guam, and Germany, that hordes of strangers became good friends overnight. Life was cheap and death entirely free. How could she have the time to think about my academic career?

To her question of what I planned to do, I replied that I would get a job on the streetcars. She rejected the proposal with: "They don't accept colored people on the streetcars."

I would like to claim an immediate fury which was followed by the noble determination to break the restricting tradition. But the truth is, my first reaction was one of disappointment. I'd pictured myself, dressed in a neat blue serge suit, my money changer swinging jauntily at my waist, and a cheery smile for the passengers which would make their own work day brighter.

From disappointment, I gradually ascended the emotional ladder to haughty indignation, and finally to that state of stubbornness where the mind is locked like the jaws of an enraged bulldog.

I would go to work on the streetcars and wear a blue serge suit. Mother gave me her support with one of her usual terse asides, "That's what you want to do? Then nothing beats a trial but a failure. Give it everything you've got. I've told you many times, 'Can't do is like Don't Care.' Neither of them have a home."

Translated, that meant there was nothing a person can't do, and there should be nothing a human being didn't care about. It was the most positive encouragement I could have hoped for.

In the offices of the Market Street Railway Company, the receptionist seemed as surprised to see me there as I was surprised to find the interior dingy and the décor drab. Somehow I had expected waxed surfaces and carpeted floors. If I had met no resistance, I might have decided against working for such a poor-mouth-looking concern. As it was, I explained that I had come to see about a job. She asked, was I sent by an agency, and when I replied that I was not, she told me they were only accepting applicants from agencies.

The classified pages of the morning papers had listed advertisements for motorettes and conductorettes and I reminded her of that. She gave me a face full of astonishment that my suspicious nature would not accept.

"I am applying for the job listed in this morning's *Chronicle* and I'd like to be presented to your personnel manager." While I spoke in supercilious accents, and looked at the room as if I had an oil well in my own backyard, my armpits were being pricked by millions of hot pointed needles. She saw her escape and dived into it.

"He's out. He's out for the day. You might call tomorrow and if he's in, I'm sure you can see him." Then she swiveled her chair around on its rusty screws and with that I was supposed to be dismissed.

"May I ask his name?"

She half turned, acting surprised to find me still there.

"His name? Whose name?"

"Your personnel manager."

We were firmly joined in the hypocrisy to play out the scene.

"The personnel manager? Oh, he's Mr. Cooper, but I'm not sure you'll find him here tomorrow. He's . . . Oh, but you can try."

"Thank you."

"You're welcome."

And I was out of the musty room and into the even mustier lobby. In the street I saw the receptionist and myself going faithfully through paces that were stale with familiarity, although I had never encountered that kind of situation before and, probably, neither had she. We were like actors who, knowing the play by heart, were still able to cry afresh over the old tragedies and laugh spontaneously at the comic situations.

The miserable little encounter had nothing to do with me, the me of me, any more than it had to do with that silly clerk. The incident was a recurring dream, concocted years before by stupid whites and it eternally came back to haunt us all. The secretary and I were like Hamlet and Laertes in the final scene, where, because of harm done by one ancestor to another, we were bound to duel to the death. Also because the play must end somewhere.

I went further than forgiving the clerk, I accepted her as a fellow victim of the same puppeteer.

On the streetcar, I put my fare into the box and the conductorette looked at me with the usual hard eyes of white contempt. "Move into the car, please move on in the car." She patted her money changer.

Her Southern nasal accent sliced my meditation and I looked deep into my thoughts. All lies, all comfortable lies. The receptionist was not innocent and neither was I. The whole charade we had played out in that crummy waiting room had directly to do with me, Black, and her, white.

I wouldn't move into the streetcar but stood on the ledge over the conductor, glaring. My mind shouted so energetically that the announcement made my veins stand out, and my mouth tighten into a prune.

I WOULD HAVE THE JOB. I WOULD BE A CONDUCTORETTE AND SLING A FULL MONEY CHANGER FROM MY BELT. I WOULD.

The next three weeks were a honeycomb of determination with apertures for the days to go in and out. The Negro organizations to whom I appealed for support bounced me back and forth like a shuttlecock on a badminton court. Why did I insist on that particular job? Openings were going begging that paid nearly twice the money. The minor officials with whom I was able to win an audience thought me mad. Possibly I was.

Downtown San Francisco became alien and cold, and the streets I had loved in a personal familiarity were unknown lanes that twisted with malicious intent. Old buildings, whose gray rococo façades housed my memories of the Forty-Niners, and Diamond Lil, Robert Service, Sutter and Jack London, were then imposing structures viciously joined to keep me out. My trips to the streetcar office were of the frequency of a person on salary. The struggle expanded. I was no longer in conflict only with the Market Street Railway but with the marble lobby of the building which housed its offices, and elevators and their operators.

During this period of strain Mother and I began our first steps on the long path toward mutual adult admiration. She never asked for reports and I didn't offer any details. But every morning she made breakfast, gave me carfare and lunch money, as if I were going to work. She comprehended the perversity of life, that in the struggle lies the joy. That I was no glory seeker was obvious to her, and that I had to exhaust every possibility before giving in was also clear.

On my way out of the house one morning she said, "Life is going to give you just what you put in it. Put your whole heart in everything you do, and pray, then you can wait." Another time she reminded me that "God helps those who help themselves." She had a store of aphorisms which she dished out as the occasion demanded. Strangely, as bored as I was with clichés, her inflection gave them something new, and set me thinking for a little while at least. Later when asked how I got my job, I was never able to say exactly. I only knew that one day, which was tiresomely like all the others before it, I sat in the Railway office, ostensibly waiting to be interviewed. The receptionist called me to her desk and shuffled a bundle of papers to me. They were job application forms. She said they had to be filled in triplicate. I had little time to wonder if I had won or not, for the standard questions reminded me of the necessity for dexterous lying. How old was I? List my previous jobs, starting from the last held and go backward to the first. How much money did I earn, and why did I leave the position? Give two references (not relatives).

Sitting at a side table my mind and I wove a cat's ladder of near truths and total lies. I kept my face blank (an old art) and wrote quickly the fable of Marguerite Johnson, aged nineteen, former companion and driver for Mrs. Annie Henderson (a White Lady) in Stamps, Arkansas.

I was given blood tests, aptitude tests, physical coordination tests, and Rorschachs, then on a blissful day I was hired as the first Negro on the San Francisco streetcars.

Mother gave me the money to have my blue serge suit tailored, and I learned to fill out work cards, operate the money changer and punch transfers. The time crowded together and at an End of Days I was swinging on the back of the rackety trolley, smiling sweetly and persuading my charges to "step forward in the car, please."

For one whole semester the street cars and I shimmied up and scooted down the sheer hills of San Francisco. I lost some of my need for the Black ghetto's shielding-sponge quality, as I clanged and cleared my way down Market Street, with its honky-tonk homes for homeless sailors, past the quiet retreat of Golden Gate Park and along closed undwelled-in-looking dwellings of the Sunset District.

My work shifts were split so haphazardly that it was easy to believe that my superiors had chosen them maliciously. Upon mentioning my suspicions to Mother, she said, "Don't worry about it. You ask for what you want, and you pay for what you get. And I'm going to show you that it ain't no trouble when you pack double."

She stayed awake to drive me out to the car barn at four thirty in the mornings, or to pick me up when I was relieved just before dawn. Her awareness of life's perils convinced her that while I would be safe on the public conveyances, she "wasn't about to trust a taxi driver with her baby."

When the spring classes began, I resumed my commitment with formal education. I was so much wiser and older, so much more independent, with a bank account and clothes that I had bought for myself, that I was sure that I had learned and earned the magic formula which would make me a part of the gay life my contemporaries led.

Not a bit of it. Within weeks, I realized that my schoolmates and I were on paths moving diametrically away from each other. They were concerned and excited over the approaching football games, but I had in my immediate past raced a car down a dark and foreign Mexican mountain. They concentrated great interest on who was worthy of being student body president, and when the metal bands would be removed from their teeth, while I remembered sleeping for a month in a wrecked automobile and conducting a streetcar in the uneven hours of the morning.

Without willing it, I had gone from being ignorant of being ignorant to being aware of being aware. And the worst part of my awareness was that I didn't know what I was aware of. I knew I knew very little, but I was certain that the things I had yet to learn wouldn't be taught to me at George Washington High School.

I began to cut classes, to walk in Golden Gate Park or wander along the shiny counter of the Emporium Department Store. When Mother discovered that I was playing truant, she told me that if I didn't want to go to school one day, if there were no tests being held, and if my school work was up to standard, all I had to do was tell her and I could stay home. She said that she didn't want some white woman calling her up to tell her something about her child that she didn't know. And she didn't want to be put in the position of lying to a white woman because I wasn't woman enough to speak up. That put an end to my truancy, but nothing appeared to lighten the long gloomy day that going to school became.

To be left alone on the tightrope of youthful unknowing is to experience the excruciating beauty of full freedom and the threat of eternal indecision. Few, if any, survive their teens. Most surrender to the vague but murderous pressure of adult conformity. It becomes easier to die and avoid conflicts than to maintain a constant battle with the superior forces of maturity.

Until recently each generation found it more expedient to plead guilty to the charge of being young and ignorant, easier to take the punishment meted out by the older generation (which had itself confessed to the same crime short years before). The command to grow up at once was more bearable than the faceless horror of wavering purpose, which was youth.

The bright hours when the young rebelled against the descending sun had to give way to twenty-four-hour periods called "days" that were named as well as numbered.

The Black female is assaulted in her tender years by all those common forces of nature at the same time that she is caught in the tripartite crossfire of masculine prejudice, white illogical hate and Black lack of power.

The fact that the adult American Negro female emerges a formidable character is often met with amazement, distaste and even belligerence. It is seldom accepted as an inevitable outcome of the struggle won by survivors and deserves respect if not enthusiastic acceptance.

A MEASURE OF FREEDOM

Jade Snow Wong

This selection is taken from the autobiography of a woman who was born in America to parents who had immigrated from China. Her parents, loyal to the ways of the Old World, demanded unquestioning obedience and respect, which Jade Snow gave. But as she matures, she feels the influence of the New World—a world where people treasure their individual independence and have the right to question authority. When this selection opens, Jade Snow has just learned that she has not won a scholarship to the four-year university. Her friend Joe suggests that she attend a two-year junior college.

So, without much enthusiasm, Jade Snow decided upon junior college. Now it was necessary to inform Mama and Daddy. She chose an evening when the family was at dinner. All of them were in their customary places, and Daddy, typically, was in conversation with Older Brother about the factory:

"Blessing, when do you think Lot Number fifty-one twenty-six will be finished? I want to ask for a check from our jobber so that I can have enough cash for next week's payroll."

To which Older Brother replied, "As soon as Mama is through with the seams in Mrs. Lee's and Mrs. Choy's bundles, the women can finish the hems. Another day, probably."

Mama had not been consulted; therefore she made no comment. Silence descended as the Wongs continued their meal, observing the well-learned precept that talk was not permissible while eating.

Jade Snow considered whether to break the silence. Three times she thought over what she had to say, and still she found it worth saying. This also was according to family precept.

"Daddy," she said, "I have made up my mind to enter junior college here in San Francisco. I will find a steady job to pay my expenses, and by working in the summers I'll try to save enough money to take me through my last two years at the university."

Then she waited. Everyone went on eating. No one said a word. Apparently no one was interested enough to be curious. But at least no one objected. It was settled.

Junior college was at first disappointing in more ways than one. There was none of the glamour usually associated with college because the institution was so young that it had not yet acquired buildings of its own. Classes were held all over the city wherever accommodations were available. The first days were very confusing to Jade Snow, especially when she discovered that she must immediately decide upon a college major.

While waiting to register, she thumbed through the catalogue in search of a clue. English . . . mathematics . . . chemistry. . . . In the last semester of high school she had found chemistry particularly fascinating: so with a feeling of assurance she wrote that as her major on the necessary forms, and went to a sign-up table.

"I wish to take the lecture and laboratory classes for Chemistry 1A," she informed the gray-haired man who presided there.

He looked at her, a trifle impatiently she thought.

"Why?"

"Because I like it." To herself she sounded reasonable.

"But you are no longer in high school. Chemistry here is a difficult subject on a university level, planned for those who are majoring in medicine, engineering, or the serious sciences."

Jade Snow set her chin stubbornly. "I still want to take Chemistry 1A."

Sharply he questioned: "What courses in mathematics have you had? What were your grades?"

Finally Jade Snow's annoyance rose to the surface. "Straight A's. But why must you ask? Do you think I would want to take a course I couldn't pass? Why don't you sign me up and let the instructor be the judge of my ability?"

"Very well," he replied stiffly. "I'll accept you in the class. And for your information, young lady, I am the instructor!"

With this inauspicious start, Jade Snow began her college career.

To take care of finances, she now

needed to look for work. Through a friend she learned that a Mrs. Simpson needed someone to help with household work. "Can you cook?" was Mrs. Simpson's first question.

Jade Snow considered a moment before answering. Certainly she could cook Chinese food, and she remembered a common Chinese saying, "A Chinese can cook foreign food as well as, if not better than, the foreigners, but a foreigner cannot cook Chinese food fit for the Chinese." On this reasoning it seemed safe to say "Yes."

After some further discussion Jade Snow was hired. Cooking, she discovered, included everything from pastries, puddings, meats, steaks, and vegetables, to sandwiches. In addition, she served the meals, washed dishes, kept the house clean, did the light laundry and ironing for Mr. and Mrs. Simpson and their career daughter—and always appeared in uniform, which she thoroughly disliked. In return she received twenty dollars a month. At night, she did her studying at home, and sometimes after a hard day she was so tired that the walk from the Simpson flat to the streetcar on Chestnut Street was a blessed respite, a time to relax and admire the moon if she could find it, and to gather fresh energy for whatever lay ahead.

Desserts, quite ignored in a Chinese household, were of first importance in the Simpson household. One particular Saturday, Jade Snow was told to bake a special meringue sponge cake with a fancy fruit filling of whipped cream and peeled and seeded grapes. Following a very special recipe of Mrs. Simpson's, she mixed it for the first time and preheated the oven. Mrs. Simpson came into the kitchen, checked and approved the prepared cake

batter, and said that she would judge when it was done. Meantime she and her husband and their guests lounged happily in the garden.

Almost an hour passed. The meringue was baking in a slow oven. The recipe said not to open the door, as the cake might fall. An hour and a quarter passed, and the pastry smelled sweetly delicate. Yet Mrs. Simpson did not come. Jade Snow wondered whether or not to call her. But she remembered that her employer disliked being disturbed when entertaining officials of her husband's company.

After an hour and forty-five minutes the cake no longer smelled delicate. Jade Snow was worn out! What could she do? At last, there was a rush of high-heeled footsteps; swish went the kitchen door, and Mrs. Simpson burst in, flushed from the sun or excitement.

"I must look at that meringue cake," she burst out.

The oven door was pulled open, and Jade Snow peered in anxiously over her employer's shoulder. Too late! It had fallen and become a tough, brown mass. Jade Snow was dumb with a crushed heart, inspecting the flattened pancake, mentally reviewing all the processes of whipping, measuring, and sifting that she had gone through for hours to achieve this unpalatable result.

Mrs. Simpson crisply broke through to her anguish, "Well, there's nothing to be done but for you to make another."

That afternoon was a torturous nightmare and a fever of activity—to manage another meringue cake, to get rolls mixed, salad greens cleaned and crisped, vegetables cut, meat broiled, the table set, and all the other details of a "company" dinner attended to. By the time she was at last washing the dishes and tidying the dining room she felt strangely vague. She hadn't taken time to eat her dinner; she was too tired anyway. How she wished that she had been asked to cook a Chinese dinner instead of this interminable American meal, especially that cake!

Of her college courses, Latin was the easiest. This was a surprise, for everyone had told her of its horrors. It was much more logical than French, almost mathematical in its orderliness and precision, and actually a snap after nine years of Chinese.

Chemistry, true to the instructor's promise, was difficult, although the classes were anything but dull. It turned out that he was a very nice person with a keen sense of humor and a gift for enlivening his lectures with stories of his own college days. There were only two girls in a class of more than fifty men— a tense blonde girl from Germany, who always ranked first; and Jade Snow, who usually took second place.

But if Latin was the easiest course and chemistry the most difficult, sociology was the most stimulating. Jade Snow had chosen it without thought, simply to meet a requirement; but that casual decision completely revolutionized her thinking, shattering her Wong-constructed conception of the order of things. This was the way it happened:

After several uneventful weeks during which the class explored the historical origins of the family and examined such terms as "norms," "mores," "folkways," there came a day when the instructor stood before them to discuss the relationship of parents and children. It was a day like many others, with the students

listening in varying attitudes of interest or indifference. The instructor was speaking casually of ideas to be accepted as standard. Then suddenly upon Jade Snow's astounded ears there fell this statement:

"There was a period in our American history when parents had children for economic reasons, to put them to work as soon as possible, especially to have them help on the farm. But now we no longer regard children in this way. Today we recognize that children are individuals, and that parents can no longer demand their unquestioning obedience. Parents should do their best to understand their children, because young people also have their rights."

The instructor went on talking, but Jade Snow heard no more, for her mind was echoing and re-echoing this startling thought. "Parents can no longer demand unquestioning obedience from their children. They should do their best to understand. Children also have their rights." For the rest of that day, while she was doing her chores at the Simpsons', while she was standing in the streetcar going home, she was busy translating the idea into terms of her own experience.

"My parents demand unquestioning obedience. Older Brother demands unquestioning obedience. By what right? I am an individual besides being a Chinese daughter. I have rights too."

Could it be that Daddy and Mama, although they were living in San Francisco in the year 1938, actually had not left the Chinese world of thirty years ago? Could it be that they were forgetting that Jade Snow would soon become a woman in a new America, not a woman in old China? In short, was it possible that Daddy and Mama could be wrong?

For days Jade Snow gave thought to little but her devastating discovery that her parents might be subject to error. As it was her habit always to act after reaching a conclusion, she wondered what to do about it. Should she tell Daddy and Mama that they needed to change their ways? One moment she thought she should, the next she thought not. At last she decided to overcome her fear in the interests of education and better understanding. She would at least try to open their minds to modern truths. If she succeeded, good! If not, she was prepared to suffer the consequences.

In this spirit of patient martyrdom she waited for an opportunity to speak.

It came, surprisingly, one Saturday. Ordinarily that was a busy day at the Simpsons', a time for entertaining, so that Jade Snow was not free until too late to go anywhere even had she had a place to go. But on this particular Saturday the Simpsons were away for the weekend, and by three in the afternoon Jade Snow was ready to leave the apartment with unplanned hours ahead of her. She didn't want to spend these rare hours of freedom in any usual way. And she didn't want to spend them alone.

"Shall I call Joe?" she wondered. She had never telephoned to a boy before and she debated whether it would be too forward. But she felt too happy and carefree to worry much, and she was confident that Joe would not misunderstand.

Even before reporting to Mama that she was home, she ran downstairs to the telephone booth and gave the operator Joe's number. His mother answered and then went to call him while Jade Snow waited in embarrassment.

"Joe." She was suddenly tongue-tied. "Joe, I'm already home."

That wasn't at all what she wanted to say. What did she want to say?

"Hello! Hello!" Joe boomed back. "What's the matter with you? Are you all right?"

"Oh, yes, I'm fine. Only, only . . . well, I'm through working for the day." That was really all she had to say, but now it sounded rather pointless.

"Isn't that wonderful? It must have been unexpected." That was what was nice and different about Joe. He always seemed to know without a lot of words. But because his teasing was never far behind his understanding he added quickly, "I suppose you're going to study and go to bed early."

Jade Snow was still not used to teasing and didn't know how to take it. With an effort she swallowed her shyness and disappointment. "I thought we might go for a walk . . . that is, if you have nothing else to do . . . if you would care to . . . if. . . ."

Joe laughed. "I'll go you one better. Suppose I take you to a movie. I'll even get all dressed up for you, and you get dressed up too."

Jade Snow was delighted. Her first movie with Joe! What a wonderful day. In happy anticipation she put on her long silk stockings, lipstick, and the nearest thing to a suit she owned—a hand-me-down jacket and a brown skirt she had made herself. Then with a bright ribbon tying back her long black hair she was ready.

Daddy didn't miss a detail of the preparations as she dashed from room to room. He waited until she was finished before he demanded, "Jade Snow, where are you going?"

"I am going out into the street," she answered.

"Did you ask my permission to go out into the street?"

"No, Daddy."

"Do you have your mother's permission to go out into the street?"

"No, Daddy."

A sudden silence from the kitchen indicated that Mama was listening.

Daddy went on: "Where and when did you learn to be so daring as to leave this house without permission of your parents? You did not learn it under my roof."

It was all very familiar. Jade Snow waited, knowing that Daddy had not finished. In a moment he came to the point.

"And with whom are you going out into the street?"

It took all the courage Jade Snow could muster, remembering her new thinking, to say nothing. It was certain that if she told Daddy that she was going out with a boy whom he did not know, without a chaperone, he would be convinced that she would lose her maidenly purity before the evening was over.

"Very well," Daddy said sharply. "If you will not tell me, I forbid you to go! You are now too old to whip."

That was the moment.

Suppressing all anger, and in a manner that would have done credit to her sociology instructor addressing his freshman class, Jade Snow carefully turned on her mentally rehearsed speech.

"That is something you should think more about. Yes, I am too old to whip. I am too old to be treated as a child. I can now think for myself, and you and Mama should not demand unquestioning obedience from me. You should understand me. There was a time in America when parents raised children to make them work, but now the foreigners regard them as individuals with rights of their own. I have worked too, but now I am an individual besides being your fifth daughter."

It was almost certain that Daddy blinked, but after the briefest pause he gathered himself together.

"Where," he demanded, "did you learn such an unfilial theory?"

Mama had come quietly into the room and slipped into a chair to listen.

"From my teacher," Jade Snow answered triumphantly, "who you taught me is supreme after you, and whose judgment I am not to question."

Daddy was feeling pushed. Thoroughly aroused, he shouted:

"A little learning has gone to your head! How can you permit a foreigner's theory to put aside the practical experience of the Chinese, who for thousands of years have preserved a most superior family pattern? Confucius had already presented an organized philosophy of manners and conduct when the foreigners were unappreciatively persecuting Christ. Who brought you up? Who clothed you, fed you, sheltered you, nursed you? Do you think you were born aged sixteen? You owe honor to us before you satisfy your personal whims."

Daddy thundered on, while Jade Snow kept silent.

"What would happen to the order of this household if each of you four children started to behave like individuals? Would we have one peaceful moment if your personal desires came before your duty? How could we maintain our self-respect if we, your parents, did not know where you were at night and with whom you were keeping company?"

With difficulty Jade Snow kept herself from being swayed by fear and the old familiar arguments. "You can be bad in the daytime as well as at night," she said defensively. "What could happen after eleven that couldn't happen before?"

Daddy was growing more excited. "Do I have to justify my judgment to you? I do not want a daughter of mine to be known as one who walks the streets at night. Have you no thought for our reputations if not for your own? If you start going out with boys, no good man will want to ask you to be his wife. You just do not know as well as we do what is good for you."

Mama fanned Daddy's wrath, "Never having been a mother, you cannot know how much grief it is to bring up a daughter. Of course we will not permit you to run the risk of corrupting your purity before marriage."

"Oh, Mama!" Jade Snow retorted. "This is America, not China. Don't you think I have any judgment? How can you think I would go out with just any man?"

"Men!" Daddy roared. "You don't know a thing about them. I tell you, you can't trust any of them."

Now it was Jade Snow who felt pushed. She delivered the balance of her declaration of independence:

"Both of you should understand that I am growing up to be a woman in a society greatly different from the one you knew in China. You expect me to work my way through college—which would not have been possible in China. You expect me to exercise judgment in choosing my employers and my jobs and in spending my own money in the American world. Then why can't I choose my friends? Of course independence is not safe. But safety isn't the only consideration. You must give me the freedom to find some answers for myself."

Mama found her tongue first. "You think you are too good for us because you have a little foreign book knowledge."

"You will learn the error of your ways after it is too late," Daddy added darkly.

By this Jade Snow knew that her parents had conceded defeat. Hoping to soften the blow, she tried to explain: "If I am to earn my living, I must learn how to get along with many kinds of people, with foreigners as well as Chinese. I intend to start finding out about them now. You must have confidence that I shall remain true to the spirit of your teachings. I shall bring back to you the new knowledge of whatever I learn."

Daddy and Mama did not accept this offer graciously. "It is as useless for you to tell me such ideas as 'The wind blows across a deaf ear.' You have lost your sense of balance," Daddy told her bluntly. "You are shameless. Your skin is yellow. Your features are forever Chinese. We are content with our proven ways. Do not try to force foreign ideas into my home. Go. You will one day tell us sorrowfully that you have been mistaken."

After that there was no further discussion of the matter. Jade Snow came and went without any questions being asked. In spite of her parents' dark predictions, her new freedom in the choice of companions did not result in a rush of undesirables. As a matter of fact, the boys she met at school were more concerned with copying her lecture notes than with anything else.

As for Joe, he remained someone to walk with and talk with. On the evening of Jade Snow's seventeenth birthday he took her up Telegraph Hill and gave her as a remembrance a sparkling grown-up bracelet with a card which read: "Here's to your making Phi Beta Kappa." And

there under the stars he gently tilted her face and gave her her first kiss.

Standing straight and awkward in her full-skirted red cotton dress, Jade Snow was caught by surprise and without words. She felt that something should stir and crash within her, in the way books and the movies described, but nothing did. Could it be that she wasn't in love with Joe, in spite of liking and admiring him? After all, he was twenty-three and probably too old for her anyway.

Still she had been kissed at seventeen, which was cause for rejoicing. Laughing happily, they continued their walk.

But while the open rebellion gave Jade Snow a measure of freedom she had not had before, and an outer show of assurance, she was deeply troubled within. It had been simple to have Daddy and Mama tell her what was right and wrong; it was not simple to decide for herself. No matter how critical she was of them, she could not discard all they stood for and accept as a substitute the philosophy of the foreigners. It took very little thought to discover that the foreign philosophy also was subject to criticism, and that for her there had to be a middle way.

In particular, she could not reject the fatalism that was at the core of all Chinese thinking and behavior, the belief that the broad pattern of an individual's life was ordained by fate although within that pattern he was capable of perfecting himself and accumulating a desirable store of good will. Should the individual not benefit by his good works, still the rewards would pass on to his children or his children's children. Epitomized by the proverbs: "I save your life, for your grandson might save mine," and "Heaven does not forget to follow the path a good man walks," this was a fundamental philosophy of Chinese life which Jade Snow found fully as acceptable as some of the so-called scientific reasoning expounded in the sociology class, where heredity and environment were assigned all the responsibility for personal success or failure.

There was good to be gained from both concepts if she could extract and retain her own personally applicable combination. She studied her neighbor in class, Stella Green, for clues. Stella had grown up reading Robert Louis Stevenson, learning to swim and play tennis, developing a taste for roast beef, mashed potatoes, sweets, aspirin tablets, and soda pop, and she looked upon her mother and father as friends. But it was very unlikely that she knew where her great-grandfather was born, or whether or not she was related to another strange Green she might chance to meet. Jade Snow had grown up reading Confucius, learning to embroider and cook rice, developing a taste for steamed fish and bean sprouts, tea, and herbs, and she thought of her parents as people to be obeyed. She not only knew where her ancestors were born but where they were buried, and how many chickens and roast pigs should be brought annually to their graves to feast their spirits. She knew all of the branches of the Wong family, the relation of each to the other, and understood why Daddy must help support the distant cousins in China who bore the sole responsibility of carrying on the family heritage by periodic visits to the burial grounds in Fragrant Mountains. She knew that one could purchase in a Chinese stationery store the printed record of her family tree relating their Wong line and other Wong lines back to the original Wong ancestors. In such a scheme the individual counted for little weighed against the family, and after sixteen years it was not easy to sever roots.

There were, alas, no books or advisers to guide Jade Snow in her search for balance between the pull from two cultures. If she chose neither to reject nor accept *in toto,* she must sift both and make her decisions alone. It would not be an easy search. But pride and determination, which Daddy had given her, prevented any thought of turning back.

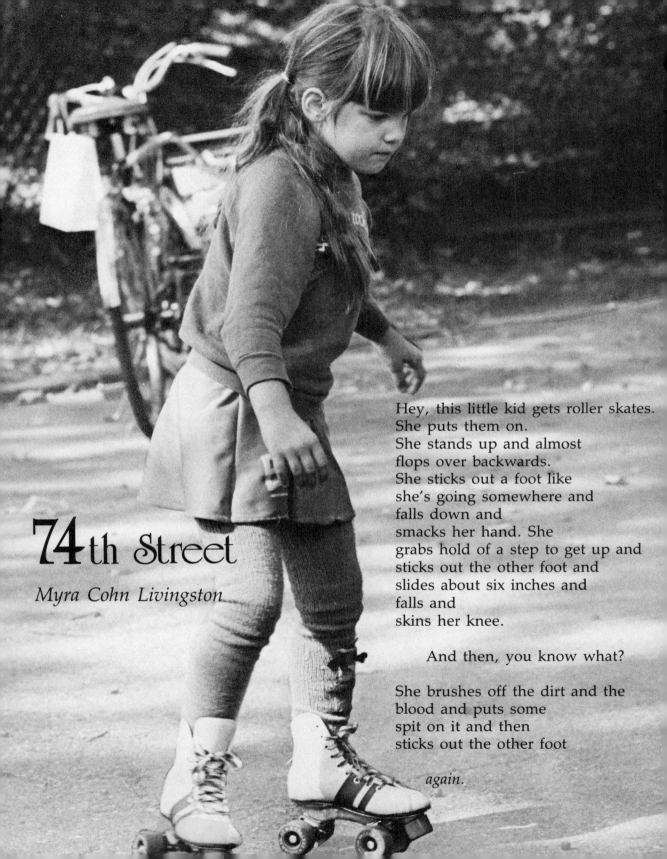

74th Street

Myra Cohn Livingston

Hey, this little kid gets roller skates.
She puts them on.
She stands up and almost
flops over backwards.
She sticks out a foot like
she's going somewhere and
falls down and
smacks her hand. She
grabs hold of a step to get up and
sticks out the other foot and
slides about six inches and
falls and
skins her knee.

And then, you know what?

She brushes off the dirt and the
blood and puts some
spit on it and then
sticks out the other foot

again.

The Three Counsels

as told by Riley Aiken

This was a boy who ran away from home. Though at heart not bad, he had three habits that were by no means good, for he would stick to no purpose, was always asking about people's affairs, and would not control his temper.

Sī señor, he ran away from home, but, do you know, he was hardly beyond the horizon when he left the highway for a trail, called to an old man to know his business, and flew into a rage when the latter did not answer.

Presently, however, the *viejito* spoke. "I am a peddler of advice," said he.

76

"What kind of advice?" asked the boy.

"It will cost you one peso to find out," was the answer.

The boy had only three pesos, but curiosity induced him to give one to the *viejito*.

"First," said the old man, "don't leave a highway for a trail."

"Is that what you call advice?" asked the boy. "You are a fraud."

"Don't you like that one?" asked the *viejito*. "Then give me another peso and lend an ear."

The boy reluctantly handed over the second of his three pesos and waited. "Second," said the *viejito*, "don't ask about things that don't pertain to you."

"*Mal ladrón*," shouted the boy, "for one peso I would kill you."

"Calm yourself, *hijito*," said the old man. "I have among my wares one more bit of advice you need. Will you buy it or not?"

The boy's curiosity was too much for him. He gave his last peso to the stranger and listened attentively for the third time.

"Don't lose your temper," laughed the old man, and before the boy could gather his wits, he had vanished into the chaparral.

Sad and empty of pocket, the youth continued on his way.

He took to the road again just as a stranger mounted on a large black horse galloped up.

"Where to, *joven*?" called he.

"To the city," said the boy.

"Then you need advice," responded the man. "Look, I will help you. One league up the road you will find a short cut. You will recognize it by my horse's tracks. It will save you many miles."

The boy thanked him and continued on his journey with the purpose of leaving the highway for the path. However, never being able to keep to a purpose, he disregarded the path.

At noon he came to a ranch house. A bandit sat beneath an arbor in front of it.

"*Pase, joven*," he called. "You are just in time for dinner."

The boy entered the house and took a chair at the table. He had waited no time when a servant placed before him a dish containing the head of a man. He was at the point of asking a question when he remembered suddenly one of his three costly bits of advice. "I had better ask no question," thought he.

"Young man," said the bandit, "what do you think of this head?"

"It is a good head," replied the boy.

"Have you no questions?" queried the bandit.

"No, señor, none."

"Would you like to see some of my keepsakes?" asked the bandit.

"If it is your pleasure to show them," said the boy, "then it will be my pleasure to see them."

A closet was opened and the boy was shown many skeletons hanging by the neck.

"How do you like my men?" asked the host.

"They are good men," answered the boy.

"*Joven*," said the bandit, "I kill all my guests. These men, like you, each in his turn stepped across my threshold to have dinner with me. Each was shown a head, but different from you, they wanted to know all about it. Their curiosity brought them to their present condition. You, however, have asked nothing about things that do not concern you, and for that reason my servants will conduct you safely from the ranch. In my corral there are three mules and a horse. The mules will be loaded with gold, and the horse will be saddled. These are yours."

Six bags of gold were tied *mancornado* (in pairs) and placed on the mules. The boy mounted the horse and with the help of the servants was soon on the highway again. "Indeed," he said to himself, "it pays to keep to the main road and it pays to ask no questions about things that do not concern one. Now I am rich."

"Halt!" called a voice from the roadside.

There stood a bandit with his arms crossed.

"What have you in those sacks?" he asked.

The boy was on the point of cursing with rage when he recalled the third bit of advice.

"It is a secret I prefer not to tell," he answered calmly.

"Speak or I shall kill you," threatened the bandit.

"If you feel that is best," said the boy, "then follow your conscience."

"Ha!" said the man, "you are a wise boy. *Adios;* may you have a pleasant journey."

This *joven* entered the city. Before many weeks had passed he had built and stocked the best store in town and was making barrels of money. Furthermore, he met and married a wealthy girl. However, the best of all was that she, too, did not leave the main road for a path, asked no questions about things that did not pertain to her, and always kept her temper.

A Precocious Autobiography

Yevgeny Yevtushenko

In 1944 I was living alone in an empty apartment in a small quiet Moscow street, Chetvertaya Meshchanskaya.

My parents were divorced. My father was somewhere in Kazakhstan with his new wife and their two children. I seldom received letters from him.

My mother was at the front. She had given up her work as a geologist to become a singer and was giving concerts for the troops.

My education was left to the street. The street taught me to swear, smoke, spit elegantly through my teeth, and to keep my fists up, always ready for a fight—a habit which I have kept to this day.

The street taught me not to be afraid of anything or anyone—this is another habit I have kept.

I realized that what mattered in the struggle for existence was to overcome my fear of those who were stronger.

The ruler of our street, Chetvertaya Meshchanskaya, was a boy of about sixteen who was nicknamed Red.

Red's shoulders were incredibly broad for a boy of his age.

Red walked masterfully up and down our street, his legs wide apart and with a slightly rolling gait, like a seaman on the deck of his ship.

From under his peaked cap, always worn back to front, his forelock tumbled down in a fiery cascade, and out of his round pockmarked face, green eyes, like a cat's, sparkled with scorn for everything and everyone crossing his path. Two or three lieutenants, in peaked caps back to front like Red's, trotted at his heels.

Red could stop any boy and say impressively the one word "money." His lieutenants would turn out the boy's pockets, and if he resisted they gave him a real beating.

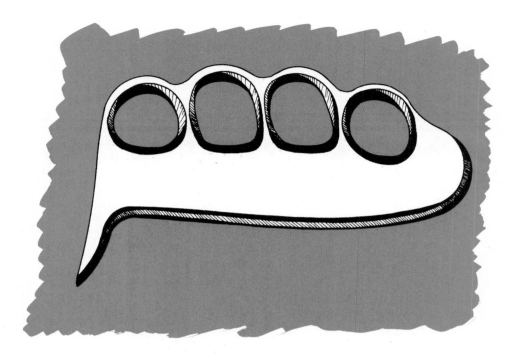

Everyone was afraid of Red. I too was afraid. I knew he carried heavy brass knuckles in his pocket.

I wanted to conquer my fear of Red.

So I wrote a poem about him.

This was my first piece of journalism in verse.

By the next day the whole street knew the piece by heart and relished it with triumphant hatred.

One morning on my way to school I suddenly came upon Red and his lieutenants. His eyes seemed to bore through me. "Ah, the poet," he drawled, smiling crookedly. "So you write verses. Do they rhyme?"

Red's hand darted into his pocket and came out armed with its brass knuckles; it flashed like lightning and struck my head. I fell down streaming with blood and lost consciousness.

This was my first payment as a poet.

I spent several days in bed.

When I went out, with my head still bandaged, I again saw Red. I struggled with instinctive fear but lost and took to my heels.

I ran all the way home. There I rolled on my bed, biting my pillow and pounding it with my fists in shame and impotent fury at my cowardice.

But then I made up my mind to vanquish it at whatever cost.

I went into training with parallel bars and weights, and after every session I would feel my muscles. They were getting harder, but slowly. Then I remembered something I had read in a book about a miraculous Japanese method of wrestling which gave an advantage to the weak over the strong. I sacrificed a week's ration card for a textbook on jujitsu.

For three weeks I hardly left home—I trained with two other boys. Finally I felt I was ready and went out.

Red was sitting on the lawn in our yard, playing Twenty-one with his lieutenants. He was absorbed in the game.

Fear was still in me and it ordered me to turn back. But I went up to the players and kicked the cards aside with my foot.

Red looked up, surprised at my boldness after my recent fight.

He got up slowly. "You looking for more?" he asked menacingly.

As before, his hand dived into his pocket for the brass knuckles. But I made a quick jabbing movement, and Red, howling with pain, rolled on the ground. Bewildered, he got up and came at me, swinging his head furiously from side to side like a bull.

I caught his wrist and squeezed slowly, as I had read in the book, until the brass knuckles dropped from his limp fingers. Nursing his hand, Red fell down again. He was sobbing and smearing the tears over his pockmarked face with his grimy fist. His lieutenants discreetly withdrew.

That day Red ceased to rule our street.

And from that day on, I knew for certain that there is no need to fear the strong. All one needs is to know the method of overcoming them. There is a special jujitsu for every strong man.

What I also learned that day was that, if I wished to be a poet, I must not only write poems but also know how to stand up for what I have written.

The New Kid

Murray Heyert

By the time Marty ran up the stairs, past the dentist's office, where it smelled like the time his father was in the hospital, past the fresh paint smell, where the new kid lived, past the garlic smell, and waited for Mommer to open the door; and threw his schoolbooks on top of the old newspapers that were piled on the sewing machine in the hall; and drank his glass of milk ("How many times must I tell you not to gulp! Are you going to stop gulping like that or must I smack your face!"); and set the empty glass in the sink under the faucet; and changed into his brown keds; and put trees into his school shoes ("How many times must I talk to you! When will you learn to take care of your clothes and not make me follow you around like this!"); and ran downstairs again, past the garlic and the paint and the hospital smells; by the time he got into the street and looked breathlessly around him, it was too late. The fellows were all out there, all ready for a game, and just waiting for Eddie Deakes to finish chalking a base against the curb.

Running up the street with all his might, Marty could see that the game would start any minute now. Out in the gutter Paulie Dahler was tossing high ones to Ray-Ray Stickerling, whose father was a bus driver and sometimes gave the fellows transfers so they could ride free. The rest were sitting on the curb, waiting for Eddie to finish making the base and listening to Gelberg, who was a Jew, explain what it meant to be bar mizvah'd, like he was going to be next month.

They did not look up as Marty galloped up to them all out of breath. Eddie finished making his base and after looking at it critically a moment, with his head on one side, moved down toward the sewer that was home plate and began drawing a scoreboard alongside it. With his nose running from excitement Marty trotted over to him.

"Just going to play with two bases?" he said, wiping his nose on the sleeve of his lumber jacket, and hoping with all his might that Eddie would think he had been there all the while and was waiting for a game like all the other fellows.

Eddie raised his head and saw that it was Marty. He gave Marty a shove. "Why don't you watch where you're walking?" he said. "Can't you see I'm making a scoreboard!"

He bent over again and with his chalk repaired the lines that Marty had smudged with his sneakers. Marty hopped around alongside him, taking care to keep his feet off the chalked box. "Gimme a game, Eddie?" he said.

"What are you asking me for?" Eddie said without looking up. "It ain't my game."

"Aw, come on, Eddie. I'll get even on you!" Marty said.

"Ask Gelberg. It's his game," Eddie said, straightening himself and shoving his chalk into his pants pocket. He trotted suddenly into the

middle of the street and ran sideways a few feet. "Here go!" he hollered. "All the way!"

From his place up near the corner Paulie Dahler heaved the ball high into the air, higher than the telephone wires. Eddie took a step back, then a step forward, then back again, and got under it.

Marty bent his knees like a catcher, pounded his fist into his palm as though he were wearing a mitt, and held out his hands. "Here go, Eddie!" he hollered. "Here go!"

Holding the ball in his hand, and without answering him, Eddie walked toward the curb, where the rest of the fellows were gathered around Gelberg. Marty straightened his knees, put down his hands, and, sniffling his nose, trotted after Eddie.

"All right, I'll choose Gelberg for sides," Eddie said.

Gelberg heaved himself off the curb and put on his punchball glove, which was one of his mother's old kid gloves, with the fingers and thumb cut off short. "Odds, once takes it," he said.

After a couple of preparatory swings of their arms they matched fingers. Gelberg won. He chose Albie Newbauer. Eddie looked around him and took Wally Reinhard. Gelberg took Ray-Ray Stickerling. Eddie took Wally Reinhard's brother Howey.

Marty hopped around on the edge of the group. "Hey, Gelberg," he hollered in a high voice. "Gimme a game, will you?"

"I got Arnie," Gelberg said.

Eddie looked around him again. "All right, I got Paulie Dahler."

They counted their men. "Choose you for up first," Gelberg said. Feeling as though he were going to cry, Marty watched them as they swung their arms, stuck out their fingers. This time Eddie won. Gelberg gathered his men around him and they trotted into the street to take up positions on the field. They hollered, "Here go!" threw the ball from first to second, then out into the field, and back again to Gelberg in the pitcher's box.

Marty ran over to him. "Gimme a game, will you, Gelberg?"

"We're all choosed up," Gelberg said, heaving a high one to Arnie out in center field.

Marty wiped his nose on his sleeve. "Come on, gimme a game. Didn't I let you lose my Spaulding Hi-Bouncer down the sewer once?"

"Want to give the kid a game?" Gelberg called to Eddie, who was seated on the curb, figuring out his batting order with his men.

"Aw, we got the sides all choosed up!" Eddie said.

Marty stuck out his lower lip and wished that he would not have to cry. "You give Howey Reinhard a game!" he said, pointing at Howey sitting on the curb next to Eddie. "He can't play any better than me!"

"Yeah," Howey yelled, swinging back his arm as though he were going to punch Marty in the jaw. "You couldn't hit the side of the house!"

"Yeah, I can play better than you any day!" Marty hollered.

"You can play left outside!" Howey said, looking around to see how the joke went over.

"Yeah, I'll get even on you!" Marty hollered, hoping that maybe they would get worried and give him a game after all.

With a fierce expression on his face, as if to indicate that he was through joking and now meant serious business, Howey sprang up from the curb and sent him staggering with a shove. Marty tried to duck, but Howey smacked him across the side of the head. Flinging his arms up about his ears, Marty scrambled down the street; for no reason at all Paulie Dahler booted him in the pants as he went by.

"I'll get even on you!" Marty yelled when he was out of reach. With a sudden movement of his legs Howey pretended to rush at him. Almost falling over himself in panic, Marty dashed toward the house, but stopped, feeling ashamed, when he saw that Howey had only wanted to make him run.

For a while he stood there on the curb, wary and ready to dive into the house the instant any of the fellows made a move toward him. But presently he saw that the game was beginning, and that none of them was paying any more attention to him. He crept toward them again and, seating himself on the curb a little distance away, watched the game start. For a moment he thought of breaking it up, rushing up to the scoreboard and smudging it with his sneakers before any one could stop him, and then dashing into the house before they caught him. Or grabbing the ball when it came near him and flinging it down the sewer. But he decided not to; the fellows would catch him in the end, smack him, and make another scoreboard or get another ball, and then he would never get a game.

Every minute feeling more and more like crying, he sat there on the curb, his elbow on his knee, his chin in his palm, and tried to think where he could get another fellow, so that they could give him a game and still have even sides. Then he lifted his chin from his palm and saw that the new kid was sitting out on the stoop in front of the house, chewing something and gazing toward the game; and all at once the feeling that he was going to cry disappeared. He sprang up from the curb.

"Hey, Gelberg!" he hollered. "If I get the new kid for even sides can I get a game?"

Without waiting for an answer he dashed down the street toward the stoop where the new kid was sitting.

"Hey, fellow!" he shouted. "Want a game? Want a game of punchball?"

He could see now that what the new kid was eating was a slice of rye bread covered with applesauce. He could see too that the new kid was smaller than he was, and had a narrow face and a large nose with a few little freckles across the bridge. He was wearing Boy Scout pants and a brown woolen pullover, and on the back of his head was a skullcap made from the crown of a man's felt hat, the edge turned up and cut into sharp points that were ornamented with brass paper clips.

All out of breath, he stopped in front of the new kid. "What do you say?" he hollered. "Want a game?"

The new kid looked at him and took another bite of rye bread. "I don't know," he said, with his mouth full of bread, turning to take another look at the fellows in the street. "I guess I got to go to the store soon."

"You don't have to go to the store right away, do you?" Marty said in a high voice.

The new kid swallowed his bread and continued looking up toward the game. "I got to stay in front of the house in case my mother calls me."

"Maybe she won't call you for a while," Marty said. He could see that the inning was ending, that they would be starting a new inning in a minute, and his legs twitched with impatience.

"I don't know," the new kid said, still looking up at the game. "Anyway, I got my good shoes on."

"Aw, I bet you can't even play punchball!" cried Marty.

The new kid looked at him with his lower lip stuck out. "Yeah, I can so play! Only I got to go to the store!"

Once more he looked undecidedly up toward the game. Marty could see that the inning was over now. He turned pleadingly to the new kid.

"You can hear her if she calls you, can't you? Can't you play just till she calls you? Come on, can't you?"

Putting the last of his rye bread into his mouth, the new kid got up from the stoop. "Well, when she calls me," he said, brushing off the seat of his pants with his hand, "when she calls me I got to quit and go to the store."

As fast as he could run Marty dashed up the street with the new kid trailing after him. "Hey, I got another man for even sides!" he yelled. "Gimme a game now? I got another man!"

The fellows looked at the new kid coming up the street behind Marty.

"You new on the block?" Howey Reinhard asked, eying the Boy Scout pants, as Marty and the new kid came up to them.

"You any good?" Gelberg demanded, bouncing the ball at his feet and looking at the skullcap ornamented with brass paper clips. "Can you hit?"

"Come on!" Marty said. He wished that they would just give him a game and not start asking a lot of questions. "I got another man for even sides, didn't I?"

"Aw, we got the game started already!" Ray-Ray Stickerling hollered.

Marty sniffled his nose, which was beginning to run again, and looked at him as fiercely as he was able. "It ain't your game!" he yelled. "It's Gelberg's game! Ain't it your game, Gelberg?"

Gelberg gave him a shove. "No one said you weren't going to get a game!" With a last bounce of his ball he turned to Eddie, who was looking the new kid over carefully.

"All right, Eddie. I'll take the new kid and you can have Marty."

Eddie drew his arm back as though he were going to hit him. "Like fun! Why don't you take Marty, if you're so wise?"

"I won the choose-up!" Gelberg hollered.

"Yeah, that was before! I'm not taking Marty!"

"I won the choose-up, didn't I?"

"Well, you got to choose up again for the new kid!"

Marty watched them as they stood up to each other, each eying the other suspiciously, and swung their arms to choose. Eddie won. "Cheating shows!" he yelled, seizing the new kid by the arm and pulling him into the group on his side.

Trying to look like the ballplayers he had seen the time his father had taken him to the Polo Grounds, Marty ran into the outfield and took the position near the curb that Gelberg had selected for him. He tried not to feel bad because Eddie had taken the new kid, that no one knew anything about, how he could hit, or anything; and that he had had to go to the loser of the choose-up. As soon as he was out in the field he leaned forward, with his hands propped on his knees, and hollered: "All right, all right, these guys can't hit!'' Then he straightened up and pounded his fist into his palm as though he were wearing a fielder's glove and shouted: ''Serve it to them on a silver platter, Gelberg! These guys are just a bunch of fan artists!'' He propped his hands on his knees again, like a big-leaguer, but all the while he felt unhappy, not nearly the way he should have felt, now that they had finally given him a game. He hoped that they would hit to him, and he would make one-handed catches over his head, run way out with his back to the ball and spear them blind, or run in with all his might and pick them right off the tops of his shoes.

A little nervous chill ran through his back as he saw Paulie Dahler get up to hit. On Gelberg's second toss Paulie stepped in and sent the ball sailing into the air. A panic seized Marty as he saw it coming at him. He took a step nervously forward, then backward, then forward again, trying as hard as he could to judge the ball. It smacked into his cupped palms, bounced out and dribbled toward the curb. He scrambled after it, hearing them shouting at him, and feeling himself getting more scared every instant. He kicked the ball with his sneaker, got his hand on it, and, straightening himself in a fever of fright, heaved it with all his strength at Ray-Ray on first. The moment the ball left his hand he knew he had done the wrong thing. Paulie was already on his way to second; and besides, the throw was wild. Ray-Ray leaped into the air, his arms flung up, but it was way over his head, bouncing beyond him on the sidewalk and almost hitting a woman who was jouncing a baby carriage at

the door of the apartment house opposite.

With his heart beating the same way it did whenever anyone chased him, Marty watched Paulie gallop across the plate. He sniffled his nose, which was beginning to run again, and felt like crying.

''Holy Moses!'' he heard Gelberg yell. ''What do you want, a basket? Can't you hold on to them once in a while?''

''Aw, the sun was in my eyes!'' Marty said.

''You wait until you want another game!'' Gelberg shouted.

Breathing hard, Ray-Ray got back on first and tossed the ball to Gelberg. ''Whose side are you on anyway?'' he hollered.

Eddie Deakes put his hands to his mouth like a megaphone. ''Attaboy, Marty!'' he yelled. ''Having you out there is like having another man on our side!''

The other fellows on the curb laughed, and Howey Reinhard made them laugh harder by pretending to catch a fly ball with the sun in his eyes, staggering around the street with his eyes screwed up and his hands cupped like a sissy, so that the wrists touched and the palms were widely separated.

No longer shouting or punching his fist into his palm, Marty took his place out in the field again. He stood there, feeling like crying, and wished that he hadn't dropped that ball, or thrown it over Ray-Ray's head. Then, without knowing why, he looked up to see whether the new kid was laughing at him like all the rest. But the new kid was sitting a little off by himself at one end of the row of fellows on the curb, and with a serious expression on his face gnawed at the skin at the side of his thumbnail. Marty began to wonder if the new kid was any good or not. He saw him sitting there, with the serious look on his face, his ears sticking out, not joking like the other fellows, and from nowhere the thought leaped into Marty's head that maybe the new kid was no good. He looked at the skinny legs, the Boy Scout pants, and the mama's-boy shoes, and all at once he began to hope that Eddie would send the new kid in to hit, so that he could know right away whether he was any good or not.

But Wally Reinhard was up next. He fouled out on one of Gelberg's twirls, and after him Howey popped up to Albie Newbauer and Eddie was out on first. The fellows ran in to watch Eddie chalk up Paulie's run on the scoreboard alongside the sewer. They were still beefing and hollering at Marty for dropping that ball, but he pretended he did not hear them and sat down on the curb to watch the new kid out in the field.

He was over near the curb, playing in closer than Paulie Dahler. Marty could see that he was not hollering "Here go!" or "All the way!" like the others, but merely stood there with that serious expression on his face and watched them throw the ball around. He held one leg bent at the ankle, so that the side of his shoe rested on the pavement, his belly was stuck out, and he chewed the skin at the side of his thumbnail.

Gelberg got up to bat. Standing in the pitcher's box, Eddie turned around and motioned his men to lay out. The new kid looked around him to see what the other fellows did, took a few steps backward, and then, with his belly stuck out again, went on chewing his thumb.

Marty felt his heart begin to beat hard. He watched Gelberg stand up to the plate and contemptuously fling back the first few pitches.

"Come on, gimme one like I like!" Gelberg hollered.

"What's the matter! You afraid to reach for them?" Eddie yelled.

"Just pitch them to me, that's all!" Gelberg said.

Eddie lobbed one in that bounced shoulder high. With a little sideways skip Gelberg lammed into it.

The ball sailed down toward the new kid. Feeling his heart begin to beat harder, Marty saw him take a hurried step backward and at the same moment fling his hands before his face and duck his head. The ball landed beyond him and bounded up on the sidewalk. For an instant the new kid hesitated, then he was galloping after it, clattering across the pavement in his polished shoes.

Swinging his arms in mock haste, Gelberg breezed across the plate. "Get a basket!" he hollered over his shoulder. "Get a basket!"

Marty let his nose run without bothering to sniffle. He jumped up from the curb and curved his hands around his mouth like a megaphone. "He's scared of the ball!" he yelled at the top of his lungs. "He's scared of the ball! That's what he is, scared of the ball!"

The new kid tossed the ball back to Eddie. "I wasn't scared!" he said, moistening his lips with his tongue. "I wasn't scared! I just couldn't see it coming!"

With an expression of despair on his face Eddie shook his head. "Holy Moses! If you can't see the ball why do you try to play punchball?" He bounced the ball hard at his feet and motioned Gelberg to send in his next batter. Arnie got up from the curb and, wiping his hands on his pants, walked toward the plate.

Marty felt his heart pounding in his chest. He hopped up and down with excitement and, seizing Gelberg by the arm, pointed at the new kid.

"You see him duck?" he yelled. "He's scared of the ball, that's what he is!" He hardly knew where to turn first. He rushed up to Ray-Ray, who was sitting on the curb making marks on the asphalt with the heel of his sneaker. "The new kid's scared to stop a ball! You see him duck!"

The new kid looked toward Marty and wet his lips with his tongue. "Yeah," he yelled, "didn't you muff one that was right in your hands?"

He was looking at Marty with a sore expression on his face, and his lower lip stuck out; and a sinking feeling went through Marty, a sudden sick feeling that maybe he had started something he would be sorry for. Behind him on the curb he could hear the fellows sniggering in that way they did when they picked on him. In the pitcher's box Eddie let out a loud cackling laugh.

"Yeah, the new kid's got your number!"

"The sun was in my eyes!" Marty said. He could feel his face getting red, and in the field the fellows were laughing. A wave of self-pity flowed through him.

"What are you picking on me for!" he yelled in a high voice. "The sun was so in my eyes. Anyway, I ain't no yellowbelly! I wasn't scared of the ball!"

The instant he said it he was sorry. He sniffled his nose uneasily as he saw Gelberg look at Ray-Ray. For an instant he thought of running into the house before anything happened. But instead he just stood there, sniffling his nose and feeling his heart beating, fast and heavy.

"You hear what he called you?" Paulie Dahler yelled at the new kid.

"You're not going to let him get away with calling you a yellowbelly, are you?" Eddie said, looking at the new kid.

The new kid wet his lips with his tongue and looked at Marty. "I wasn't scared!" he said. He shifted the soles of his new-looking shoes on the pavement. "I wasn't scared! I just couldn't see it coming, that's all!"

Eddie was walking toward the new kid now, bouncing the ball slowly in front of him as he walked. In a sudden panic Marty looked back toward the house where Old Lady Kipnis lived. She always broke up fights; maybe she would break up this one; maybe she wouldn't even let it get started. But she wasn't out on her porch. He sniffled his nose, and with all his might hoped that the kid's mother would call him to go to the store.

"Any kid that lets himself be called a yellowbelly must be a yellowbelly!" Albie Newbauer said, looking around him for approval.

"Yeah," Gelberg said. "I wouldn't let anyone call me a yellowbelly."

With a sudden shove Eddie sent the new kid scrambling forward toward Marty. He tried to check himself by stiffening his body and twisting to one side, but it was no use. Before he could recover his balance another shove made him stagger forward.

Marty sniffled his nose and looked at the kid's face close in front of him. It seemed as big as the faces he saw in the movies; and he could see that the kid's nose was beginning to run just like his own; and he could see in the corner of his mouth a crumb of the rye bread he had eaten on the stoop. For a moment the kid's eyes looked squarely into Marty's, so that he could see the little dark specks in the colored part around the pupil. Then the glance slipped away to one side; and all at once Marty had a feeling that the new kid was afraid of him.

"You gonna let him get away with calling you a yellowbelly?" he heard Eddie say. From the way it sounded he knew that the fellows were on his side now. He stuck out his jaw and waited for the new kid to answer.

"I got to go to the store!" the new kid said. There was a scared look on his face and he took a step back from Marty.

Paulie Dahler got behind him and shoved him against Marty. Although he tried not to, Marty couldn't help flinging his arms up before his face. But the new kid only backed away and kept his arms at his sides. A fierce excitement went through Marty as he saw how scared the look on the kid's face was. He thrust his chest up against the new kid.

"Yellowbelly!" he hollered, making his voice sound tough. "Scared of the ball!"

The new kid backed nervously away, and there was a look on his face as though he wanted to cry.

"Yeah, he's scared!" Eddie yelled.

"Slam him, Marty!" Wally Reinhard hollered. "The kid's scared of you!"

"Aw, sock the yellowbelly!" Marty heard Gelberg say, and he smacked the kid as hard as he could on the shoulder. The kid screwed up his face to keep from crying and tried to back through the fellows ringed around him.

"Lemme alone!" he yelled.

Marty looked at him fiercely, with his jaw thrust forward, and felt his heart beating. He smacked the kid again, making him stagger against Arnie in back of him.

"Yeah, yellowbelly!" Marty hollered, feeling how the fellows were on his side, and how scared the new kid was. He began smacking him again and again on the shoulder.

"Three, six, nine, a bottle of wine, I can fight you any old time!" he yelled. With each word he smacked the kid on the shoulder or arm. At the last word he swung with all his strength. He meant to hit the kid on the shoulder, but at the last instant, even while his arm was swinging, something compelled him to change his aim; his fist caught the kid on the mouth with a hard, wet, socking sound. The shock of his knuckles against the kid's mouth, and that sound of it, made Marty want to hit him again and again. He put his head down and began swinging wildly, hitting the new kid without any aim on the head and shoulders and arms.

The new kid buried his head in his arms and began to cry. "Lemme alone!" he yelled. He tried to rush through the fellows crowded around him.

With all his might Marty smacked him on the side of the head. Rushing up behind him, Arnie smacked him too. Paulie Dahler shoved the skullcap, with its paper-clip ornaments, over the kid's eyes; and as he went by Gelberg booted him in the pants.

Crying and clutching his cap, the new kid scampered over to the curb out of reach.

"I'll get even on you!" he cried.

With a fierce expression on his face Marty made a sudden movement of his legs and pretended to rush at him. The kid threw his arms about his head and darted down the street toward the house. When he saw that Marty was not coming after him he sat down on the stoop; and Marty could see him rubbing his knuckles against his mouth.

Howey Reinhard was making fun of the new kid, scampering up and down the pavement with his arms wrapped around his head and hollering, "Lemme alone! Lemme alone!" The fellows laughed, and although he was breathing hard, and his hand hurt from hitting the kid, Marty had to laugh too.

"You see him duck when that ball came at him?" he panted at Paulie Dahler.

Paulie shook his head. "Boy, just wait until we get the yellowbelly in the schoolyard!"

"And on Halloween," Gelberg said. "Wait until we get him on Halloween with our flour stockings!" He gave Marty a little shove and made as though he were whirling an imaginary flour stocking round his head.

Standing there in the middle of the street, Marty suddenly thought of Halloween, of the winter and snowballs, of the schoolyard. He saw himself whirling a flour stocking around his head and rushing at the new kid, who scampered in terror before him, hollering, "Lemme alone! Lemme alone!" As clearly as if it were in the movies, he saw himself flinging snowballs and the new kid backed into a corner of the schoolyard, with his hands over his face. Before he knew what he was doing, Marty turned fiercely toward the stoop where the new kid was still sitting, rubbing his mouth and crying.

"Hey, yellowbelly!" Marty hollered; and he pretended he was going to rush at the kid.

Almost falling over himself in fright, the new kid scrambled inside the house. Marty stood in the middle of the street and sniffled his nose. He shook his fist at the empty doorway.

"You see him run?" he yelled, so loud that it made his throat hurt. "Boy, you see him run?" He stood there shaking his fist, although the new kid was no longer there to see him. He could hardly wait for the winter, for Halloween, or the very next day in the schoolyard.

excerpt from
To Kill a Mockingbird

Harper Lee

Atticus was feeble: he was nearly fifty. When Jem and I asked him why he was so old, he said he got started late, which we felt reflected upon his abilities and manliness. He was much older than the parents of our school contemporaries, and there was nothing Jem or I could say about him when our classmates said, ''My father—''

Jem was football crazy. Atticus was never too tired to play keep-away, but when Jem wanted to tackle him, Atticus would say, ''I'm too old for that, son.''

Our father didn't do anything. He worked in an office, not in a drugstore. Atticus did not drive a dumptruck for the county, he was not the sheriff, he did not farm, work in a garage, or do anything that could possibly arouse the admiration of anyone.

Besides that, he wore glasses. He was nearly blind in his left eye, and said left eyes were the tribal curse of the Finches. Whenever he wanted to see something well, he turned his head and looked from his right eye.

He did not do the things our schoolmates' fathers did: he never went hunting, he did not play poker or fish or drink or smoke. He sat in the livingroom and read.

With these attributes, however, he would not remain as inconspicuous as we wished him to: that year, the school buzzed with talk about him defending Tom Robinson, none of which was complimentary. About my bout with Cecil Jacobs when I committed myself to a policy of cowardice, word got around that Scout Finch wouldn't fight any more, her daddy wouldn't let her. This was not entirely correct: I wouldn't fight publicly for Atticus, but the family was private ground. I would fight anyone from a third cousin upwards tooth and nail. Francis Hancock, for example, knew that.

When he gave us our air-rifles, Atticus wouldn't teach us to shoot. Uncle Jack instructed us in the rudiments thereof; he said Atticus wasn't interested in guns. Atticus said to Jem one day, "I'd rather you shot at tin cans in the back yard, but I know you'll go after birds. Shoot all the bluejays you want, if you can hit 'em, but remember it's a sin to kill a mockingbird."

That was the only time I ever heard Atticus say it was a sin to do something, and I asked Miss Maudie about it.

"Your father's right," she said. "Mockingbirds don't do one thing but make music for us to enjoy. They don't eat up people's gardens, don't nest in corncribs, they don't do one thing but sing their hearts out for us. That's why it's a sin to kill a mockingbird."

"Miss Maudie, this is an old neighborhood, ain't it?"

"Been here longer than the town."

"Nome, I mean the folks on our street are all old. Jem and me's the only children around here. Mrs. Dubose is close on to a hundred and Miss Rachel's old and so are you and Atticus."

"I don't call fifty very old," said Miss Maudie tartly. "Not being wheeled around yet, am I? Neither's your father. But I must say Providence was kind enough to burn down that old mausoleum of mine, I'm too old to keep it up—maybe you're right Jean Louise, this is a settled neighborhood. You've never been around young folks much, have you?"

"Yessum, at school."

"I mean young grown-ups. You're lucky, you know. You and Jem have the benefit of your father's age. If your father was thirty you'd find life quite different."

"I sure would. Atticus can't do anything. . . ."

"You'd be surprised," said Miss Maudie. "There's life in him yet."

"What can he do?"

"Well, he can make somebody's will so airtight can't anybody meddle with it."

"Shoot . . ."

"Well, did you know he's the best checker-player in this town? Why, down at the Landing when we were coming up, Atticus Finch could beat everybody on both sides of the river."

"Good heavens, Miss Maudie, Jem and me beat him all the time."

"It's about time you found out it's because he lets you. Did you know he can play a Jew's Harp?"

This modest accomplishment served to make me even more ashamed of him.

"*Well . . .*" she said.

"Well, what, Miss Maudie?"

"Well nothing. Nothing—it seems with all that you'd be proud of him. Can't everybody play a Jew's Harp. Now keep out of the way of the carpenters. You'd better go home, I'll be in my azaleas and can't watch you. Plank might hit you."

I went to the back yard and found Jem plugging away at a tin can, which seemed stupid with all the bluejays around. I returned to the front yard and busied myself for two hours erecting a complicated breastworks at the side of the porch, consisting of a tire, an orange crate, the laundry hamper, the porch chairs, and a small U.S. flag Jem gave me from a popcorn box.

When Atticus came home to dinner, he found me crouched down aiming across the street. "What are you shooting at?"

"Miss Maudie's rear end."

Atticus turned and saw my generous target bending over her bushes. He pushed his hat to the back of his head and crossed the street. "Maudie," he called, "I thought I'd better warn you. You're in considerable peril."

Miss Maudie straightened up and looked toward me. She said, "Atticus, you are a devil."

When Atticus returned he told me to break camp. "Don't you ever let me catch you pointing that gun at anybody again," he said.

I wished my father was a devil. I sounded out Calpurnia on the subject. "Mr. Finch? Why, he can do lots of things."

"Like what?" I asked.

Calpurnia scratched her head. "Well, I don't rightly know," she said.

Jem underlined it when he asked Atticus if he was going out for the Methodists and Atticus said he'd break his neck if he did, he was just too old for that sort of thing. The Methodists were trying to pay off their church mortgage and had challenged the Baptists to a game of touch football. Everybody in town's father was playing, it seemed, except Atticus. Jem said he didn't even want to go, but he was unable to resist football in any form, and he stood gloomily on the sidelines with Atticus and me watching Cecil Jacob's father make touchdowns for the Baptists.

One Saturday Jem and I decided to go exploring with our air-rifles to see if we could find a rabbit or a squirrel. We had gone about five hundred yards beyond the Radley Place when I noticed Jem squinting at something down the street. He had turned his head to one side and was looking out of the corners of his eyes.

"Whatcha looking at?"

"That old dog down yonder," he said.

"That's old Tim Johnson, ain't it?"

"Yeah."

Tim Johnson was the property of Mr. Harry Johnson who drove the Mobile bus and lived on the southern edge of town. Tim was a liver-colored bird dog, the pet of Maycomb.

"What's he doing?"

"I don't know, Scout. We better go home."

"Aw, Jem, it's February."

"I don't care, I'm gonna tell Cal."

We raced home and ran to the kitchen.

"Cal," said Jem, "can you come down the sidewalk a minute?"

"What for, Jem? I can't come down the sidewalk every time you want me."

"There's somethin' wrong with an old dog down yonder."

Calpurnia sighed. "I can't wrap up any dog's foot now. There's some gauze in the bathroom, go get it and do it yourself."

Jem shook his head. "He's sick, Cal. Something's wrong with him."

"What's he doin', trying to catch his tail?"

"No, he's doin' like this."

Jem gulped like a goldfish, hunched his shoulders and twitched his torso. "He's goin' like that, only not like he means to."

"Are you telling me a story, Jem Finch?" Calpurnia's voice hardened.

"No, Cal, I swear I'm not."

"Was he runnin'?"

"No, he's just moseyin' along, so slow you can't hardly tell it. He's comin' this way."

Calpurnia rinsed her hands and followed Jem into the yard. "I don't see any dog," she said.

She followed us beyond the Radley Place and looked where Jem pointed. Tim Johnson was not much more than a speck in the distance, but he was closer to us. He walked erratically, as if his right legs were shorter than his left legs. He reminded me of a car stuck in a sandbed.

"He's gone lopsided," said Jem.

Calpurnia stared, then grabbed us by the shoulders and ran us home. She shut the wood door behind us, went to the telephone and shouted, "Gimme Mr. Finch's office!"

"Mr. Finch!" she shouted. "This is Cal. I swear there's a mad dog down the street a piece—he's comin' this way, yes sir, he's—Mr. Finch, I declare he is—old Tim Johnson, yes sir . . . yessir . . . yes—"

She hung up and shook her head when we tried to ask her what Atticus had said. She rattled the telephone hook and said, "Miss Eula May—now ma'am, I'm through talkin' to Mr. Finch, please don't connect me no more—listen, Miss Eula May, can you call Miss Rachel and Miss Stephanie Crawford and whoever's got a phone on this street and tell 'em a mad dog's comin'? Please ma'am!"

Calpurnia listened. "I know it's February, Miss Eula May, but I know a mad dog when I see one. Please ma'am hurry!"

Calpurnia asked Jem, "Radley's got a phone?"

Jem looked in the book and said no. "They won't come out anyway, Cal."

"I don't care, I'm gonna tell 'em."

She ran to the front porch, Jem and I at her heels. "You stay in that house!" she yelled.

Calpurnia's message had been received by the neighborhood. Every wood door within our range of vision was closed tight. We saw no trace of Tim Johnson. We watched Calpurnia running toward the Radley Place, holding her skirt and apron above her knees. She went up to the front steps and banged on the door. She got no answer, and she shouted, "Mr. Nathan, Mr. Arthur, mad dog's comin'! Mad dog's comin'!"

"She's supposed to go around in back," I said.

Jem shook his head. "Don't make any difference now," he said.

Calpurnia pounded on the door in vain. No one acknowledged her warning; no one seemed to have heard it.

As Calpurnia sprinted to the back porch a black Ford swung into the driveway. Atticus and Mr. Heck Tate got out.

Mr. Heck Tate was the sheriff of Maycomb County. He was as tall as Atticus, but thinner. He was long-nosed, wore boots with shiny metal eye-holes, boot pants and a lumber jacket. His belt had a row of bullets sticking in it. He carried a heavy rifle. When he and Atticus reached the porch, Jem opened the door.

"Stay inside, son," said Atticus. "Where is he, Cal?"

"He oughta be here by now," said Calpurnia, pointing down the street.

"Not runnin', is he?" asked Mr. Tate.

"Naw, sir, he's in the twitchin' stage, Mr. Heck."

"Should we go after him, Heck?" asked Atticus.

"We better wait, Mr. Finch. They usually go in a straight line, but you never can tell. He might follow the curve—hope he does or he'll go straight in the Radley back yard. Let's wait a minute."

"Don't think he'll get in the Radley yard," said Atticus. "Fence'll stop him. He'll probably follow the road. . . ."

I thought mad dogs foamed at the mouth, galloped, leaped and lunged at throats, and I thought they did it in August. Had Tim Johnson behaved thus, I would have been less frightened.

Nothing is more deadly than a deserted, waiting street. The trees were still, the mockingbirds were silent, the carpenters at Miss Maudie's house had vanished. I heard Mr. Tate sniff, then blow his nose. I saw him shift his gun to the crook of his arm. I saw Miss Stephanie Crawford's face framed in the glass window of her front door. Miss Maudie appeared and stood beside her. Atticus put his foot on the rung of a chair and rubbed his hand slowly down the side of his thigh.

"There he is," he said softly.

Tim Johnson came into sight, walking dazedly in the inner rim of the curve parallel to the Radley house.

"Look at him," whispered Jem. "Mr. Heck said they walked in a straight line. He can't even stay in the road."

"He looks more sick than anything," I said.

"Let anything get in front of him and he'll come straight at it."

Mr. Tate put his hand to his forehead and leaned forward. "He's got it all right, Mr. Finch."

Tim Johnson was advancing at a snail's pace, but he was not playing or sniffing at foliage; he seemed dedicated to one course and motivated by an invisible force that was inching him toward us. We could see him shiver like a horse shedding flies;

his jaw opened and shut; he was alist, but he was being pulled gradually toward us.

"He's lookin' for a place to die," said Jem.

Mr. Tate turned around. "He's far from dead, Jem, he hasn't got started yet."

Tim Johnson reached the side street that ran in front of the Radley Place, and what remained of his poor mind made him pause and seem to consider which road he would take. He made a few hesitant steps and stopped in front of the Radley gate; then he tried to turn around, but was having difficulty.

Atticus said, "He's within range, Heck. You better get him before he goes down the side street—goodness knows who's around the corner. Go inside, Cal."

Calpurnia opened the screen door, latched it behind her, then unlatched it and held onto the hook. She tried to block Jem and me with her body, but we looked out from beneath her arms.

"Take him, Mr. Finch." Mr. Tate handed the rifle to Atticus; Jem and I nearly fainted.

"Don't waste time, Heck," said Atticus. "Go on."

"Mr. Finch, this is a one-shot job."

Atticus shook his head vehemently: "Don't just stand there, Heck! He won't wait all day for you—"

"For heaven's sake, Mr. Finch, look where he is! Miss and you'll go straight into the Radley house! I can't shoot that well and you know it!"

"I haven't shot a gun in thirty years—"

Mr. Tate almost threw the rifle at Atticus. "I'd feel mighty comfortable if you did now," he said.

In a fog, Jem and I watched our father take the gun and walk out into the middle of the street. He walked quickly, but I thought he moved like an underwater swimmer: time had slowed to a nauseating crawl.

When Atticus raised his glasses Calpurnia murmured, "Heaven help him," and put her hands to her cheeks.

Atticus pushed his glasses to his forehead; they slipped down, and he dropped them in the street. In the silence, I heard them crack. Atticus rubbed his eyes and chin; we saw him blink hard.

In front of the Radley gate, Tim Johnson had made up what was left of his mind. He had finally turned himself around, to pursue his original course up our street. He made two steps forward, then stopped and raised his head. We saw his body go rigid.

With movements so swift they seemed simultaneous, Atticus's hand yanked a ball-tipped lever as he brought the gun to his shoulder.

The rifle cracked. Tim Johnson leaped, flopped over and crumpled on the sidewalk in a brown-and-white heap. He didn't know what hit him.

Mr. Tate jumped off the porch and ran to the Radley Place. He stopped in front of the dog, squatted, turned around and tapped his finger on his forehead above his left eye. "You were a little to the right, Mr. Finch," he called.

"Always was," answered Atticus. "If I had my 'druthers I'd take a shotgun."

He stooped and picked up his glasses, ground the broken lenses to powder under his heel, and went to Mr. Tate and stood looking at Tim Johnson.

Doors opened one by one, and the neighborhood slowly came alive.

Miss Maudie walked down the steps with Miss Stephanie Crawford.

Jem was paralyzed. I pinched him to get him moving, but when Atticus saw us coming he called, "Stay where you are."

When Mr. Tate and Atticus returned to the yard, Mr. Tate was smiling. "I'll have Zeebo collect him," he said. "You haven't forgot much, Mr. Finch. They say it never leaves you."

Atticus was silent.

"Atticus?" said Jem.

"Yes?"

"Nothin'."

"I saw that, One-Shot Finch!"

Atticus wheeled around and faced Miss Maudie. They looked at one another without saying anything, and Atticus got into the sheriff's car. "Come here," he said to Jem. "Don't you go near that dog, you understand? Don't go near him, he's just as dangerous dead as alive."

"Yes, sir," said Jem. "Atticus—"

"What, son?"

"Nothing."

"What's the matter with you, boy, can't you talk?" said Mr. Tate, grinning at Jem. "Didn't you know your daddy's—"

"Hush, Heck," said Atticus, "let's go back to town."

When they drove away, Jem and I went to Miss Stephanie's front steps. We sat waiting for Zeebo to arrive in the garbage truck.

Jem sat in numb confusion, and Miss Stephanie said, "Uh, uh, uh, who 'da thought of a mad dog in February? Maybe he wasn't mad, maybe he was just crazy. I'd hate to see Harry Johnson's face when he gets in from the Mobile run and finds Atticus Finch's shot his dog. Bet he was just full of fleas from somewhere—"

Miss Maudie said Miss Stephanie'd be singing a different tune if Tim Johnson was still coming up the street, that they'd find out soon enough, they'd send his head to Montgomery.

Jem became vaguely articulate: " 'd you see him, Scout? You see him just standing there? . . . 'n' all of a sudden he just relaxed all over, an' it looked like that gun was a part of him . . . an' he did it so quick, like . . . I hafta aim for ten minutes 'fore I can hit somethin'. . . ."

Miss Maudie grinned wickedly. "Well now, Miss Jean Louise," she said, "still think your father can't do anything? Still ashamed of him?"

"Nome," I said meekly.

"Forgot to tell you the other day that besides playing the Jew's Harp, Atticus Finch was the deadest shot in Maycomb County in his time."

"Dead shot . . ." echoed Jem.

"That's what I said, Jem Finch. Guess you'll change *your* tune now. The very idea, didn't you know his nickname was Ol' One-Shot when he was a boy? Why, down at the Landing when he was coming up, if he shot fifteen times and hit fourteen doves he'd complain about wasting ammunition."

"He never said anything about that," Jem muttered.

"Never said anything about it, did he?"

"No ma'am."

"Wonder why he never goes huntin' now," I said.

"Maybe I can tell you," said Miss Maudie. "If your father's anything, he's civilized in his heart. Marksmanship's a gift of God, a talent—oh, you have to practice to make it perfect, but shootin's different from playing the piano or the like. I think maybe he put his gun down when he realized that God had given him an unfair advantage over most living things. I guess he decided he wouldn't shoot till he had to, and he had to today."

"Looks like he'd be proud of it," I said.

"People in their right minds never take pride in their talents," said Miss Maudie.

We saw Zeebo drive up. He took a pitchfork from the back of the garbage truck and gingerly lifted Tim Johnson. He pitched

the dog onto the truck, then poured something from a gallon
jug on and around the spot where Tim fell. "Don't yawl come
over here for a while," he called.

When he went home I told Jem we'd really have something
to talk about at school on Monday. Jem turned on me.

"Don't say anything about it, Scout," he said.

"What? I certainly am. Ain't everybody's daddy the deadest
shot in Maycomb County."

Jem said, "I reckon if he'd wanted us to know it, he'da told
us. If he was proud of it, he'da told us."

"Maybe it just slipped his mind," I said.

"Naw, Scout, it's something you wouldn't understand. Atticus is real old, but I wouldn't care if he couldn't do anything—I wouldn't care if he couldn't do a blessed thing."

Jem picked up a rock and threw it jubilantly at the carhouse. Running after it, he called back: "Atticus is a gentleman, just like me!"

Battle Won Is Lost

Phil George

They said, "You are no longer a lad."
    I nodded.
They said, "Enter the council lodge."
    I sat.
They said, "Our lands are at stake."
    I scowled.
They said, "We are at war."
    I hated.
They said, "Prepare red war symbols."
    I painted.
They said, "Count coups."
    I cringed.
They said, "Desperate warriors fight best."
    I charged.
They said, "Some will be wounded."
    I bled.
They said, "To die is glorious."
    They lied.

What Shall He Tell That Son?

Carl Sandburg

A father sees a son nearing manhood.
What shall he tell that son?
"Life is hard; be steel; be a rock."
And this might stand him for the storms
and serve him for humdrum and monotony
and guide him amid sudden betrayals
and tighten him for slack moments.
"Life is a soft loam; be gentle; go easy."
And this too might serve him.
Brutes have been gentled where lashes failed.
The growth of a frail flower in a path up
has sometimes shattered and split a rock.
A tough will counts. So does desire.
So does a rich soft wanting.
Without rich wanting nothing arrives.

One who knows nothing
is confident in everything.

U·R·A·S·H·I·M·A

retold by Miriam Cox

The fisher lad Urashima caught a tortoise on his line one day. A pity to harm it, he thought, for these creatures are said to live a thousand years. He allowed it to slip back into the sea, and again baited his hook for a fish. But the day was warm, and the youth soon fell fast asleep as his boat drifted idly on the quiet waters.

"Urashima, Urashima!" Through his dreams came the sound of his name being called again and again. He awoke to find the tortoise by his boat. "You were kind to me," it said. "Let me repay by taking you down to the Palace of the Dragon King where the Sea Princess herself may thank you."

Here was adventure! Eagerly Urashima climbed on the creature's broad back and down they glided through the sea lanes into the shining depths.

It was not long before he could see the delicate tracery of towers, pillars, and bridges spiraling up through the emerald waters. Then it seemed as if the rainbow had fallen into the sea, for a magnificent procession of fish—silver, green, gold, red— formed on either side to escort them to the Dragon King's palace.

When the pearled gates swung open, the lad drew back in awe. Before him was a land of enchantment. Here all the four seasons presented their glories at once: spring with its blossoming cherry and silken-winged butterflies; summer's gardenias bending over shimmering pools; autumn's blaze of maple leaves; winter's white embroidery on tree and fern.

But the beauty of the Sea Princess who came forward to greet him eclipsed all of these wonders, and when she spoke it was as if every singing bird had given her its sweetest note. "You were kind to my messenger, the tortoise," she said. "Stay with us as long as you wish in this land of eternal youth that we may show our gratitude." She clapped her hands, and a great company of fishes glided in bearing on their fins coral trays heaped with delicacies. While the princess and Urashima feasted, other merry little fishes entertained them with song and dance.

For three years he stayed in the Palace of the Dragon King, finding new delights with every hour. But then he began to worry about his aged parents. How they must be grieving at his strange disappearance!

"Let me return for one day to my home," he said to the Sea Princess. "Then I will come back to dwell forever in this beautiful realm."

"I had hoped to make you so happy that you would never leave," she answered sadly, for she had fallen in love with the gentle lad from the great world above the waters. "But if you must go, take this gift." She handed him a small box. "It contains a valuable treasure—one that should not be seen by mortal eyes. Take it as a token of my love, but I entreat you, do not open it!"

Urashima promised, and mounting the tortoise, was swiftly borne upward to earth. But as he stepped upon the beach, he found to his amazement that everything had changed. Where was the old tree under which he had dozed so often? Where was his father's house? The stream ran through the village as always, but now it was spanned by a new bridge that he had never seen before.

Bewildered, he stopped an old woman and asked, "Where is Urashima's home? What has become of his parents?"

She stared at him suspiciously. "Urashima? I have lived here eighty years and never have I heard of Urashima." She started to hobble away and then turned back. "Wait! Vaguely I remember hearing my old grandmother tell about a fisher lad by that name who was drowned at sea. But that was three hundred years ago!"

Tears welled into Urashima's eyes. How could he have forgotten that in the country of the Sea King one day was like a hundred years! Now everyone he loved on earth was gone! He would go back at once to his dear princess in the place where the four seasons displayed their glories at once, and where fishes danced on their tails and played musical instruments with their fins.

But where was the tortoise? How could he return? What if he were never to see his princess again! The box! Surely in the box he could discover the secret of returning to the sea. Perhaps she had given it to him for that very reason.

With trembling fingers he lifted the lid. A wreath of white smoke coiled out, wove itself into a delicate column above his head for a moment, and then drifted out over the sea. Now Urashima felt a change come over him. His limbs suddenly felt stiff and tired; his eyes became so dim that shore and sea faded away into a vague mist; the wind caught at a long white beard that fell to his waist.

"The princess had sealed my youth in the box, and I have let it go!" He staggered forward, lifted his arms imploringly to the sea, and then fell upon the sand. Urashima was dead.

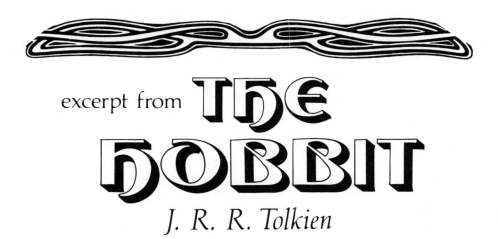

excerpt from THE HOBBIT

J. R. R. Tolkien

An Unexpected Party

In a hole in the ground there lived a hobbit. Not a nasty, dirty, wet hole, filled with the ends of worms and an oozy smell, nor yet a dry, bare, sandy hole with nothing in it to sit down on or to eat: it was a hobbit-hole, and that means comfort.

It had a perfectly round door like a porthole, painted green, with a shiny yellow brass knob in the exact middle. The door opened on to a tube-shaped hall like a tunnel: a very comfortable tunnel without smoke, with panelled walls, and floors tiled and carpeted, provided with polished chairs, and lots and lots of pegs for hats and coats—the hobbit was fond of visitors. The tunnel wound on and on, going fairly but not quite straight into the side of the hill—The Hill, as all the people for many miles round called it—and many little round doors opened out of it, first on one side and then on another. No going upstairs for the hobbit: bedrooms, bathrooms, cellars, pantries (lots of these), wardrobes (he had whole rooms devoted to clothes), kitchens, dining-rooms, all were on the same floor, and indeed on the same passage. The best rooms were all on the lefthand side (going in), for these were the only ones to have windows, deep-set round windows looking over his garden and meadows beyond, sloping down to the river.

This hobbit was a very well-to-do hobbit, and his name was Baggins. The Bagginses had lived in the neighbourhood of The Hill for time out of mind, and people considered them very respectable, not only because most of them were rich, but also because they never had any adventures or did anything unexpected: you could tell what a Baggins would say on any question without the bother of asking him. This is a story of how a Baggins had an adventure, and found himself doing and saying things altogether unexpected. He may have lost the neighbours' respect, but he gained—well, you will see whether he gained anything in the end.

The mother of our particular hobbit—what is a hobbit? I suppose hobbits need some description nowadays, since they have become rare and shy of the Big People, as they call us. They are (or were) a little people, about half our height, and smaller than the bearded Dwarves. Hobbits have no beards. There is little or no magic about them, except the ordinary everyday sort which helps them to disappear quietly and quickly when large stupid folk like you and me come blundering along, making a noise like elephants which they can hear a mile off. They are inclined to be fat in the stomach; they dress in bright colours (chiefly green and yellow); wear no shoes, because their feet grow natural leathery soles and thick warm brown hair like the stuff on their heads (which is curly); have long clever brown fingers, good-natured faces, and laugh deep fruity laughs (especially after dinner, which they have twice a day when they can get it). Now you know enough to go on with. As I was saying, the mother of this hobbit—of Bilbo Baggins, that is— was the fabulous Belladonna Took, one of the three remarkable daughters of the Old Took, head of the hobbits who lived across The Water, the small river that ran at the foot of The Hill. It was often said (in other families) that long ago one of the Took ancestors must have taken a fairy wife. That was, of course, absurd, but certainly there was still something not entirely hobbit-like about them, and once in a while members of the Took-clan would go and have adventures. They discreetly disappeared, and the family hushed it up; but the fact remained that the Tooks were not as respectable as the Bagginses, though they were undoubtedly richer.

Not that Belladonna Took ever had any adventures after she became Mrs. Bungo Baggins. Bungo, that was Bilbo's father, built the most luxurious hobbit-hole for her (and partly with her money) that was to be found either under The Hill or over The Hill or across The Water, and there they remained to the end of their days. Still it is probable that Bilbo, her only son, although he looked and behaved exactly like a second edition of his solid and comfortable father, got something a bit queer in his makeup from the Took side, something that only waited for a chance to come out. The chance never arrived, until Bilbo Baggins was grown up, being about fifty years old or so, and living in the beautiful hobbit-hole built by his father, which I have just described for you, until he had in fact apparently settled down immovably.

By some curious chance one morning long ago in the quiet of the world, when there was less noise and more green, and the hobbits were still numerous and prosperous, and Bilbo Baggins was standing at his door after breakfast smoking an enormous long wooden pipe that reached nearly down to his woolly toes (neatly brushed)—Gandalf came by. Gandalf! If you had heard only a quarter of what I have heard about him, and I have only heard very little of all there is to hear, you would be prepared for any sort of remarkable tale. Tales and adventures sprouted up all over the place wherever he went, in the most extraordinary fashion. He had not been down that way under The Hill for ages and ages, not since his friend the Old Took died, in fact, and the hobbits had almost forgotten what he looked like. He had been away over The Hill and across The Water on business of his own since they were all small hobbit-boys and hobbit-girls.

All that the unsuspecting Bilbo saw that morning was an old man with a staff. He had a tall pointed blue hat, a long grey cloak, a silver scarf over which a white beard hung down below his waist, and immense black boots.

"Good morning!" said Bilbo, and he meant it. The sun was shining, and the grass was very green. But Gandalf looked at him from under long bushy eyebrows that stuck out further than the brim of his shady hat.

"What do you mean?" he said. "Do you wish me a good morning, or mean that it is a good morning whether I want it or not; or that you feel good this morning; or that it is a morning to be good on?"

"All of them at once," said Bilbo. "And a very fine morning for a pipe of tobacco out of doors, into the bargain. If you have a pipe about you, sit down and have a fill of mine! There's no hurry, we have all the day before us!" Then Bilbo sat down on a seat by his door, crossed his legs, and blew out a beautiful grey ring of smoke that sailed up into the air without breaking and floated away over The Hill.

"Very pretty!" said Gandalf. "But I have no time to blow smoke-rings this morning. I am looking for someone to share in an adventure that I am arranging, and it's very difficult to find anyone."

"I should think so—in these parts! We are plain quiet people and have no use for adventures. Nasty disturbing uncomfortable things! Make you late for dinner! I can't think what anybody sees in them," said our Mr. Baggins, and stuck one thumb behind his braces, and blew out another even bigger smoke-ring. Then he took out his morning letters, and began to read, pretending to take no more notice of the old man. He had decided that he was not quite his sort, and wanted him to go away. But the old man did not move. He stood leaning on his stick and gazing at the hobbit without saying anything, till Bilbo got quite uncomfortable and even a little cross.

"Good morning!" he said at last. "We don't want any adventures here, thank you. You might try over The Hill or across The Water." By this he meant that the conversation was at an end.

"What a lot of things you do use Good morning for!" said Gandalf. "Now you mean that you want to get rid of me, and that it won't be good till I move off."

"Not at all, not at all, my dear sir! Let me see, I don't think I know your name?"

"Yes, yes, my dear sir—and I do know your name, Mr. Bilbo Baggins. And you do know my name, though you don't remember that I belong to it. I am Gandalf, and Gandalf means me! To think that I should have lived to be good-morninged by Belladonna Took's son, as if I was selling buttons at the door!"

"Gandalf, Gandalf! Good gracious me! Not the wandering wizard that gave Old Took a pair of magic diamond studs that fastened themselves and never came undone till ordered? Not the fellow who used to tell such wonderful tales at parties, about dragons and goblins and giants and the rescue of princesses and the unexpected luck of widows' sons? Not the man that used to make such particularly excellent fireworks! I remember those! Old Took used to have them on Midsummer's

Eve. Splendid! They used to go up like great lilies and snapdragons and laburnums of fire and hang in the twilight all evening!" You will notice already that Mr. Baggins was not quite so prosy as he liked to believe, also that he was very fond of flowers. "Dear me!" he went on. "Not the Gandalf who was responsible for so many quiet lads and lasses going off into the Blue for mad adventures. Anything from climbing trees to visiting Elves—or sailing in ships, sailing to other shores! Bless me, life used to be quite inter—I mean, you used to upset things badly in these parts once upon a time. I beg your pardon, but I had no idea you were still in business."

"Where else should I be?" said the wizard. "All the same I am pleased to find you remember something about me. You seem to remember my fireworks kindly, at any rate, and that is not without hope. Indeed for your old grandfather Took's sake, and for the sake of poor Belladonna, I will give you what you asked for."

"I beg your pardon, I haven't asked for anything!"

"Yes, you have! Twice now. My pardon. I give it you. In fact I will go so far as to send you on this adventure. Very amusing for me, very good for you—and profitable too, very likely, if you ever get over it."

"Sorry! I don't want any adventures, thank you. Not today. Good morning! But please come to tea—any time you like! Why not tomorrow? Come tomorrow! Good-bye!" With that the hobbit turned and scuttled inside his round green door, and shut it as quickly as he dared, not to seem rude. Wizards after all are wizards.

"What on earth did I ask him to tea for!" he said to himself, as he went to the pantry. He had only just had breakfast, but he thought a cake or two and a drink of something would do him good after his fright.

Gandalf in the meantime was still standing outside the door, and laughing long but quietly. After a while he stepped up, and with the spike of his staff scratched a queer sign on the hobbit's beautiful green front-door. Then he strode away, just about the time when Bilbo was finishing his second cake and beginning to think that he had escaped adventures very well.

The next day he had almost forgotten about Gandalf. He did not remember things very well, unless he put them down on his Engagement Tablet: like this: *Gandalf Tea Wednesday.* Yesterday he had been too flustered to do anything of the kind.

Just before tea-time there came a tremendous ring on the front-door bell, and then he remembered! He rushed and put on the kettle, and put out another cup and saucer, and an extra cake or two, and ran to the door.

"I am so sorry to keep you waiting!" he was going to say, when he saw that it was not Gandalf at all. It was a dwarf with a blue beard tucked into a golden belt, and very bright eyes under his dark-green hood. As soon as the door was opened, he pushed inside, just as if he had been expected.

He hung his hooded cloak on the nearest peg, and "Dwalin at your service!" he said with a low bow.

"Bilbo Baggins at yours!" said the hobbit, too surprised to ask any questions for the moment. When the silence that followed had become uncomfortable, he added: "I am just about to take tea; pray come and have some with me." A little stiff perhaps, but he meant it kindly. And what would you do, if an uninvited dwarf came and hung his things up in your hall without a word of explanation?

They had not been at table long, in fact they had hardly reached the third cake, when there came another even louder ring at the bell.

"Excuse me!" said the hobbit, and off he went to the door.

"So you have got here at last!" was what he was going to say to Gandalf this time. But it was not Gandalf. Instead there was a very old-looking dwarf on the step with a white beard and a scarlet hood; and he too hopped inside as soon as the door was open, just as if he had been invited.

"I see they have begun to arrive already," he said when he caught sight of Dwalin's green hood hanging up. He hung his red one next to it, and "Balin at your service!" he said with his hand on his breast.

"Thank you!" said Bilbo with a gasp. It was not the correct thing to say, but *they have begun to arrive* had flustered him badly. He liked visitors, but he liked to know them before they arrived, and he preferred to ask them himself. He had a horrible thought that the cakes might run short, and then he—as the host: he knew his duty and stuck to it however painful—he might have to go without.

"Come along in, and have some tea!" he managed to say after taking a deep breath.

"A little beer would suit me better, if it is all the same to you, my good sir," said Balin with the white beard. "But I don't mind some cake—seed-cake, if you have any."

"Lots!" Bilbo found himself answering, to his own surprise; and he found himself scuttling off, too, to the cellar to fill a pint beer-mug, and to the pantry to fetch two beautiful round seed-cakes which he had baked that afternoon for his after-supper morsel.

When he got back Balin and Dwalin were talking at the table like old friends (as a matter of fact they were brothers). Bilbo plumped down the beer and the cake in front of them, when loud came a ring at the bell again, and then another ring.

"Gandalf for certain this time," he thought as he puffed along the passage. But it was not. It was two more dwarves, both with blue hoods, silver belts, and yellow beards; and each of them carried a bag of tools and a spade. In they hopped, as soon as the door began to open—Bilbo was hardly surprised at all.

"What can I do for you, my dwarves?" he said.

"Kili at your service!" said the one. "And Fili!" added the other; and they both swept off their blue hoods and bowed.

"At yours and your family's!" replied Bilbo, remembering his manners this time.

"Dwalin and Balin here already, I see," said Kili. "Let us join the throng!"

"Throng!" thought Mr. Baggins. "I don't like the sound of that. I really must sit down for a minute and collect my wits, and have a drink." He had only just had a sip—in the corner, while the four dwarves sat around the table, and talked about mines and gold and troubles with the goblins, and the depredations of dragons, and lots of other things which he did not understand, and did not want to, for they sounded much too adventurous—when, *ding-dong-a-ling-dang*, his bell rang again, as if some naughty little hobbit-boy was trying to pull the handle off.

"Someone at the door!" he said, blinking.

"Some four, I should say by the sound," said Fili. "Besides, we saw them coming along behind us in the distance."

The poor little hobbit sat down in the hall and put his head in his hands, and wondered what had happened, and what was going to happen, and whether they would all stay to supper. Then the bell rang again louder than ever, and he had to run to the door. It was not four after all, it was FIVE. Another dwarf had come along while he was wondering in the hall. He had hardly turned the knob, before they were all inside, bowing and saying "at your service" one after another. Dori, Nori, Ori, Oin, and Gloin were their names; and very soon two purple hoods, a grey hood, a brown hood, and a white hood were hanging on the pegs, and off they marched with their broad hands stuck in their gold and silver belts to join the others. Already it had almost become a throng. Some called for ale, and some for porter, and one for coffee, and all of them for cakes; so the hobbit was kept very busy for a while.

A big jug of coffee had just been set in the hearth, the seed-cakes were gone, and the dwarves were starting on a round of buttered scones, when there came—a loud knock. Not a ring, but a hard rat-tat on the hobbit's beautiful green door. Somebody was banging with a stick!

Bilbo rushed along the passage, very angry, and altogether bewildered and bewuthered—this was the most awkward Wednesday he ever remembered. He pulled open the door with a jerk, and they all fell in, one on top of the other. More dwarves, four more! And there was Gandalf behind, leaning on his staff and laughing. He had made quite a dent on the beautiful door; he had also, by the way, knocked out the secret mark that he had put there the morning before.

"Carefully! Carefully!" he said. "It is not like you, Bilbo, to keep friends waiting on the mat, and then open the door like a pop-gun! Let me introduce Bifur, Bofur, Bombur, and especially Thorin!"

"At your service!" said Bifur, Bofur, and Bombur standing in a row. Then they hung up two yellow hoods and a pale green one; and also a sky-blue one with a long silver tassel. This last belonged to Thorin, an enormously important dwarf, in fact no other than the great Thorin Oakenshield himself, who was not at all pleased at falling flat on Bilbo's mat with Bifur, Bofur, and Bombur on top of him. For one thing Bombur was immensely fat and heavy. Thorin indeed was very haughty, and said nothing about *service*; but poor Mr. Baggins said he was sorry so many times, that at last he grunted "pray don't mention it," and stopped frowning.

"Now we are all here!" said Gandalf, looking at the row of thirteen hoods—the best detachable party hoods—and his own hat hanging on the pegs. "Quite a merry gathering! I hope there is something left for the late-comers to eat and drink! What's that? Tea! No thank you! A little red wine, I think, for me."

"And for me," said Thorin.

"And raspberry jam and apple-tart," said Bifur.

"And mince-pies and cheese," said Bofur.

"And pork-pie and salad," said Bombur.

"And more cakes—and ale—and coffee, if you don't mind," called the other dwarves through the door.

"Put on a few eggs, there's a good fellow!" Gandalf called after him, as the hobbit stumped off to the pantries. "And just bring out the cold chicken and pickles!"

"Seems to know as much about the inside of my larders as I do myself!" thought Mr. Baggins, who was feeling positively flummoxed, and was beginning to wonder whether a most wretched adventure had not come right into his house. By the time he had got all the bottles and dishes and knives and forks and glasses and plates and spoons and things piled up on big trays, he was getting very hot, and red in the face, and annoyed.

"Confusticate and bebother these dwarves!" he said aloud. "Why don't they come and lend a hand?" Lo and behold! there stood Balin and Dwalin at the door of the kitchen, and Fili and Kili behind them, and before he could say *knife* they had whisked the trays and a couple of small tables into the parlour and set out everything afresh.

Gandalf sat at the head of the party with the thirteen dwarves all round: and Bilbo sat on a stool at the fireside, nibbling at a biscuit (his appetite was quite taken away), and trying to look as if this was all perfectly ordinary and not in the least an adventure. The dwarves ate and ate, and talked and talked, and time got on. At last they pushed their chairs back, and Bilbo made a move to collect the plates and glasses.

"I suppose you will all stay to supper?" he said in his politest unpressing tones.

"Of course!" said Thorin. "And after. We shan't get through the business till late, and we must have some music first. Now to clear up!"

Thereupon the twelve dwarves—not Thorin, he was too important, and stayed talking to Gandalf—jumped to their feet, and made tall piles of all the things. Off they went, not waiting for trays, balancing columns of plates, each with a bottle on the top, with one hand, while the hobbit ran after them almost squeaking with fright: "please be careful!" and "please, don't trouble! I can manage." But the dwarves only started to sing:

> *Chip the glasses and crack the plates!*
> *Blunt the knives and bend the forks!*
> *That's what Bilbo Baggins hates—*
> *Smash the bottles and burn the corks!*
>
> *Cut the cloth and tread on the fat!*
> *Pour the milk on the pantry floor!*
> *Leave the bones on the bedroom mat!*
> *Splash the wine on every door!*

Dump the crocks in a boiling bowl;
  Pound them up with a thumping pole;
And when you've finished, if any are whole,
  Send them down the hall to roll!

That's what Bilbo Baggins hates!
So, carefully! carefully with the plates!

And of course they did none of these dreadful things, and everything was cleaned and put away safe as quick as lightning, while the hobbit was turning round and round in the middle of the kitchen trying to see what they were doing. Then they went back, and found Thorin with his feet on the fender smoking a pipe. He was blowing the most enormous smoke-rings, and wherever he told one to go, it went—up the chimney, or behind the clock on the mantelpiece, or under the table, or round and round the ceiling; but wherever it went it was not quick enough to escape Gandalf. Pop! he sent a smaller smoke-ring from his short clay-pipe straight through each one of Thorin's. Then Gandalf's smoke-ring would go green and come back to hover over the wizard's head. He had quite a cloud of them about him already, and in the dim light it made him look strange and sorcerous. Bilbo stood still and watched—he loved smoke-rings—and then he blushed to think how proud he had been yesterday morning of the smoke-rings he had sent up the wind over The Hill.

"Now for some music!" said Thorin. "Bring out the instruments!"

Kili and Fili rushed for their bags and brought back little fiddles; Dori, Nori, and Ori brought out flutes from somewhere inside their coats; Bombur produced a drum from the hall; Bifur and Bofur went out too, and came back with clarinets that they had left among the walking-sticks. Dwalin and Balin said: "Excuse me, I left mine in the porch!" "Just bring mine in with you," said Thorin. They came back with viols as big as themselves, and with Thorin's harp wrapped in a green cloth. It was a beautiful golden harp, and when Thorin struck it the music began all at once, so sudden and sweet that Bilbo forgot everything else, and was swept away into dark lands under strange moons, far over The Water and very far from his hobbit-hole under The Hill.

The dark came into the room from the little window that opened in the side of The Hill; the firelight flickered—it was

April—and still they played on, while the shadow of Gandalf's beard wagged against the wall.

The dark filled all the room, and the fire died down, and the shadows were lost, and still they played on. And suddenly first one and then another began to sing as they played, deep-throated singing of the dwarves in the deep places of their ancient homes; and this is like a fragment of their song, if it can be like their song without their music.

Far over the misty mountains cold
To dungeons deep and caverns old
We must away ere break of day
To seek the pale enchanted gold.

The dwarves of yore made mighty spells,
While hammers fell like ringing bells
In places deep, where dark things sleep,
In hollow halls beneath the fells.

For ancient king and elvish lord
There many a gleaming golden hoard
They shaped and wrought, and light they caught
To hide in gems on hilt of sword.

On silver necklaces they strung
The flowering stars, on crowns they hung
The dragon-fire, in twisted wire
They meshed the light of moon and sun.

Far over the misty mountains cold
To dungeons deep and caverns old
We must away, ere break of day,
To claim our long-forgotten gold.

Goblets they carved there for themselves
And harps of gold; where no man delves
There lay they long, and many a song
Was sung unheard by men or elves.

The pines were roaring on the height,
The winds were moaning in the night.
The fire was red, it flaming spread;
The trees like torches blazed with light.

The bells were ringing in the dale
And men looked up with faces pale;
The dragon's ire more fierce than fire
Laid low their towers and houses frail.

The mountain smoked beneath the moon;
The dwarves, they heard the tramp of doom.
They fled their hall to dying fall
Beneath his feet, beneath the moon.

Far over the misty mountains grim
To dungeons deep and caverns dim
We must away, ere break of day,
To win our harps and gold from him!

As they sang the hobbit felt the love of beautiful things made by hands and by cunning and by magic moving through him, a fierce and jealous love, the desire of the hearts of dwarves. Then something Tookish woke up inside him, and he wished to go and see the great mountains, and hear the pine-trees and the waterfalls, and explore the caves, and wear a sword instead of a walking-stick. He looked out of the window. The stars were out in a dark sky above the trees. He thought of the jewels of the dwarves shining in dark caverns. Suddenly in the wood beyond The Water a flame leapt up—probably somebody lighting a wood-fire—and he thought of plundering dragons settling on his quiet Hill and kindling it all to flames. He shuddered; and very quickly he was plain Mr. Baggins of Bag-End, Under-Hill, again.

He got up trembling. He had less than half a mind to fetch the lamp, and more than half a mind to pretend to, and go and hide behind the beer barrels in the cellar, and not come out again until all the dwarves had gone away. Suddenly he found that the music and the singing had stopped, and they were all looking at him with eyes shining in the dark.

"Where are you going?" said Thorin, in a tone that seemed to show that he guessed both halves of the hobbit's mind.

"What about a little light?" said Bilbo apologetically.

"We like the dark," said the dwarves. "Dark for dark business! There are many hours before dawn."

"Of course!" said Bilbo, and sat down in a hurry. He missed the stool and sat in the fender, knocking over the poker and shovel with a crash.

"Hush!" said Gandalf. "Let Thorin speak!" And this is how Thorin began.

"Gandalf, dwarves and Mr. Baggins! We are now together in the house of our friend and fellow conspirator, this most excellent and audacious hobbit—may the hair on his toes never fall out! all praise to his wine and ale!—" He paused for breath and for a polite remark from the hobbit, but the compliments were quite lost on poor Bilbo Baggins, who was wagging his mouth in protest at being called *audacious* and worst of all *fellow conspirator*, though no noise came out, he was so flummoxed. So Thorin went on:

"We are met to discuss our plans, our ways, means, policy and devices. We shall soon before the break of day start on our long journey, a journey from which some of us, or perhaps all of us (except our friend and counsellor, the ingenious wizard Gandalf) may never return. It is a solemn moment. Our object is, I take it, well known to us all. To the estimable Mr. Baggins, and perhaps to one or two of the younger dwarves (I think I should be right in naming Kili and Fili, for instance), the exact situation at the moment may require a little brief explanation——"

This was Thorin's style. He was an important dwarf. If he had been allowed, he would probably have gone on like this until he was out of breath, without telling any one there anything that was not known already. But he was rudely interrupted. Poor Bilbo couldn't bear it any longer. At *may never return* he began to feel a shriek coming up inside, and very soon it burst out like the whistle of an engine coming out of a tunnel. All the dwarves sprang up knocking over the table. Gandalf struck a blue light on the end of his magic staff, and in its firework glare the poor little hobbit could be seen kneeling on the hearthrug, shaking like a jelly that was melting. Then he fell flat on the floor, and kept on calling out "struck by lightning, struck by lightning!" over and over again; and that was all they could get out of him for a long time. So they took him and laid him out of the way on the drawing-room sofa with a drink at his elbow, and they went back to their dark business.

"Excitable little fellow," said Gandalf, as they sat down again. "Gets funny queer fits, but he is one of the best, one of the best—as fierce as a dragon in a pinch."

If you have ever seen a dragon in a pinch, you will realize that this was only poetical exaggeration applied to any hobbit, even to Old Took's great-granduncle Bullroarer, who was so huge (for a hobbit) that he could ride a horse. He charged the ranks of the goblins of Mount Gram in the Battle of the Green Fields, and knocked their king Golfimbul's head clean off with a wooden club. It sailed a hundred yards through the air and went down a rabbit-hole, and in this way the battle was won and the game of Golf invented at the same moment.

In the meanwhile, however, Bullroarer's gentler descendant was reviving in the drawing-room. After a while and a drink he crept nervously to the door of the parlour. This is what he heard, Gloin speaking: "Humph!" (or some snort more or less like that). "Will he do, do you think? It is all very well for Gandalf to talk about this hobbit being fierce, but one shriek like that in a moment of excitement would be enough to wake the dragon and all his relatives, and kill the lot of us. I think it sounded more like fright than excitement! In fact, if it had not been for the sign on the door, I should have been sure we had come to the wrong house. As soon as I clapped eyes on the little fellow bobbing and puffing on the mat, I had my doubts. He looks more like a grocer than a burglar!"

Then Mr. Baggins turned the handle and went in. The Took side had won. He suddenly felt he would go without bed and breakfast to be thought fierce. As for *little fellow bobbing on the mat* it almost made him really fierce. Many a time afterwards the Baggins part regretted what he did now, and he said to himself: "Bilbo, you were a fool; you walked right in and put your foot in it."

"Pardon me," he said, "if I have overheard words that you were saying. I don't pretend to understand what you are talking about, or your reference to burglars, but I think I am right in believing" (this is what he called being on his dignity) "that you think I am no good. I will show you. I have no signs on my door—it was painted a week ago—, and I am quite sure you have come to the wrong house. As soon as I saw your funny faces on the door-step, I had my doubts. But treat it as the right one. Tell me what you want done, and I will try it, if I have to walk from here to the East of East and fight the wild Were-worms in the Last Desert. I had a great-great-great-grand-uncle once, Bullroarer Took, and——"

"Yes, yes, but that was long ago," said Gloin. "I was talking about *you*. And I assure you there is a mark on this door—the usual one in the trade, or used to be. *Burglar wants a good job, plenty of Excitement and reasonable Reward*, that's how it is usually read. You can say *Expert Treasure-hunter* instead of *Burglar* if you like. Some of them do. It's all the same to us. Gandalf told us that there was a man of the sort in these parts looking for a Job at once, and that he had arranged for a meeting here this Wednesday tea-time."

"Of course there is a mark," said Gandalf. "I put it there myself. For very good reasons. You asked me to find the fourteenth man for your expedition, and I chose Mr. Baggins. Just let any one say I chose the wrong man or the wrong house, and you can stop at thirteen and have all the bad luck you like, or go back to digging coal."

He scowled so angrily at Gloin that the dwarf huddled back in his chair; and when Bilbo tried to open his mouth to ask a question, he turned and frowned at him and stuck out his bushy eyebrows, till Bilbo shut his mouth tight with a snap. "That's right," said Gandalf. "Let's have no more argument. I have chosen Mr. Baggins and that ought to be enough for all of you. If I say he is a Burglar, a Burglar he is, or will be when the time comes. There is a lot more in him than you guess, and a deal more than he has any idea of himself. You may (possibly) all live to thank me yet. Now Bilbo, my boy, fetch the lamp, and let's have a little light on this!"

On the table in the light of a big lamp with a red shade he spread a piece of parchment rather like a map.

"This was made by Thror, your grandfather, Thorin," he said in answer to the dwarves' excited questions. "It is a plan of the Mountain."

"I don't see that this will help us much," said Thorin disappointedly after a glance. "I remember the Mountain well enough and the lands about it. And I know where Mirkwood is, and the Withered Heath where the great dragons bred."

"There is a dragon marked in red on the Mountain," said Balin, "but it will be easy enough to find him without that, if ever we arrive there."

"There is one point that you haven't noticed," said the wizard, "and that is the secret entrance. You see that rune on the West side, and the hand pointing to it from the other runes? That marks a hidden passage to the Lower Halls."

"It may have been secret once," said Thorin, "but how do we know that it is secret any longer? Old Smaug has lived there long enough now to find out anything there is to know about those caves."

"He may—but he can't have used it for years and years."

"Why?"

"Because it is too small. 'Five feet high the door and three may walk abreast' say the runes, but Smaug could not creep into a hole that size, not even when he was a young dragon, certainly not after devouring so many of the dwarves and men of Dale."

"It seems a great big hole to me," squeaked Bilbo (who had no experience of dragons and only of hobbit-holes). He was getting excited and interested again, so that he forgot to keep his mouth shut. He loved maps, and in his hall there hung a large one of the Country Round with all his favourite walks marked on it in red ink. "How could such a large door be kept secret from everybody outside, apart from the dragon?" he asked. He was only a little hobbit you must remember.

"In lots of ways," said Gandalf. "But in what way this one has been hidden we don't know without going to see. From what it says on the map I should guess there is a closed door which has been made to look exactly like the side of the Mountain. That is the usual dwarves' method—I think that is right, isn't it?"

"Quite right," said Thorin.

"Also," went on Gandalf, "I forgot to mention that with the map went a key, a small and curious key. Here it is!" he said, and handed to Thorin a key with a long barrel and intricate wards, made of silver. "Keep it safe!"

"Indeed I will," said Thorin, and he fastened it upon a fine chain that hung about his neck and under his jacket. "Now things begin to look more hopeful. This news alters them much for the better. So far we have had no clear idea what to do. We thought of going East, as quiet and careful as we could, as far as the Long Lake. After that the trouble would begin—."

"A long time before that, if I know anything about the roads East," interrupted Gandalf.

"We might go from there up along the River Running," went on Thorin taking no notice, "and so to the ruins of Dale— the old town in the valley there, under the shadow of the Mountain. But we none of us liked the idea of the Front Gate. The river runs right out of it through the great cliff at the South of the Mountain, and out of it comes the dragon too—far too often, unless he has changed."

"That would be no good," said the wizard, "not without a mighty Warrior, even a Hero. I tried to find one; but warriors are busy fighting one another in distant lands, and in this neighbourhood heroes are scarce, or simply not to be found. Swords in these parts are mostly blunt, and axes are used for trees, and shields as cradles or dishcovers; and dragons are comfortably far-off (and therefore legendary). That is why I settled on *burglary*—especially when I remembered the existence of a Side-door. And here is our little Bilbo Baggins, *the* burglar,

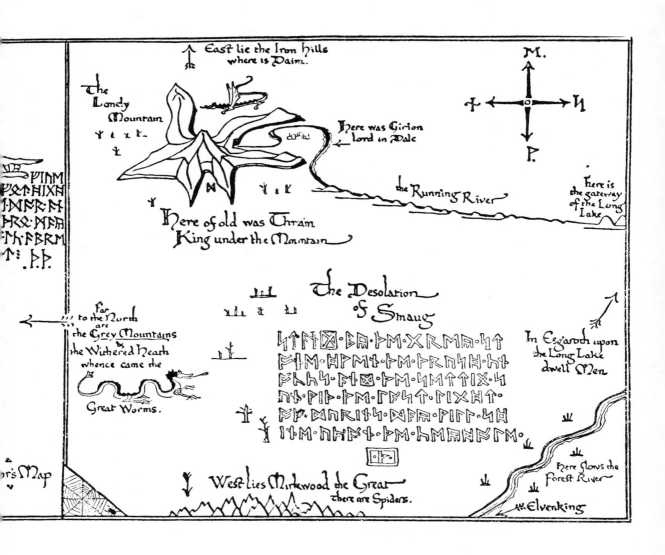

East lie the Iron hills where is Dain.

M.

P.

the Lonely Mountain

Here was Girion lord in Dale

the Running River

Here is the gateway of the Long Lake

Here of old was Thrain King under the Mountain

The Desolation of Smaug

Far to the North are the Grey Mountains & the Withered Heath whence came the Great Worms.

In Esgaroth upon the Long Lake dwell Men

Here flows the Forest River

or's Map

West lies Mirkwood the Great there are Spiders.

Elvenking

the chosen and selected burglar. So now let's get on and make some plans."

"Very well then," said Thorin, "supposing the burglar-expert gives us some ideas or suggestions." He turned with mock-politeness to Bilbo.

"First I should like to know a bit more about things," said he, feeling all confused and a bit shaky inside, but so far still Tookishly determined to go on with things. "I mean about the gold and the dragon, and all that, and how it got there, and who it belongs to, and so on and further."

"Bless me!" said Thorin, "haven't you got a map? and didn't you hear our song? and haven't we been talking about all this for hours?"

"All the same, I should like it all plain and clear," said he obstinately, putting on his business manner (usually reserved for people who tried to borrow money off him), and doing his best to appear wise and prudent and professional and live up to Gandalf's recommendation. "Also I should like to know about risks, out-of-pocket expenses, time required and remuneration, and so forth"—by which he meant: "What am I going to get out of it? and am I going to come back alive?"

"O very well," said Thorin. "Long ago in my grandfather Thror's time our family was driven out of the far North, and came back with all their wealth and their tools to this Mountain on the map. It had been discovered by my far ancestor, Thrain the Old, but now they mined and they tunnelled and they made huger halls and greater workshops—and in addition I believe they found a good deal of gold and a great many jewels too. Anyway they grew immensely rich and famous, and my grandfather was King under the Mountain again and treated with great reverence by the mortal men, who lived to the South, and were gradually spreading up the Running River as far as the valley overshadowed by the Mountain. They built the merry town of Dale there in those days. Kings used to send for our smiths, and reward even the least skilful most richly. Fathers would beg us to take their sons as apprentices, and pay us handsomely, especially in food-supplies, which we never bothered to grow or find for ourselves. Altogether those were good days for us, and the poorest of us had money to spend and to lend, and leisure to make beautiful things just for the fun of it, not to speak of the most marvellous and magical toys, the like of which is not to be found in the world now-a-days. So my grandfather's halls became full of armour and jewels and carvings and cups, and the toymarket of Dale was the wonder of the North.

"Undoubtedly that was what brought the dragon. Dragons steal gold and jewels, you know, from men and elves and dwarves, wherever they can find them; and they guard their plunder as long as they live (which is practically forever, unless they are killed), and never enjoy a brass ring of it. Indeed they hardly know a good bit of work from a bad, though they usually have a good notion of the current market value; and they can't make a thing for themselves, not even mend a little loose scale of their armour. There were lots of dragons in the North in those days, and gold was probably getting scarce up there, with the dwarves flying south or getting killed, and all the general waste and destruction that dragons make going from bad to worse. There was a most specially greedy, strong and wicked worm called Smaug. One day he flew up into the air and came south. The first we heard of it was a noise like a hurricane coming from the North, and the pine-trees on the Mountain creaking and cracking in the wind. Some of the dwarves who happened to be outside (I was one luckily—a fine adventurous lad in those days, always wandering about, and it saved my life that day)—well, from a good way off we saw the dragon settle on our mountain in a spout of flame. Then he came down the slopes and when he reached the woods they all went up in fire. By that time all the bells were ringing in Dale and the warriors were arming. The dwarves rushed out of their great gate; but there was the dragon waiting for them. None escaped that way. The river rushed up in steam and a fog fell on Dale, and in the fog the dragon came on them and destroyed most of the warriors—the usual unhappy story, it was only too common in those days. Then he went back and crept in through the Front Gate and routed out all the halls, and lanes, and tunnels, alleys, cellars, mansions and passages. After that there were no dwarves left alive inside, and he took all their wealth for himself. Probably, for that is the dragons' way, he has piled it all up in a great heap far inside, and sleeps on it for a bed. Later he used to crawl out of the great gate and come by night to Dale, and carry away people, especially maidens, to eat, until Dale was ruined, and all the people dead or gone. What goes on there now I don't know for certain, but I don't suppose anyone lives nearer to the Mountain than the far edge of the Long Lake now-a-days.

"The few of us that were well outside sat and wept in hiding, and cursed Smaug; and there we were unexpectedly joined by my father and my grandfather with singed beards. They looked very grim but they said very little. When I asked how they had got away, they told me to hold my tongue, and said that one day in the proper time I should know. After that we went away, and we have had to earn our livings as best we could up and down the lands, often enough sinking as low as blacksmith-work or even coal-mining. But we have never forgotten our stolen treasure. And even now, when I will allow we have a good bit laid by and are not so badly off"—here Thorin stroked the gold chain round his neck—"we still mean to get it back, and to bring our curses home to Smaug—if we can.

"I have often wondered about my father's and my grandfather's escape. I see now they must have had a private Side-door which only they knew about. But apparently they made a map, and I should like to know how Gandalf got hold of it, and why it did not come down to me, the rightful heir."

"I did not 'get hold of it,' I was given it," said the wizard. "Your grandfather Thror was killed, you remember, in the mines of Moria by Azog the Goblin—"

"Curse his name, yes," said Thorin.

"And Thrain your father went away on the twenty-first of April, a hundred years ago last Thursday, and has never been seen by you since—"

"True, true," said Thorin.

"Well, your father gave me this to give to you; and if I have chosen my own time and way of handing it over, you can hardly blame me, considering the trouble I had to find you. Your father could not remember his own name when he gave me the paper, and he never told me yours; so on the whole I think I ought to be praised and thanked. Here it is," said he handing the map to Thorin.

"I don't understand," said Thorin, and Bilbo felt he would have liked to say the same. The explanation did not seem to explain.

"Your grandfather," said the wizard slowly and grimly, "gave the map to his son for safety before he went to the mines of Moria. Your father went away to try his luck with the map after your grandfather was killed; and lots of adventures of a most unpleasant sort he had, but he never got near the Mountain. How he got there I don't know, but I found him a prisoner in the dungeons of the Necromancer."

"Whatever were you doing there?" asked Thorin with a shudder, and all the dwarves shivered.

"Never you mind. I was finding things out, as usual; and a nasty dangerous business it was. Even I, Gandalf, only just escaped. I tried to save your father, but it was too late. He was witless and wandering, and had forgotten almost everything except the map and the key."

"We have long ago paid the goblins of Moria," said Thorin; "we must give a thought to the Necromancer."

"Don't be absurd! He is an enemy quite beyond the powers of all the dwarves put together, if they could all be collected again from the four corners of the world. The one thing your father wished was for his son to read the map and use the key. The dragon and the Mountain are more than big enough tasks for you!"

"Hear, hear!" said Bilbo, and accidentally said it aloud.

"Hear what?" they all said turning suddenly towards him, and he was so flustered that he answered, "Hear what I have got to say!"

"What's that?" they asked.

"Well, I should say that you ought to go East and have a look round. After all there is the Side-door, and dragons must sleep sometimes, I suppose. If you sit on the door-step long enough, I daresay you will think of something. And well, don't you know, I think we have talked long enough for one night, if you see what I mean. What about bed, and an early start, and all that? I will give you a good breakfast before you go."

"Before *we* go, I suppose you mean," said Thorin. "Aren't you the burglar? And isn't sitting on the door-step your job, not to speak of getting inside the door? But I agree about bed and breakfast. I like eggs with my ham, when starting on a journey: fried not poached, and mind you don't break 'em."

After all the others had ordered their breakfasts without so much as a please (which annoyed Bilbo very much), they all got up. The hobbit had to find room for them all, and filled all his spare-rooms and made beds on chairs and sofas, before he got them all stowed and went to his own little bed very tired and not altogether happy. One thing he did make his mind up about was not to bother to get up very early and cook everybody else's wretched breakfast. The Tookishness was wearing off, and he was not now quite so sure that he was going on any journey in the morning.

As he lay in bed he could hear Thorin still humming to himself in the best bedroom next to him:

Far over the misty mountains cold
To dungeons deep and caverns old
We must away, ere break of day,
To find our long-forgotten gold.

Bilbo went to sleep with that in his ears, and it gave him very uncomfortable dreams. It was long after the break of day, when he woke up.

The Sin of Madame Phloi

Lilian Jackson Braun

From the very beginning Madame Phloi felt an instinctive distaste for the man who moved into the apartment next door. He was fat, and his trouser cuffs had the unsavory odor of fire hydrant.

They met for the first time in the decrepit elevator as it lurched up to the tenth floor of the old building, once fashionable but now coming apart at the seams. Madame Phloi had been out for a stroll in the city park, chewing city grass and chasing faded butterflies, and as she and her companion stepped on the elevator for the slow ride upward, the car was already half filled with the new neighbor.

The fat man and the Madame presented a contrast that was not unusual in this apartment house, which had a brilliant past and no future. He was bulky, uncouth, sloppily attired. Madame Phloi was a long-legged, blue-eyed aristocrat whose creamy fawn coat shaded into brown at the extremities.

The Madame deplored fat men. They had no laps, and of what use is a lapless human? Nevertheless, she gave him the common courtesy of a sniff at his trouser cuffs and immediately backed away, twitching her nose and breathing through the mouth.

"*GET* that cat away from me," the fat man roared, stamping his feet thunderously at Madame Phloi. Her companion pulled on the leash, although there was no need—the Madame, with one backward leap, had retreated to a safe corner of the elevator, which shuddered and continued its groaning ascent.

"Don't you like animals?" asked the gentle voice at the other end of the leash.

"Filthy, sneaky beasts," the fat man said with a snarl. "Last place I lived, some lousy cat got in my room and et my parakeet."

"I'm sorry to hear that. Very sorry. But you don't need to worry about Madame Phloi and Thapthim. They never leave the apartment except on a leash."

"You got *TWO?* That's just fine, that is! Keep 'em away from me, or I'll break their rotten necks. I ain't wrung a cat's neck since I was fourteen, but I remember how."

And with the long black box he was carrying, the fat man lunged at the impeccable Madame Phloi, who sat in her corner, flat-eared and tense. Her fur bristled, and she tried to dart away. Even when her companion picked her up in protective arms, Madame Phloi's body was taut and trembling.

Not until she was safely home in her modest but well-cushioned apartment did she relax. She walked stiff-legged to the sunny spot on the carpet where Thapthim was sleeping and licked the top of his head. Then she had a complete bath herself—to rid her coat of the fat man's odor. Thapthim did not wake.

This drowsy, unambitious, amiable creature—her son—was a puzzle to Madame Phloi, who was sensitive and spirited herself. She didn't try to understand him; she merely loved him. She spent hours washing his paws and breast and other parts he could easily have reached with his own tongue. At dinnertime she chewed slowly so there would be something left on her plate for his dessert, and he always gobbled the extra portion hungrily. And when he slept, which was most of the time, she kept watch by his side, sitting with a tall, regal posture until she swayed with weariness. Then she made herself into a small bundle and dozed with one eye open.

Thapthim was lovable, to be sure. He appealed to other cats, large and small dogs, people, and even ailurophobes in a limited way. He had a face like a beautiful flower and large blue eyes, tender and trusting. Ever since he was a kitten, he had been willing to purr at the touch of a hand—any hand. Eventually he became so agreeable that he purred if anyone looked at him across the room. What's more, he came when called; he gratefully devoured whatever was served on his dinner plate; and when he was told to get down, he got down.

His wise parent disapproved of this uncatly conduct; it indicated a certain lack of character, and no good would come of it. By her own example she tried to guide him. When dinner was served, she gave the plate a haughty sniff and walked away, no matter how tempting the dish. That was the way it was done by any self-respecting feline. In a minute or two she returned and condescended to dine, but never with open enthusiasm.

Furthermore, when human hands reached out, the catly thing was to bound away, lead them a chase, flirt a little before allowing oneself to be caught and cuddled. Thapthim, sorry to say, greeted any friendly overture by rolling over, purring, and looking soulful.

From an early age he had known the rules of the apartment:

No sleeping in a cupboard with the pots and pans.

Sitting on the table with the inkwell is permissible.

Sitting on the table with the coffeepot is never allowed.

The sad truth was that Thapthim obeyed these rules. Madame Phloi, on the other hand, knew that a rule was a challenge, and it was a matter of integrity to violate it. To obey was to sacrifice one's dignity. . . . It seemed that her son would never learn the true values in life.

To be sure, Thapthim was adored for his good nature in the human world of inkwells and coffeepots. But Madame Phloi was equally adored— and for the correct reasons. She was respected for her independence, admired for her clever methods of getting her own way, and loved for the cowlick on her white breast, the kink in her tail, and the squint in her delphinium-blue eyes. She was more truly Siamese than her son. Her face was small and perky. By cocking her head and staring with heart-melting eyes, slightly crossed, she could charm a porterhouse steak out from under a knife and fork.

Until the fat man and his black box moved in next door, Madame Phloi had never known an unfriendly soul. She had two companions in her tenth-floor apartment—genial creatures without names who came and went a good deal. One was an easy mark for between-meal snacks; a tap on his ankle always produced a spoonful of cottage cheese. The other served as a hot-water bottle on cold nights, and punctually obliged whenever the Madame wished to have her underside stroked or her cheekbones massaged.

This second one also murmured compliments in a gentle voice that made one squeeze one's eyes in pleasure.

Life was not all love and cottage cheese, however. Madame Phloi had her regular work. She was official watcher and listener for the household.

There were six windows that needed watching, for a wide ledge ran around the building flush with the tenth-floor windowsills, and this was a promenade for pigeons. They strutted, searched their feathers, and ignored the Madame, who sat on the sill and watched them dispassionately but thoroughly through the window screen.

While watching was a daytime job, listening was done after dark and required greater concentration. Madame Phloi listened for noises in the walls. She heard termites chewing, pipes sweating, and sometimes the ancient plaster cracking; but mostly she listened to the ghosts of generations of deceased mice.

One evening, shortly after the incident in the elevator, Madame Phloi was listening, Thapthim was asleep, and the other two were quietly turning pages of books, when a strange and horrendous sound came from the wall. The Madame's ears flicked to attention, then flattened against her head.

An interminable screech was coming out of that wall, like nothing the Madame had ever heard before. It chilled the blood and tortured the eardrums. So painful was the shrillness that Madame Phloi threw back her head and complained with a piercing howl of her own. The strident din even waked Thapthim. He looked

133

about in alarm, shook his head wildly, and clawed at his ears to get rid of the offending noise.

The others heard it, too.

"Listen to that!" said the one with the gentle voice.

"It must be that new man next door," said the other. "It's incredible."

"I can't imagine anyone so crude producing anything so exquisite. Is it Prokofiev he's playing?"

"No, I think it's Bartók."

"He was carrying his violin in the elevator today. He tried to hit Phloi with it."

"He's a nut. . . . Look at the cats—apparently they don't care for violin."

Madame Phloi and Thapthim, bounding from the room, collided with each other as they rushed to hide under the bed.

That was not the only kind of noise which emanated from the adjoining apartment in those upsetting days after the fat man moved in. The following evening, when Madame Phloi walked into the living room to commence her listening, she heard a fluttering sound dimly through the wall, accompanied by highly conversational chirping. This was agreeable music, and she settled down on the sofa to enjoy it, tucking her brown paws neatly under her creamy body.

Her contentment was soon disturbed, however, when the fat man's voice burst through the wall like thunder.

"Look what you done, you dirty skunk!" he bellowed. "Right in my fiddle! Get back in your cage before I brain you."

There was a frantic beating of wings.

"*GET* down off that window, or I'll bash your head in."

This threat brought only a torrent of chirping.

"Shut up, you stupid cluck! Shut up and get back in the cage, or I'll . . ."

There was a splintering crash, and after that all was quiet except for an occasional pitiful "Peep!"

Madame Phloi was fascinated. In fact, when she resumed her watching the next day, pigeons seemed rather insipid entertainment. She had waked the family that morning in her usual way—by staring intently at their foreheads as they slept. Then she and Thapthim had a game of hockey in the bathtub with a ping-pong ball, followed by a dish of mackerel, and after breakfast the Madame took up her post at the living-room window. Everyone had left for the day, but not before opening the window and placing a small cushion on the chilly marble sill.

There she sat—Madame Phloi—a small but alert package of fur, sniffing the welcome summer air, seeing all, and knowing all. She knew, for example, that the person who was at that moment walking down the tenth-floor hallway, wearing old tennis shoes and limping slightly, would halt at the door of her apartment, set down his pail, and let himself in with a passkey.

Indeed, she hardly bothered to turn her head when the window washer entered. He was one of her regular court of admirers. His odor was friendly, although it suggested damp basements and floor mops, and

134

he talked sensibly—indulging in none of that falsetto foolishness with which some people insulted the Madame's intelligence.

"Hop down, kitty," he said in a musical voice. "Charlie's gotta take out that screen. See, I brought you some cheese."

He held out a modest offering of rat cheese, and Madame Phloi investigated it. Unfortunately it was the wrong variety, and she shook one fastidious paw at it.

"Mighty fussy cat," Charlie laughed. "Well, now, you set there and watch Charlie clean this here window. Don't you go jumpin' out on the ledge, because Charlie ain't runnin' after you. No sir! That old ledge, she's startin' to crumble. Someday them pigeons'll stamp their feet hard, and down she goes! . . . Hey, lookit the broken glass out here. Somebody busted a window."

Charlie sat on the marble sill and pulled the upper sash down in his lap, and while Madame Phloi followed his movements carefully, Thapthim sauntered into the room, yawning and stretching, and swallowed the cheese.

"Now Charlie puts the screen back in, and you two guys can watch them crazy pigeons some more. This screen, she's comin' apart, too. Whole buildin' seems to be crackin' up."

Remembering to replace the cushion on the cool, hard sill, he then went on to clean the next window, and the Madame resumed her post, sitting on the very edge of the cushion so that Thapthim could have most of it.

The pigeons were late that morning, probably frightened away by the window washer. It was while Madame Phloi patiently waited for the first visitor to skim in on a blue-gray wing that she noticed the tiny opening in the screen. Every aperture, no matter how small, was a temptation; she had to prove she could wriggle through any tight space, whether there was a good reason or not.

She waited until Charlie had limped out of the apartment before she began pushing at the screen with her nose, first gingerly and then stubbornly. Inch by inch the rusted mesh ripped away from the frame until the whole corner formed a loose flap, and Madame Phloi slithered through— nose and ears, slender shoulders, dainty Queen Anne forefeet, svelte torso, lean flanks, hind legs like steel springs, and finally, proud brown tail. For the first time in her life she found herself on the pigeon promenade. She gave a delicious shudder.

Inside the screen the lethargic Thapthim, jolted by this strange turn of affairs, watched his daring parent with a quarter inch of his pink tongue hanging out. They touched noses briefly through the screen, and the Madame proceeded to explore. She advanced cautiously and with mincing step, for the pigeons had not been tidy in their habits.

The ledge was about two feet wide. To its edge Madame Phloi moved warily, nose down and tail high. Ten stories below there were moving objects, but nothing of interest, she decided. Walking daintily along the extreme edge to avoid the broken glass, she ventured in the direction of the fat man's apartment, impelled by some half-forgotten curiosity.

His window stood open and unscreened, and Madame Phloi peered in politely. There, sprawled on the floor, lay the fat man himself, snorting and heaving his immense paunch in a kind of rhythm. It always alarmed her to see a human on the floor, which she considered feline domain. She licked her nose apprehensively and stared at him with enormous eyes, one iris hypnotically off-center. In a dark corner of the room something fluttered and squawked, and the fat man waked.

"SHcrrff! *GET* out of here!" he shouted, struggling to his feet.

In three leaps Madame Phloi crossed the ledge back to her own window and pushed through the screen to safety. Looking back to see if the fat man might be chasing her and being reassured that he wasn't, she washed Thapthim's ears and her own paws and sat down to wait for pigeons.

Like any normal cat, Madame Phloi lived by the Rule of Three. She resisted every innovation three times before accepting it, tackled an obstacle three times before giving up, and tried each new activity three times before tiring of it. Consequently she made two more sallies to the pigeon promenade and eventually convinced Thapthim to join her.

Together they peered over the edge at the world below. The sense of freedom was intoxicating. Recklessly,

Thapthim made a leap at a low-flying pigeon and landed on his mother's back. She cuffed his ear in retaliation. He poked her nose. They grappled and rolled over and over on the ledge, oblivious of the long drop below them, taking playful nips of each other's hide and snarling guttural expressions of glee.

Suddenly and instinctively Madame Phloi scrambled to her feet and crouched in a defensive position. The fat man was leaning from his window.

"Here, kitty, kitty," he was saying in one of those despised falsetto voices, offering some tidbit in a saucer. The Madame froze, but Thapthim turned his beautiful trusting eyes on the stranger and advanced along the ledge. Purring and waving his tail cordially, he walked into the trap. It all happened in a matter of seconds: the saucer was withdrawn, and a long black box was swung at Thapthim like a ball bat, sweeping him off the ledge and into space. He was silent as he fell.

When the family came home, laughing and chattering, with their arms full of packages, they knew at once something was amiss. No one greeted them at the door. Madame Phloi hunched moodily on the windowsill staring at a hole in the screen, and Thapthim was not to be found.

"Look at the screen!" cried the gentle voice.

"I'll bet he got out on the ledge."

"Can you lean out and look? Be careful."

"You hold Phloi."

"Do you see him?"

"Not a sign of him! There's a lot of glass scattered around, and the window's broken next door."

"Do you suppose that man . . .? I feel sick."

"Don't worry, dear. We'll find him. . . . There's the doorbell! Maybe someone's bringing him home."

It was Charlie standing at the door. He fidgeted uncomfortably. " 'Scuse me, folks," he said. "You missin' one of your kitties?"

"Yes! Have you found him?"

"Poor little guy," said Charlie. "Found him lyin' right under your windows—where the bushes is thick."

"He's dead!" the gentle one moaned.

"Yes, ma'am. That's a long way down."

"Where is he now?"

"I got him down in the basement, ma'am. I'll take care of him real nice. I don't think you'd want to see the poor guy."

Still Madame Phloi stared at the hole in the screen and waited for Thapthim. From time to time she checked the other windows, just to be sure. As time passed and he did not return, she looked behind the radiators and under the bed. She pried open the cupboard door where the pots and pans were stored. She tried to burrow her way into the closet. She sniffed all around the front door. Finally she stood in the middle of the living room and called loudly in a high-pitched, wailing voice.

Later that evening Charlie paid another visit to the apartment.

"Only wanted to tell you, ma'am, how nice I took care of him," he said. "I got a box that was just the right size. A white box, it was. And I wrapped him up in a piece of old blue curtain. The color looked real pretty with his fur. And I buried the little guy right under your window behind the bushes."

And still the Madame searched, returning again and again to watch the ledge from which Thapthim had disappeared. She scorned food. She rebuffed any attempts at consolation. And all night she sat wide-eyed and waiting in the dark.

The living-room window was now tightly closed, but the following day the Madame—after she was left by herself in the lonely apartment—went to work on the bedroom screens. One was new and hopeless, but the second screen was slightly corroded, and she was soon nosing through a slit that lengthened as she struggled out onto the ledge.

Picking her way through the broken glass, she approached the spot where Thapthim had vanished. And then it all happened again. There he was—the fat man—reaching forth with a saucer.

"Here, kitty, kitty."

Madame Phloi hunched down and backed away.

"Kitty want some milk?" It was that ugly falsetto, but she didn't run home this time. She crouched there on the ledge, a few inches out of reach.

"Nice kitty. Nice kitty."

Madame Phloi crept with caution toward the saucer in the outstretched fist, and stealthily the fat man extended another hand, snapping his fingers as one would call a dog.

The Madame retreated diagonally—half toward home and half toward the dangerous brink.

"Here, kitty. Here, kitty," he cooed, leaning farther out. But muttering, he said, "You dirty sneak! I'll get you if it's the last thing I ever do. Comin' after my bird, weren't you?"

Madame Phloi recognized danger with all her senses. Her ears went back, her whiskers curled, and her white underside hugged the ledge.

A little closer she moved, and the fat man made a grab for her. She jerked back a step, with unblinking eyes fixed on his sweating face. He was furtively laying the saucer aside, she noticed, and edging his fat paunch farther out the window.

Once more she advanced almost into his grasp, and again he lunged at her with both powerful arms.

The Madame leaped lightly aside.

"This time I'll get you, you stinkin' cat," he cried, and raising one knee to the windowsill, he threw himself at Madame Phloi. As she slipped through his fingers, he landed on the ledge with all his weight.

A section of it crumbled beneath him. He bellowed, clutching at the air, and at the same time a streak of creamy brown flashed out of sight. The fat man was not silent as he fell.

As for Madame Phloi, she was found doubled in half in a patch of sunshine on her living-room carpet, innocently washing her fine brown tail.

PYGMALION AND GALATEA

retold by

Miriam Cox

On the island of Cyprus lived a talented young sculptor named Pygmalion. The statues he carved were so lifelike that they seemed actually to breathe; yet they were far more beautiful than real human beings.

Travelers came from great distances to admire his work. But if the visitors were women, they were certain to be turned away abruptly. For Pygmalion was a woman-hater. Not only had he decided never to marry, but he scorned even to talk to girls.

Naturally the pretty maidens of the village tried to change this harsh attitude and dreamed up all kinds of little tricks to attract his attention, for Pygmalion was handsome as well as gifted. But all their efforts were useless; he would have nothing to do with any of them, preferring to toil from morning until night upon one beautiful work of art after another.

Oddly enough, however, when an unusually fine piece of ivory came into his possession one day, he decided to fashion it into the statue of a woman. After all, he couldn't go on forever making sculptures only of men and animals. In this statue he would express all his ideals of supreme beauty. It would be interesting to show misguided men that living women were quite inferior, by comparison!

Long before the statue was completed, Pygmalion knew that it would be his masterpiece. The mellow ivory seemed to welcome the lightest touch of his delicate chisels, and it was as

if his very soul were being molded into his new creation. He could hardly wait to finish it. Often he worked all through the night, and felt cheated when at last he had to stop for food and sleep.

At last the statue was complete, and Pygmalion stood in awe before it. He had achieved his goal; here truly was matchless beauty; this was perfection. The figure glowed with an inner radiance that made the softly curved lips seem about to open into a welcoming smile. It was as if a living maiden would descend gracefully from the marble pedestal at any moment.

For several days Pygmalion could not bear to leave his statue for a moment, so entranced was he by her beauty. Then he began to search the shops for trinkets, pretty robes, and jewels. Lovingly he adorned his statue with them, almost imagining that he could hear her happy laughter as she accepted his gifts.

She became so real to him that he gave her a name, Galatea, and told her of his hopes and sorrows just as if she was a living woman. Finally he had to admit the truth to himself: he had fallen in love at last, but with a cold ivory statue of his own making. What could be more hopeless? Gradually his joy in her began to turn to deep sadness. If only she were real!

Now each year a great festival was held in honor of Aphrodite, the goddess of love and beauty. The people of Cyprus especially loved this day because it was to their island that the goddess had first been blown by the breezes after rising from the ocean foam.

All day long her temple was thronged with worshipers who offered incense at the altar, decked her statue with garlands, and presented gifts. In the crowd were many unhappy lovers who had come to ask for her aid, because it was well known that Aphrodite was interested in the course of true love. Occasionally she would even lend mortals her magic belt, which enabled its wearer to inspire love in others.

Pygmalion had always felt deep devotion for Aphrodite, for he worshiped beauty. But as he approached her shrine, he was troubled. Could he tell her of the deep desire in his heart? Would she listen to such a plea as his, knowing that he had always hated women? Hesitantly he placed his offerings on her altar and pleaded, "Grant me, O Goddess of Love and Beauty, the greatest of all gifts: let me have a maiden like the ivory Galatea for my wife. Or better still. . . ." But at that moment the flames of the altar leaped high into the air. Could this mean that Aphrodite favored his prayer?

Pygmalion was excited as he hurried home, flung open his door, and went to his lovely Galatea. He touched her delicately chiseled hand; it felt warm and soft! As he watched spellbound, scarlet flooded into her lips and a breeze from the open doorway caressed hair that fell like a golden fountain over her white shoulders.

With a happy cry, Pygmalion stepped forward to embrace her; then he stopped. So often he had imagined that this was happening, only to awake to cruel disappointment. But this time it was not a dream. Violet eyes shining with love, Galatea stepped down from her marble pedestal into his eager arms. Aphrodite had answered the prayer in his heart: his statue had been granted the gift of life and was his to adore forever.

LUCY GRAY

William Wordsworth

Oft I had heard of Lucy Gray:
And, when I crossed the wild,
I chanced to see at break of day
The solitary child.

No mate, no comrade Lucy knew;
She dwelt on a wide moor,
—The sweetest thing that ever grew
Beside a human door!

You yet may spy the fawn at play,
The hare upon the green;
But the sweet face of Lucy Gray
Will never more be seen.

"To-night will be a stormy night—
You to the town must go;
And take a lantern, Child, to light
Your mother through the snow."

"That, Father! will I gladly do:
'Tis scarcely afternoon—
The minster-clock has just struck two,
And yonder is the moon!"

At this the Father raised his hook,
And snapped a faggot-band;
He plied his work;—and Lucy took
The lantern in her hand.

Not blither is the mountain roe:
With many a wanton stroke
Her feet disperse the powdery snow,
That rises up like smoke.

The storm came on before its time:
She wandered up and down;
And many a hill did Lucy climb:
But never reached the town.

The wretched parents all that night
Went shouting far and wide;
But there was neither sound nor sight
To serve them for a guide.

At day-break on a hill they stood
That overlooked the moor;
And thence they saw the bridge of wood,
A furlong from their door.

They wept—and, turning homeward, cried,
"In heaven we all shall meet";
—When in the snow the mother spied
The print of Lucy's feet.

Then downwards from the steep hill's edge
They tracked the footmarks small;
And through the broken hawthorn hedge,
And by the long stone-wall;

And then an open field they crossed;
The marks were still the same;
They tracked them on, nor ever lost;
And to the bridge they came.

They followed from the snowy bank
Those footmarks, one by one,
Into the middle of the plank;
And further there were none!

—Yet some maintain that to this day
She is a living child;
That you may see sweet Lucy Gray
Upon the lonesome wild.

O'er rough and smooth she trips along,
And never looks behind;
And sings a solitary song
That whistles in the wind.

END
Langston Hughes

There are
No clocks on the wall
And no time,
No shadows that move
From dawn to dusk
Across the floor.

There is neither light
Nor dark
Outside the door.

There is no door!

THE MAN WHO DISAPPEARED... INTO THIN AIR

Stephen Mooser

The summer of 1880 had been a real scorcher in Tennessee. From one end of the state to the other, farmers' fields lay dry and brown. For David Lang of Gallitin, Tennessee, the dry spell was especially worrisome. His cows and horses needed the grass he grew in his fields.

On September 23, Mr. Lang stood in his yard and looked out at his 40-acre farm. It was noon. Nearby, his two children, Sarah, age 11, and George, age eight, were playing. Mr. Lang had just bought them a little wagon. They laughed as they pulled it about the dusty yard.

"The fields look terrible," Mr. Lang said to his wife. "I don't know what we'll do if it doesn't rain."

"We'll work out something," said Mrs. Lang. "Don't worry."

Mr. Lang sighed and headed out into the open field. "I'm going to look over the farm," he said. "I won't be long."

Mrs. Lang watched her husband walk away. There was nothing to block her view. No trees. No rocks. Just short brown grass stretching toward the horizon.

Just then a buggy came down the road. In it were Mr. Lang's brother-in-law and a friend, Judge Peck. The judge waved to Mr. Lang. He turned around and waved back. He looked as if he was about to speak. Then, quite suddenly, it happened.

David Lang disappeared . . . into thin air!

Just like that. Before their very eyes, he was gone.

Mrs. Lang screamed, and so did the judge. Everyone, including the children, ran into the field. They looked for holes or big cracks in the ground. They found none.

They called Mr. Lang's name. There was no answer.

Then someone rang a large bell. Neighbors came running from miles around.

145

"What happened?" everyone asked.

"He was there . . . then he wasn't," said Mrs. Lang.

"It's true," said the judge. "I saw it too."

Judge Peck led the neighbors out into the field. He showed them where Mr. Lang had been standing. They began to stamp the dry ground, looking for holes. But they didn't find any.

Before long it grew dark. Scores of torches were lit; then the search went on beneath their eerie glare. The Langs and their neighbors searched all through the night and into the next day. They looked everywhere. They tried everything. But they didn't turn up a clue.

For more than a week, people searched the Langs' farm. At one point, geologists were called in. They dug into the field and tested the soil. When their findings were made public, the mystery only deepened. The report read, "Under the field we found nothing but solid rock."

It was strange—and scary too. Some of Mrs. Lang's friends were afraid to visit her. And all the farmhands left in fear.

The following year, more weird things happened. The cows and horses refused to graze near the spot where Mr. Lang had vanished. So the grass in that area grew much taller than in the surrounding pasture. There was something strange, almost unearthly, about the spot. Even insects seemed to shy away from the tall grass.

Then, one day in 1881, David Lang spoke!

The Lang children were playing near the tall grass. One of them looked at the place where Mr. Lang had disappeared and called, "Father, Father. Are you there?"

There was no answer.

Then both children called for their father. They called out four times. Suddenly, they heard an answer.

"Help, help me please!"

Their mouths fell open. It was their father! They could hear him, but they couldn't see him. The words just floated out of the air.

They quickly ran to get their mother. She hurried to the spot.

"David! David!" she cried. "Where are you?"

"Help me, help me," came the answer.

"Where are you?" she repeated.

But "Help me" was the only answer she ever got. Over the next few days, the scene was repeated. Mrs. Lang would call out, and her husband's voice would answer with the same words. In time, the cries began to fade away. At last, like Mr. Lang himself, they disappeared. And he was never heard from again.

Where did he go? No one knows for sure. But here are some of the possibilities:

Mr. Lang passed into another dimension. There may be places where time and space are warped. Perhaps he just happened to be in the wrong place at the wrong time. (If this is true, why haven't more people vanished? Why didn't anything else disappear from the spot where he was standing?)

He was picked up by an invisible UFO. (If so, why was his voice heard in the same spot seven months later?)

Mr. Lang was murdered by his wife. To cover up the crime, she devised this strange story. (This doesn't make much sense. How could she have talked four other people into going along with her crazy plan? Among the four were her two children and a judge!)

Was it a time warp, a UFO, a murder? We may never know. All we know is that the disappearance of David Lang is one of the greatest mysteries of our time.

The Birds

Daphne du Maurier

On December third, the wind changed overnight and it was winter. Until then, the autumn had been mellow, soft. The earth was rich where the plow had turned it.

Nat Hocken, because of a wartime disability, had a pension and did not work full time at the farm. He worked three days a week, and they gave him the lighter jobs. Although he was married, with children, his was a solitary disposition; he liked best to work alone.

It pleased him when he was given a bank to build up, or a gate to mend, at the far end of the peninsula, where the sea surrounded the farmland on either side. Then, at midday, he would pause and eat the meat pie his wife had baked for him and, sitting on the cliff's edge, watch the birds.

In autumn, great flocks of them came to the peninsula, restless, uneasy, spending themselves in motion; now wheeling, circling in the sky; now settling to feed on the rich, new-turned soil; but even when they fed, it was as though they did so without hunger, without desire.

Restlessness drove them to the skies again. Crying, whistling, calling, they skimmed the placid sea and left the shore.

Make haste, make speed, hurry and begone; yet where, and to what purpose? The restless urge of autumn, unsatisfying, sad, had put a spell upon them, and they must spill themselves of motion before winter came.

Perhaps, thought Nat, a message comes to the birds in autumn, like a warning. Winter is coming. Many of

them will perish. And, like people who, apprehensive of death before their time, drive themselves to work or folly, the birds do likewise; tomorrow we shall die.

The birds had been more restless than ever this fall of the year. Their agitation more remarked because the days were still.

As Mr. Trigg's tractor traced its path up and down the western hills, and Nat, hedging, saw it dip and turn, the whole machine and the man upon it were momentarily lost in the great cloud of wheeling, crying birds.

Nat remarked upon them to Mr. Trigg when the work was finished for the day.

"Yes," said the farmer, "there are more birds about than usual. I have a notion the weather will change. It will be a hard winter. That's why the birds are restless."

The farmer was right. That night the weather turned.

The bedroom in the cottage faced east. Nat woke just after two and heard the east wind, cold and dry. It sounded hollow in the chimney, and a loose slate rattled on the roof. Nat listened, and he could hear the sea roaring in the bay. He drew the blanket round him, leaned closer to the back of his wife, deep in sleep. Then he heard the tapping on the windowpane. It continued until, irritated by the sound, Nat got out of bed and went to the window. He opened it; and, as he did so, something brushed his hand, jabbing at his knuckles, grazing the skin. Then he saw the flutter of wings and the thing was gone again, over the roof, behind the cottage.

It was a bird. What kind of bird he could not tell. The wind must have driven it to shelter on the sill.

He shut the window and went back to bed, but, feeling his knuckles wet, put his mouth to the scratch. The bird had drawn blood.

Frightened, he supposed, bewildered, seeking shelter, the bird had stabbed at him in the darkness. Once more he settled himself to sleep.

Presently the tapping came again—this time, more forceful, more insistent. And now his wife woke at the sound and, turning in the bed, said to him, "See to the window, Nat; it's rattling."

"I've already been to it," he told her. "There's some bird there, trying to get in."

"Send it away," she said. "I can't sleep with that noise."

He went to the window for the second time, and now when he opened it, there was not one bird on the sill but half a dozen; they flew straight into his face.

He shouted, striking out at them with his arms, scattering them; like the first one, they flew over the roof and disappeared.

He let the window fall and latched it.

Suddenly a frightened cry came from the room across the passage where the children slept.

"It's Jill," said his wife, roused at the sound.

There came a second cry, this time from both children. Stumbling into their room, Nat felt the beating of wings about him in the darkness. The window was wide open. Through it came the birds, hitting first the ceiling and the walls, then swerving in mid-flight and turning to the children in their beds.

"It's all right, I'm here," shouted Nat, and the children flung themselves, screaming, upon him, while in the darkness the birds rose and dived, and came for him again.

"What is it, Nat? What's happened?" his wife called. Swiftly he pushed the children through the door to the passage and shut it upon them, so that he was alone in their bedroom with the birds.

He seized a blanket from the nearest bed and, using it as a weapon, flung it to right and left about him.

He felt the thud of bodies, heard the fluttering of wings; but the birds were not yet defeated, for again and again they returned to the assault, jabbing his hands, his head, their little stabbing beaks sharp as pointed forks.

The blanket became a weapon of defense. He wound it about his head, and then, in greater darkness, beat at the birds with his bare hands. He dared not stumble to the door and open it lest the birds follow him.

How long he fought with them in the darkness he could not tell; but at last the beating of the wings about him lessened, withdrew; and, through the dense blanket, he was aware of light.

He waited, listened; there was no sound except the fretful crying of one of the children from the bedroom beyond.

He took the blanket from his head and stared about him. The cold gray morning light exposed the room.

Dawn and the open window had called the living birds; the dead lay on the floor.

Sickened, Nat went to the window and stared out across his patch of garden to the fields.

It was bitter cold, and the ground had all the hard, black look of the frost that the east wind brings. The sea, fiercer now with turning tide, white-capped and steep, broke harshly in the bay. Of the birds there was no sign.

Nat shut the window and the door of the small bedroom and went back across the passage to his own room.

His wife sat up in bed, one child asleep beside her; the smaller one in her arms, his face bandaged.

"He's sleeping now," she whispered. "Something must have cut him; there was blood at the corners of his eyes. Jill said it was the birds. She said she woke up and the birds were in the room."

His wife looked up at Nat, searching his face for cònfirmation. She looked terrified, bewildered. He did not want her to know that he also was shaken, dazed almost, by the events of the past few hours.

"There are birds in there," he said. "Dead birds, nearly fifty of them."

He sat down on the bed beside his wife.

"It's the hard weather," he said. "It must be that; it's the hard weather. They aren't the birds, maybe, from around here. They've been driven down from upcountry."

"But, Nat," whispered his wife, "it's only this night that the weather turned. They can't be hungry yet. There's food for them out there in the fields."

"It's the weather," repeated Nat. "I tell you, it's the weather."

His face, too, was drawn and tired, like hers. They stared at one another for a while without speaking.

Nat went to the window and looked out. The sky was hard and leaden, and the brown hills that had gleamed in the sun the day before looked dark and bare. Black winter had descended in a single night.

The children were awake now. Jill was chattering, and young Johnny was crying once again. Nat heard his wife's voice, soothing, comforting them as he went downstairs.

Presently they came down. He had breakfast ready for them.

"Did you drive away the birds?" asked Jill.

"Yes, they've all gone now," Nat said. "It was the east wind brought them in."

"I hope they won't come again," said Jill.

"I'll walk with you to the bus," Nat said to her.

Jill seemed to have forgotten her experience of the night before. She danced ahead of him, chasing the leaves, her face rosy under her pixy hood.

All the while Nat searched the hedgerows for the birds, glanced over them to the fields beyond, looked to the small wood above the farm where the rooks and jackdaws gathered; he saw none. Soon the bus came ambling up the hill.

Nat saw Jill onto the bus, then turned and walked back toward the farm. It was not his day for work, but he wanted to satisfy himself that all was well. He went to the back door of the farmhouse; he heard Mrs. Trigg singing, the wireless making a background for her song.

"Are you there, missus?" Nat called.

She came to the door, beaming, broad, a good-tempered woman.

"Hullo, Mr. Hocken," she said. "Can you tell me where this cold is coming from? Is it Russia? I've never seen such a change. And it's going on, the wireless says. Something to do with the Arctic Circle."

"We didn't turn on the wireless this morning," said Nat. "Fact is, we had trouble in the night."

"Kiddies poorly?"

"No." He hardly knew how to explain. Now, in daylight, the battle of the birds would sound absurd.

He tried to tell Mrs. Trigg what had happened, but he could see from her eyes that she thought his story was the result of nightmare following a heavy meal.

"Sure they were real birds?" she said, smiling.

"Mrs. Trigg," he said, "there are fifty dead birds—robins, wrens, and such—lying low on the floor of the children's bedroom. They went for me; they tried to go for young Johnny's eyes."

Mrs. Trigg stared at him doubtfully. "Well, now," she answered. "I suppose the weather brought them; once in the bedroom they wouldn't know where they were. Foreign birds maybe, from that Arctic Circle."

"No," said Nat. "They were the birds you see about here every day."

"Funny thing," said Mrs. Trigg. "No explaining it, really. You ought to write up and ask the *Guardian*. They'd have some answer for it. Well, I must be getting on."

Nat walked back along the lane to his cottage. He found his wife in the kitchen with young Johnny.

"See anyone?" she asked.

"Mrs. Trigg," he answered. "I don't think she believed me. Anyway, nothing wrong up there."

"You might take the birds away," she said. "I daren't go into the room to make the beds until you do. I'm scared."

"Nothing to scare you now," said Nat. "They're dead, aren't they?"

He went up with a sack and dropped the stiff bodies into it, one by one. Yes, there were fifty of them all told. Just the ordinary, common birds of the hedgerow; nothing as large even as a thrush. It must have been fright that made them act the way they did.

He took the sack out into the garden and was faced with a fresh problem. The ground was frozen solid, yet no snow had fallen; nothing had happened in the past hours but the coming of the east wind. It was unnatural, queer. He could see the white-capped seas breaking in the bay. He decided to take the birds to the shore and bury them.

When he reached the beach below the headland, he could scarcely stand, the force of the east wind was so strong. It was low tide; he crunched his way over the shingle to the softer sand and then, his back to the wind, opened up his sack.

He ground a pit in the sand with his heel, meaning to drop the birds into it; but, as he did so, the force of the wind lifted them as though in flight again, and they were blown away from him along the beach, tossed like feathers, spread and scattered.

The tide will take them when it turns, he said to himself.

He looked out to sea and watched the crested breakers, combing green. They rose stiffly, curled, and broke again; and, because it was ebb tide, the roar was distant, more remote, lacking the sound and thunder of the flood.

Then he saw them. The gulls. Out there, riding the seas.

What he had thought at first were the whitecaps of the waves were gulls. Hundreds, thousands, tens of thousands.

They rose and fell in the troughs of the seas, heads to the wind, like a mighty fleet at anchor, waiting on the tide.

Nat turned; leaving the beach, he climbed the steep path home.

Someone should know of this. Someone should be told. Something was happening, because of the east wind and the weather, that he did not understand.

As he drew near the cottage, his wife came to meet him at the door. She called to him, excited. "Nat," she said, "it's on the wireless. They've just read out a special news bulletin. It's not only here, it's everywhere. In London, all over the country. Something has happened to the birds. Come listen; they're repeating it."

Together they went into the kitchen to listen to the announcement.

"Statement from the Home Office, at 11 A.M. this morning. Reports from all over the country are coming in hourly about the vast quantity of birds flocking above towns, villages, and outlying districts, causing obstruction and damage, and even attacking individuals. It is thought that the Arctic air stream at present covering the British Isles is causing birds to migrate south in immense numbers, and that intense hunger may drive these birds to attack human beings. Householders are warned to see to their windows, doors, and chimneys, and to take reasonable precautions for the safety of their children. A further statement will be issued later."

A kind of excitement seized Nat. He looked at his wife in triumph. "There you are," he said. "I've been telling myself all morning there's something wrong. And, just now, down on the beach, I looked out to sea and there were gulls, thousands of them, riding on the sea, waiting."

"What are they waiting for, Nat?" she asked.

He stared at her. "I don't know," he said slowly.

He went over to the drawer where he kept his hammer and other tools.

"What are you going to do, Nat?"

"See to the windows and the chimneys, like they tell you to."

"You think they would break in with the windows shut? Those wrens and robins and such? Why, how could they?"

He did not answer. He was not thinking of the robins and the wrens. He was thinking of the gulls.

He went upstairs and worked there the rest of the morning, boarding the windows of the bedrooms, filling up the chimney bases.

"Dinner's ready." His wife called him from the kitchen.

"All right. Coming down."

When dinner was over and his wife was washing up, Nat switched on the one o'clock news. The same announcement was repeated, but the news bulletin enlarged upon it. "The flocks of birds have caused dislocation in all areas," said the announcer, "and in London, the mass was so dense at ten o'clock this morning that it seemed

153

like a vast, black cloud. The birds settled on rooftops, on window ledges, and on chimneys. The species included blackbird, thrush, the common house sparrow, and, as might be expected in the metropolis, a vast quantity of pigeons, starlings, and that frequenter of the London river, the black-headed gull. The sight was so unusual that traffic came to a standstill in many thoroughfares, work was abandoned in shops and offices, and the streets and pavements were crowded with people standing about to watch the birds."

The announcer's voice was smooth and suave; Nat had the impression that he treated the whole business as he would an elaborate joke. There would be others like him, hundreds of them, who did not know what it was to struggle in darkness with a flock of birds.

Nat switched off the wireless. He got up and started work on the kitchen windows. His wife watched him, young Johnny at her heels.

"What they ought to do," she said, "is to call the Army out and shoot the birds."

"Let them try," said Nat. "How'd they set about it?"

"I don't know. But something should be done. They ought to do something."

Nat thought to himself that "they" were no doubt considering the problem at that very moment, but whatever "they" decided to do in London and the big cities would not help them here, nearly three hundred miles away.

"How are we off for food?" he asked.

"It's shopping day tomorrow, you know that. I don't keep uncooked food

about. Butcher doesn't call till the day after. But I can bring back something when I go in tomorrow."

Nat did not want to scare her. He looked in the larder for himself and in the cupboard where she kept her tins.

They could hold out for a couple of days.

He went on hammering the boards across the kitchen windows. Candles. They were low on candles. That must be another thing she meant to buy tomorrow. Well, they must go early to bed tonight. That was, if—

He got up and went out the back door and stood in the garden, looking down toward the sea.

There had been no sun all day, and now, at barely three o'clock, a kind of darkness had already come; the sky was sullen, heavy, colorless like salt. He could hear the vicious sea drumming on the rocks.

He walked down the path halfway to the beach. And then he stopped. He could see the tide had turned. The gulls had risen. They were circling, hundreds of them, thousands of them, lifting their wings against the wind.

It was the gulls that made the darkening of the sky.

And they were silent. They just went on soaring and circling, rising, falling, trying their strength against the wind. Nat turned. He ran up the path back to the cottage.

"I'm going for Jill," he said to his wife.

"What's the matter?" she asked. "You've gone quite white."

"Keep Johnny inside," he said. "Keep the door shut. Light up now and draw the curtains."

"It's only gone three," she said.

"Never mind. Do what I tell you."

He looked inside the toolshed and took the hoe.

He started walking up the lane to the bus stop. Now and again he glanced back over his shoulder; he could see the gulls had risen higher now, their circles were broader, they were spreading out in huge formation across the sky.

He hurried on. Although he knew the bus would not come before four o'clock, he had to hurry.

He waited at the top of the hill. There was half an hour still to go.

The east wind came whipping across the fields from the higher ground. In the distance he could see the clay hills, white and clean against the heavy pallor of the sky.

Something black rose from behind them, like a smudge at first, then widening, becoming deeper. The smudge became a cloud; and the cloud divided again into five other clouds, spreading north, east, south, and west; and then they were not clouds at all but birds.

He watched them travel across the sky within two or three hundred feet of him. He knew, from their speed, that they were bound inland; they had no business with the people here on the peninsula. They were rooks, crows, jackdaws, magpies, jays—all birds that usually preyed upon the smaller species, but bound this afternoon on some other mission.

He went to the telephone call box, stepped inside, lifted the receiver. The exchange would pass the message on. "I'm speaking from the highway," he said, "by the bus stop. I want to report large formations of birds traveling upcountry. The gulls are also forming in the bay."

"All right," answered the voice, laconic, weary.

"You'll be sure and pass this message on to the proper quarter?"

"Yes. Yes." Impatient now, fed up. The buzzing note resumed.

She's another, thought Nat. She doesn't care.

The bus came lumbering up the hill. Jill climbed out.

"What's the hoe for, Dad?"

"I just brought it along," he said. "Come on now, let's get home. It's cold; no hanging about. See how fast you can run."

He could see the gulls now, still silent, circling the fields, coming in toward the land.

"Look, Dad; look over there. Look at all the gulls."

"Yes. Hurry now."

"Where are they flying to? Where are they going?"

"Upcountry, I dare say. Where it's warmer."

He seized her hand and dragged her after him along the lane.

"Don't go so fast. I can't keep up."

The gulls were copying the rooks and the crows. They were spreading out, in formation, across the sky. They headed, in bands of thousands, to the four compass points.

"Dad, what is it? What are the gulls doing?"

They were not intent upon their flight, as the crows, as the jackdaws, had been. They still circled overhead. Nor did they fly so high. It was as though they waited upon some signal;

as though some decision had yet to be given.

"I wish the gulls would go away." Jill was crying. "I don't like them. They're coming closer to the lane."

He started running, swinging Jill after him. As they went past the farm turning, he saw the farmer backing his car into the garage. Nat called to him.

"Can you give us a lift?" he said.

Mr. Trigg turned in the driver's seat and stared at them. Then a smile came to his cheerful, rubicund face. "It looks as though we're in for some fun," he said. "Have you seen the gulls? Jim and I are going to take a crack at them. Everyone's gone bird crazy, talking of nothing else. I hear

you were troubled in the night. Want a gun?"

Nat shook his head.

The small car was packed, but there was room for Jill on the back seat.

"I don't want a gun," said Nat, "but I'd be obliged if you'd run Jill home. She's scared of the birds."

"Okay," said the farmer. "I'll take her home. Why don't you stop behind and join the shooting match? We'll make the feathers fly."

Jill climbed in, and, turning the car, the driver sped up the lane. Nat followed after. Trigg must be crazy. What use was a gun against a sky of birds?

They were coming in now toward the farm, circling lower in the sky. The

farm, then, was their target. Nat increased his pace toward his own cottage. He saw the farmer's car turn and come back along the lane. It drew up beside him with a jerk.

"The kid has run inside," said the farmer. "Your wife was watching for her. Well, what do you make of it? They're saying in town the Russians have done it. The Russians have poisoned the birds."

"How could they do that?" asked Nat.

"Don't ask me. You know how stories get around."

"Have you boarded your windows?" asked Nat.

"No. Lot of nonsense. I've had more to do today than to go round boarding up my windows."

"I'd board them now if I were you."

"Garn. You're windy. Like to come to our place to sleep?"

"No, thanks all the same."

"All right. See you in the morning. Give you a gull breakfast."

The farmer grinned and turned his car to the farm entrance. Nat hurried on. Past the little wood, past the old barn, and then across the stile to the remaining field. As he jumped the stile, he heard the whir of wings. A black-backed gull dived down at him from the sky. It missed, swerved in flight, and rose to dive again. In a moment, it was joined by others—six, seven, a dozen.

Nat dropped his hoe. The hoe was useless. Covering his head with his arms, he ran toward the cottage.

They kept coming at him from the air—noiseless, silent, save for the beating wings. The terrible, fluttering wings. He could feel the blood on his hands, his wrists, upon his neck. If only he could keep them from his eyes. Nothing else mattered.

With each dive, with each attack, they became bolder. And they had no thought for themselves. When they dived low and missed, they crashed, bruised and broken, on the ground.

As Nat ran, he stumbled, kicking their spent bodies in front of him.

He found the door and hammered upon it with his bleeding hands. "Let me in," he shouted. "It's Nat. Let me in."

Then he saw the gannet, poised for the dive, above him in the sky.

The gulls circled, retired, soared, one with another, against the wind.

Only the gannet remained. One single gannet, above him in the sky. Its wings folded suddenly to its body. It dropped like a stone.

Nat screamed; and the door opened.

He stumbled across the threshold, and his wife threw her weight against the door.

They heard the thud of the gannet as it fell.

His wife dressed his wounds. They were not deep. The backs of his hands had suffered most, and his wrists. Had he not worn a cap, the birds would have reached his head. As for the gannet—the gannet could have split his skull.

The children were crying, of course. They had seen the blood on their father's hands.

"It's all right now," he told them. "I'm not hurt."

His wife was ashen. "I saw them overhead," she whispered. "They began collecting just as Jill ran in with Mr. Trigg. I shut the door fast, and it jammed. That's why I couldn't open it at once when you came."

"Thank God, the birds waited for me," he said. "Jill would have fallen at once. They're flying inland, thousands of them. Rooks, crows, all the bigger birds. I saw them from the bus stop. They're making for the towns."

"But what can they do, Nat?"

"They'll attack. Go for everyone out in the streets. Then they'll try the windows, the chimneys."

"Why don't the authorities do something? Why don't they get the Army, get the machine guns?"

"There's been no time. Nobody's prepared. We'll hear what they have to say on the six o'clock news."

"I can hear the birds," Jill said. "Listen, Dad."

Nat listened. Muffled sounds came from the windows, from the door. Wings brushing the surface, sliding, scraping, seeking a way of entry. The sound of many bodies pressed together, shuffling on the sills. Now and again came a thud, a crash, as some bird dived and fell.

Some of them will kill themselves that way, he thought, but not enough. Never enough.

"All right," he said aloud. "I've got boards over the windows, Jill. The birds can't get in."

He went and examined all the windows. He found wedges—pieces of old tin, strips of wood and metal—and fastened them at the sides of the windows to reinforce the boards.

His hammering helped to deafen the sound of the birds, the shuffling, the tapping, and—more ominous—the splinter of breaking glass.

"Turn on the wireless," he said.

He went upstairs to the bedrooms and reinforced the windows there. Now he could hear the birds on the roof—the scraping of claws, a sliding, jostling sound.

He decided the whole family must sleep in the kitchen and keep up the fire. He was afraid of the bedroom chimneys. The boards he had placed at their bases might give way. In the kitchen, they would be safe because of the fire.

He would have to make a joke of it. Pretend to the children they were playing camp. If the worst happened and the birds forced an entry by way of the bedroom chimneys, it would be hours, days perhaps, before they could break down the doors. The birds would be imprisoned in the bedrooms. They could do no harm there. Crowded together, they would stifle and die. He began to bring the mattresses downstairs.

At the sight of them, his wife's eyes widened in apprehension.

"All right," he said cheerfully. "We'll all sleep together in the kitchen tonight. More cozy, here by the fire. Then we won't be worried by those silly old birds tapping at the windows."

He made the children help him rearrange the furniture, and he took the precaution of moving the dresser against the windows.

We're safe enough now, he thought. We're snug and tight. We can hold out. It's just the food that worries me. Food and coal for the fire. We've enough for two or three days, not more. By that time——

No use thinking ahead as far as that. And they'd be given directions on the wireless.

And now, in the midst of many problems, he realized that only dance music was coming over the air. He knew the reason. The usual programs had been abandoned; this only happened at exceptional times.

At six o'clock the records ceased. The time signal was given. There was a pause, and then the announcer spoke. His voice was solemn, grave. Quite different from midday.

"This is London," he said. "A national emergency was proclaimed at four o'clock this afternoon. Measures are being taken to safeguard the lives and property of the population, but it must be understood that these are not easy to effect immediately, owing to the unforeseen and unparalleled nature of the present crisis. Every householder must take precautions about his own building. Where several people live together, as in flats and hotels, they must unite to do the utmost that they can to prevent entry. It is absolutely imperative that every individual stay indoors tonight.

"The birds, in vast numbers, are attacking anyone on sight, and have already begun an assault upon buildings; but these, with due care, should be impenetrable.

"The population is asked to remain calm.

"Owing to the exceptional nature of the emergency, there will be no further transmission from any broadcasting station until 7 A.M. tomorrow."

They played "God Save the Queen." Nothing more happened.

Nat switched off the set. He looked at his wife. She stared back at him.

"We'll have supper early," suggested Nat. "Something for a treat—toasted cheese, eh? Something we all like."

He winked and nodded at his wife. He wanted the look of dread, of apprehension, to leave her face.

He helped with the supper, whistling, singing, making as much clatter as he could. It seemed to him that the shuffling and the tapping were not so intense as they had been at first, and presently he went up to the bedrooms and listened. He no longer heard the jostling for place upon the roof.

They've got reasoning powers, he thought. They know it's hard to break in here. They'll try elsewhere.

Supper passed without incident. Then, when they were clearing away, they heard a new sound, a familiar droning.

His wife looked up at him, her face alight.

"It's planes," she said. "They're sending out planes after the birds. That will get them. Isn't that gunfire? Can't you hear guns?"

It might be gunfire, out at sea. Nat could not tell. Big naval guns might have some effect upon the gulls out at sea, but the gulls were inland now. The guns couldn't shell the shore because of the population.

"It's good, isn't it," said his wife, "to hear the planes?"

Catching her enthusiasm, Jill jumped up and down with Johnny. "The planes will get the birds."

Just then they heard a crash about two miles distant. Followed by a second, then a third. The droning became more distant, passed away out to sea.

"What was that?" asked his wife.

"I don't know," answered Nat. He did not want to tell her that the sound they had heard was the crashing of aircraft.

It was, he had no doubt, a gamble on the part of the authorities to send out reconnaissance forces, but they might have known the gamble was suicidal. What could aircraft do against birds that flung themselves to death against propeller and fuselage, but hurtle to the ground themselves?

"Where have the planes gone, Dad?" asked Jill.

"Back to base," he said. "Come on now, time to tuck down for bed."

There was no further drone of aircraft, and the naval guns had ceased. Waste of life and effort, Nat said to himself. We can't destroy enough of them that way. Cost too heavy. There's always gas. Maybe they'll try spraying with gas, mustard gas. We'll be warned first, of course, if they do. There's one thing, the best brains of the country will be on it tonight.

Upstairs in the bedrooms all was quiet. No more scraping and stabbing at the windows. A lull in battle. The wind hadn't dropped, though. Nat could still hear it roaring in the chimneys. And the sea breaking down on the shore.

Then he remembered the tide. The tide would be on the turn. Maybe the lull in battle was because of the tide. There was some law the birds obeyed, and it had to do with the east wind and the tide.

He glanced at his watch. Nearly eight o'clock. It must have gone high water an hour ago. That explained the lull. The birds attacked with the flood tide.

He reckoned the time limit in his head. They had six hours to go without attack. When the tide turned again, around one-twenty in the morning, the birds would come back.

He called softly to his wife and whispered to her that he would go out and see how they were faring at the farm, see if the telephone was still working there so that they might get news from the exchange.

"You're not to go," she said at once, "and leave me alone with the children. I can't stand it."

"All right," he said, "all right. I'll wait till morning. And we can get the wireless bulletin then, too, at seven. But when the tide ebbs again, I'll try for the farm; they may let us have bread and potatoes."

His mind was busy again, planning against emergency. They would not have milked, of course, this evening. The cows would be standing by the gate, waiting; the household would be inside, battened behind boards as they were here at the cottage.

That is, if they had had time to take precautions.

Softly, stealthily, he opened the back door and looked outside.

It was pitch-dark. The wind was blowing harder than ever, coming in steady gusts, icy, from the sea.

He kicked at the step. It was heaped with birds. These were the suicides, the divers, the ones with broken necks. Wherever he looked, he saw dead birds. The living had flown seaward with the turn of the tide. The gulls would be riding the seas now, as they had done in the forenoon.

In the far distance on the hill, something was burning. One of the aircraft that had crashed; the fire, fanned by the wind, had set light to a stack.

He looked at the bodies of the birds. He had a notion that if he stacked them, one upon the other, on the window sills, they would be added protection against the next attack.

Not much, perhaps, but something. The bodies would have to be clawed at, pecked, and dragged aside before the living birds gained purchase on the sills and attacked the panes.

He set to work in the darkness. It was queer. He hated touching the dead birds, but he went on with his work. He noticed, grimly, that every windowpane was shattered. Only the boards had kept the birds from breaking in.

He stuffed the cracked panes with bleeding bodies of the birds and felt his stomach turn. When he had finished, he went back into the cottage and barricaded the kitchen door, making it doubly secure.

His wife had made him cocoa; he drank it thirstily. He was very tired: "All right," he said, smiling, "don't worry. We'll get through."

He lay down on his mattress and closed his eyes.

He dreamed uneasily because, through his dreams, ran the dread of something forgotten. Some piece of work that he should have done. It was connected, in some way, with the burning aircraft.

It was his wife, shaking his shoulder, who awoke him finally.

"They've begun," she sobbed. "They've started this last hour. I can't listen to it any longer alone. There's something smells bad, too, something burning."

Then he remembered. He had forgotten to make up the fire.

The fire was smoldering, nearly out. He got up swiftly and lighted the lamp.

The hammering had started at the windows and the door, but it was not that he minded now. It was the smell of singed feathers.

The smell filled the kitchen. He knew what it was at once. The birds were coming down the chimney, squeezing their way down to the kitchen range.

He got sticks and paper and put them on the embers, then reached for the can of kerosene.

"Stand back," he shouted to his wife. He threw some of the kerosene onto the fire.

The flame roared up the pipe, and down into the fire fell the scorched, blackened bodies of the birds.

The children waked, crying. "What is it?" asked Jill. "What's happened?"

Nat had no time to answer her. He was raking the bodies from the chimney, clawing them out onto the floor.

The flames would drive the living birds away from the chimney top. The lower joint was the difficulty, though. It was choked with the smoldering, helpless bodies of the birds caught by fire.

He scarcely heeded the attack on the windows and the door. Let them beat their wings, break their backs, lose their lives, in the desperate attempt to force entry into his home. They would not break in.

"Stop crying," he called to the children. "There's nothing to be afraid of. Stop crying."

He went on raking out the burning, smoldering bodies as they fell into the fire.

This'll fetch them, he said to himself. The draft and the flames together. We're all right as long as the chimney doesn't catch.

Amid the tearing at the window boards came the sudden, homely striking of the kitchen clock. Three o'clock.

A little more than four hours to go. He could not be sure of the exact time of high water. He reckoned the tide would not turn much before half past seven.

He waited by the range. The flames were dying. But no more blackened bodies fell from the chimney. He thrust his poker up as far as it could go and found nothing.

The danger of the chimney's being choked up was over. It could not happen again, not if the fire was kept burning day and night.

I'll have to get more fuel from the farm tomorrow, he thought. I can do all that with the ebb tide. It can be worked; we can fetch what we need when the tide's turned. We've just got to adapt ourselves, that's all.

They drank tea and cocoa, ate slices of bread. Only half a loaf left, Nat noticed. Never mind, though; they'd get by.

If they could hang on like this until seven, when the first news bulletin came through, they would not have done too badly.

"Give us a smoke," he said to his wife. "It will clear away the smell of the scorched feathers."

"There's only two left in the packet," she said. "I was going to buy you some."

"I'll have one," he said.

He sat with one arm around his wife and the other around Jill, with Johnny on his lap, the blankets heaped about them on the mattress.

"You can't help admiring the beggars," he said. "They've got persistency. You'd think they'd tire of the game, but not a bit of it."

Admiration was hard to sustain. The tapping went on and on; and a new, rasping note struck Nat's ear, as though a sharper beak than any hitherto had come to take over from its fellows.

He tried to remember the names of birds; he tried to think which species would go for this particular job.

It was not the tap of the woodpecker. That would be light and frequent. This was more serious; if it continued long, the wood would splinter as the glass had done.

Then he remembered the hawks. Could the hawks have taken over from the gulls? Were there buzzards now upon the sills, using talons as well as beaks? Hawks, buzzards, kestrels, falcons; he had forgotten the birds of prey. Three hours to go; and, while they waited, the sound of the splintering wood, the talons tearing at the wood.

Nat looked about him, seeing what furniture he could destroy to fortify the door.

The windows were safe because of the dresser. He was not certain of the door. He went upstairs; but when he reached the landing, he paused and listened.

There was a soft patter on the floor of the children's room. The birds had broken through.

The other bedroom was still clear. He brought out the furniture to pile at the head of the stairs should the door of the children's bedroom go.

"Come down, Nat. What are you doing?" called his wife.

"I won't be long," he shouted. "I'm just making everything shipshape up here."

He did not want her to come. He did not want her to hear the pattering in the children's bedroom, the brushing of those wings against the door.

After he suggested breakfast, he found himself watching the clock, gazing at the hands that went so slowly around the dial. If his theory was not correct, if the attack did not cease with the turn of the tide, he knew they were beaten. They could not continue through the long day without air, without rest, without fuel.

A crackling in his ears drove away the sudden, desperate desire for sleep.

"What is it? What now?" he said sharply.

"The wireless," said his wife. "I've been watching the clock. It's nearly seven."

The comfortable crackling of the wireless brought new life.

They waited. The kitchen clock struck seven.

The crackling continued. Nothing else. No chimes. No music.

They waited until a quarter past. No news bulletin came through.

"We heard wrong," he said. "They won't be broadcasting until eight o'clock."

They left the wireless switched on. Nat thought of the battery, wondered how much power was left in the battery. If it failed, they would not hear the instructions.

"It's getting light," whispered his wife. "I can't see it but I can feel it. And listen! The birds aren't hammering so loud now."

She was right. The rasping, tearing sound grew fainter every moment. So did the shuffling, the jostling for place upon the step, upon the sills. The tide was on the turn.

By eight there was no sound at all. Only the wind. And the crackling of the wireless. The children, lulled at last by the stillness, fell asleep.

At half past eight Nat switched the wireless off.

"We'll miss the news," said his wife.

"There isn't going to be any news," said Nat. "We've got to depend upon ourselves."

He went to the door and slowly pulled away the barricades. He drew the bolts and, kicking the broken bodies from the step outside the door, breathed the cold air.

He had six working hours before him, and he knew he must reserve his strength to the utmost, not waste it in any way.

Food and light and fuel; these were the most necessary things. If he could get them, they could endure another night.

He stepped into the garden; and, as he did so, he saw the living birds. The gulls had gone to ride the sea, as they had done before. They sought sea food and the buoyancy of the tide before they returned to the attack.

Not so the land birds. They waited and watched.

Nat saw them on the hedgerows, on the soil, crowded in the trees, outside in the field—line upon line of birds, still, doing nothing. He went to the end of his small garden.

The birds did not move. They merely watched him.

I've got to get food, Nat said to himself. I've got to go to the farm to get food.

He went back to the cottage. He saw to the windows and the door.

"I'm going to the farm," he said.

His wife clung to him. She had seen the living birds from the open door.

"Take us with you," she begged. "We can't stay here alone. I'd rather die than stay here alone."

"Come on, then," he said. "Bring baskets and Johnny's pram. We can load up the pram."

They dressed against the biting wind. His wife put Johnny in the pram, and Nat took Jill's hand.

"The birds," Jill whimpered. "They're all out there in the fields."

"They won't hurt us," he said. "Not in the light."

They started walking across the field toward the stile, and the birds did not move. They waited, their heads turned to the wind.

When they reached the turning to the farm, Nat stopped and told his wife to wait in the shelter of the hedge with the two children. "But I want to see Mrs. Trigg," she protested. "There are lots of things we can borrow if they went to market yesterday, and——"

"Wait here," Nat interrupted. "I'll be back in a moment."

The cows were lowing, moving restlessly in the yard, and he could see a gap in the fence where the sheep had knocked their way through to roam unchecked in the front garden before the farmhouse.

No smoke came from the chimneys. Nat was filled with misgiving. He did not want his wife or the children to go down to the farm.

He went down alone, pushing his way through the herd of lowing cows, who turned this way and that, distressed, their udders full.

He saw the car standing by the gate. Not put away in the garage.

All the windows of the farmhouse were smashed. There were many dead gulls lying in the yard and around the house.

The living birds perched on the group of trees behind the farm and on the roof of the house. They were quite still. They watched him. Jim's body lay in the yard. What was left of it. His gun was beside him.

The door of the house was shut and bolted, but it was easy to push up a smashed window and climb through.

Trigg's body was close to the telephone. He must have been trying to get through to the exchange when the birds got him. The receiver was off the hook, and the instrument was torn from the wall.

No sign of Mrs. Trigg. She would be upstairs. Was it any use going up? Sickened, Nat knew what he would find there.

Thank God, he said to himself, there were no children.

He forced himself to climb the stairs, but halfway up he turned and descended again. He could see Mrs. Trigg's legs protruding from the open bedroom door. Beside her were the bodies of black-backed gulls and an umbrella, broken. It's no use doing anything, Nat thought. I've only got five hours; less than that. The Triggs would understand. I must load up with what I can find.

He tramped back to his wife and children.

"I'm going to fill up the car with stuff," he said. "We'll take it home and return for a fresh load."

"They must have gone to friends," he said.

"Shall I come and help you, then?"

"No, there's a mess down there. Cows and sheep all over the place. Wait; I'll get the car. You can sit in the car."

Her eyes watched his all the time he was talking. He believed she understood. Otherwise, she certainly would have insisted on helping him find the bread and groceries.

They made three journeys altogether, to and from the farm, before he was satisfied they had everything they needed. It was surprising, once he started thinking, how many things were necessary.

Probably the most important of all was planking for the windows. He had to go around searching for timber. He wanted to renew the boards on all the windows at the cottage.

On the final journey he drove the car to the bus stop and got out and went to the telephone box.

He waited a few minutes, jangling the hook. No good, though. The line was dead. He climbed onto a bank and looked over the countryside, but there was no sign of life at all, nothing in the fields but the waiting, watching birds.

Some of them slept; he could see their beaks tucked into their feathers.

You'd think they'd be feeding, he said to himself, not just standing that way.

Then he remembered. They were gorged with food. They had eaten their fill during the night. That was why they did not move this morning.

He lifted his face to the sky. It was colorless, gray. The bare trees looked bent and blackened by the east wind.

The cold did not affect the living birds, waiting out there in the fields.

This is the time they ought to get them, Nat said to himself. They're a sitting target now. They must be doing this all over the country. Why don't our aircraft take off now and spray them with mustard gas? What are all our chaps doing? They must know; they must see for themselves.

He went back to the car and got into the driver's seat.

"Go quickly past that second gate," whispered his wife. "The postman's lying there. I don't want Jill to see."

It was a quarter to one by the time they reached the cottage. Only an hour to go.

"Better have dinner," said Nat. "Hot up something for yourself and the children, some of that soup. I've no time to eat now. I've got to unload all this stuff from the car."

He got everything inside the cottage. It could be sorted later. Give them all something to do during the long hours ahead.

First he must see to the windows and the door.

He went around the cottage methodically, testing every window and the door. He climbed onto the roof, also, and fixed boards across every chimney except the kitchen's.

The cold was so intense he could hardly bear it, but the job had to be done. Now and again he looked up, searching the sky for aircraft. None came. As he worked, he cursed the inefficiency of the authorities.

He paused, his work on the bedroom chimney finished, and looked out to sea. Something was moving out there. Something gray and white among the breakers.

"Good old Navy," he said. "They never let us down. They're coming down channel; they're turning into the bay."

He waited, straining his eyes toward the sea. He was wrong, though. The Navy was not there. It was the gulls rising from the sea. And the massed flocks in the fields, with ruffled feathers, rose in formation from the ground and, wing to wing, soared upward to the sky.

The tide had turned again.

Nat climbed down the ladder and went inside the cottage. The family were at dinner. It was a little after two.

He bolted the door, put up the barricade, and lighted the lamp.

"It's nighttime," said young Johnny.

His wife had switched on the wireless once again. The crackling sound came, but nothing else.

"I've been all round the dial," she said, "foreign stations and all. I can't get anything but the crackling."

"Maybe they have the same trouble," he said. "Maybe it's the same right through Europe."

They ate in silence.

The tapping began at the windows, at the door, the rustling, the jostling, the pushing for position on the sills. The first thud of the suicide gulls upon the step.

When he had finished dinner, Nat planned, he would put the supplies away, stack them neatly, get everything shipshape. The boards were strong against the windows and across the chimneys. The cottage was filled with stores, with fuel, with all they needed for the next few days.

His wife could help him, and the children too. They'd tire themselves out between now and a quarter to nine, when the tide would ebb; then, he'd tuck them down on their mattresses, see that they slept good and sound until three in the morning.

He had a new scheme for the windows, which was to fix barbed wire in front of the boards. He had brought a great roll of it from the farm. The nuisance was, he'd have to work at this in the dark, when the lull came between nine and three. Pity he had not thought of it before. Still, as long as the wife and kids slept—that was the main thing.

The smaller birds were at the windows now. He recognized the light tap-tapping of their beaks and the soft brush of their wings.

The hawks ignored the windows. They concentrated their attack upon the door.

Nat listened to the tearing sound of splintering wood, and wondered how many million years of memory were stored in those little brains, behind the stabbing beaks, the piercing eyes, now giving them this instinct to destroy mankind with all the deft precision of machines.

"I'll smoke that last cigarette," he said to his wife. "Stupid of me. It was the one thing I forgot to bring from the farm."

He reached for it, switched on the crackling wireless.

He threw the empty packet onto the fire and watched it burn.

I am part of all that I have met.

The Story of Keesh

Jack London

The winter darkness, when the north gales make their long sweep across the ice pack and the air is filled with flying white and no man may venture forth, is the chosen time for the telling of how Keesh, from the poorest igloo in the village, rose to power.

Keesh lived long ago on the rim of the polar sea. He was a bright boy, healthy and strong, who had seen thirteen years. His father had been a very brave man who had met his death in a time of famine, when he sought to save the lives of his people by taking that of a great polar bear. In his eagerness, he had come to close grapples with the bear, and his bones had been crushed. But the bear had had much meat on him, so the people were saved.

Keesh was his only son and lived alone with his mother. But people are forgetful, and the deed of his father was forgotten. Keesh being but a boy, and his mother only a woman, they, too, were swiftly forgotten. Soon they were reduced to living in the meanest of all the igloos.

At a council one night in the big igloo of Klosh-Kwan, who was chief, Keesh showed the blood that ran in his veins and the manhood that stiffened his back. With the dignity of an elder, he rose to his feet and waited for silence amid the babble of voices.

"It is true that meat is apportioned me and mine," he said. "But it is ofttimes old and tough, this meat, and, moreover, it has an unusual quantity of bones."

The hunters, both the grizzled and gray and the lusty and young, were aghast—a child that talked like a grown man and said harsh things to their very faces!

Steadily and with seriousness, Keesh went on. "Because I know my father, Bok, was a great hunter, I speak these words. It is said that Bok brought home more meat than any of the best hunters, that with his own hands he attended to the division of it, that with his own eyes he saw to it that the least old woman and the last old man received fair share."

"Na! Na!" the men cried. "Put the child out!" "Send him off to bed!"

He waited calmly till the uproar died down.

"My mother has no one save me; wherefore I speak. As I say, though Bok be dead because he hunted overkeenly, it is just that I, who am his son, and that Ikeega, who is my mother and was his wife, should have meat in plenty so long as there is meat in plenty in the tribe. I, Keesh, the son of Bok, have spoken."

He sat down.

"That a boy should speak in council!" old Ugh-Gluk was mumbling.

"Shall the babes in arms tell us men the things we shall do?" Massuk demanded in a loud voice. "Am I a man that I should be made a mock by every child that cries for meat?"

Their anger boiled to white heat. They ordered him to bed, threatened that he should have no meat at all, and promised him sore beatings. Keesh's eyes began to flash and his blood to pound darkly under his skin. In the midst of the abuse, he sprang to his feet.

"Hear me, ye men!" he cried. "Take this now for my last word. Bok, my father, was a great hunter. I, too, his son, shall go and hunt the meat that I eat. And be it known now, that the division of that which I kill shall be fair. And no widow nor weak one shall cry in the night because there is no meat, when the strong men are groaning in great pain because they have eaten overmuch. And in the days to come there shall be shame upon the strong men who have eaten overmuch. I, Keesh, have said it!"

Jeers and scornful laughter followed him out of the igloo, but his jaw was set and he went his way, looking neither to right nor to left.

The next day he went forth along the shore line where the ice and the land met together. Those who saw him go noted that he carried his bow, with a goodly supply of bone-barbed arrows, and that across his shoulders was his father's big hunting spear. And there was laughter, and much talk, at the event. It was an unprecedented occurrence. Never did boys of his tender age go forth to hunt, much less to hunt alone. Also, there were shaking of heads and prophetic mutterings. The other women looked pityingly at Ikeega, and her face was grave and sad.

"He will be back ere long," they said cheeringly.

"Let him go; it will teach him a lesson," the hunters said. "He will come back shortly, and he will be meek and soft of speech in the days to follow."

But a day passed, and a second, and on the third a wild gale blew, and there was no Keesh. Ikeega tore her hair and put soot of the seal oil on her face in token of her grief; and the women assailed the men with bitter words in that they had mistreated the boy and sent him to his death; and the men made no answer, preparing to go in search of the body when the storm abated.

Early the next morning, however, Keesh strode into the village. He came not shamefacedly. Across his shoulders he bore a burden of fresh-killed meat. There was importance in his step and arrogance in his speech.

"Go, ye men, with the dogs and sledges, and take my trail for the better part of a day's travel," he said. "There is much meat on the ice—a she-bear and two half-grown cubs."

Ikeega was overcome with joy, but he received her demonstrations in manlike fashion, saying, "Come, Ikeega, let us eat. And after that I shall sleep, for I am weary."

He passed into their igloo and ate profoundly, and, after that, he slept for twenty running hours.

There was much doubt at first, much doubt and discussion. The killing of a polar bear is very dangerous, but thrice dangerous is it, and three times

thrice, to kill a mother bear with her cubs. The men could not bring themselves to believe that the boy Keesh, single-handed, had accomplished so great a marvel.

But the women spoke of the fresh-killed meat he had brought on his back, and this was an overwhelming argument against the men's unbelief. Finally, the men departed, grumbling greatly that in all probability, if the thing were so, he had neglected to cut up the carcasses.

Now, in the north it is very necessary that this should be done as soon as the kill is made. If not, the meat freezes so solidly as to turn the edge of the sharpest knife, and a three-hundred-pound bear, frozen stiff, is no easy thing to put upon a sled and haul over the rough ice. However, arriving at the spot, they found not only the kill, which they had doubted, but that Keesh had quartered the beasts in true hunter fashion and removed the entrails.

Thus began the mystery of Keesh, a mystery that deepened and deepened with the passing of the days. His very next trip he killed a young bear, nearly full grown, and, on the trip following, a large male bear and his mate. He was ordinarily gone from three to four days, though it was nothing unusual for him to stay away a week at a time on the ice field. Always he declined company on these expeditions, and the people marveled.

"How does he do it?" they demanded of one another. "Never does he take a dog with him, and dogs are of such great help."

"Why dost thou hunt only bear?" Klosh-Kwan once ventured to ask him.

Keesh made fitting answer. "It is well known that there is more meat on the bear," he said.

However, there was also talk of witchcraft in the village. "He hunts with evil spirits," some of the people contended, "wherefore his hunting is rewarded. How else can it be, save that he hunts with evil spirits?"

"Mayhap they be not evil, but good, these spirits," others said. "It is known that his father was a mighty hunter. May not his father hunt with him so that he may attain excellence and patience and understanding? Who knows?"

Nonetheless, his success continued, and the less skillful hunters were often kept busy hauling in his meat. In the division of it, Keesh was just. As his father had done before him, he saw to it that the least old woman and the last old man received a fair portion, keeping no more for himself than his needs required. Because of this and of his merit as a hunter, he was looked upon with respect and even awe; and there was even talk of making him chief after old Klosh-Kwan. Because of the things he had done, they looked for him to appear in the council, but he never came, and they were ashamed to ask.

"I am minded to build me an igloo," he said one day to Klosh-Kwan and a number of the hunters. "It shall be a large igloo, wherein Ikeega and I can dwell in comfort."

"Aye," they nodded gravely.

"But I have no time. My business is hunting, and it takes all my time. So it is but just that the men and women of the village, who eat my meat, should build me my igloo."

The igloo was built accordingly, on a generous scale that exceeded even the dwelling of Klosh-Kwan. Keesh and his mother moved into it, and it was the first prosperity she had enjoyed since the death of Bok. Nor was material prosperity alone hers, for, because of her wonderful son and the position he had given her, she came to be looked upon as the first woman in all the village; and the women were given to visiting her, to asking her advice, and to quoting her wisdom when arguments arose among themselves or with the men.

But it was the mystery of Keesh's marvelous hunting that took chief place in all their minds. And one day Ugh-Gluk taxed him with witchcraft to his face.

"It is charged," Ugh-Gluk said ominously, "that thou dealest with evil spirits, wherefore thy hunting is rewarded."

"Is not the meat good?" Keesh made answer. "Has one in the village yet to fall sick from the eating of it? How dost thou know that witchcraft be concerned? Or dost thou guess, in the dark, merely because of the envy that consumes thee?"

Ugh-Gluk withdrew, discomfited, the women laughing at him as he walked away. However, in the council one night after long deliberation, it was determined to put spies on Keesh's track when he went forth to hunt, so that his methods might be learned. So on his next trip Bim and Bawn, two young men, the craftiest of hunters, followed after him, taking care not to be seen. After five days they came back, their eyes bulging and their tongues a-tremble, to tell what they had seen. The council was hastily called in Klosh-Kwan's dwelling, and Bim took up the tale.

"Brothers! As was commanded, we journeyed on the trail of Keesh, and cunningly we journeyed, so that he might not know. And midway of the first day, he picked up with a great he-bear. It was a very great bear."

"None greater," Bawn corroborated and went on himself. "Yet was the bear not inclined to fight, for he turned away and made off slowly over the ice. This we saw from the rocks of the shore, and the bear came toward us, and after him came Keesh, very much unafraid. And he shouted harsh words after the bear, and waved his arms about, and made much noise. Then did the bear grow angry, and rise up on his hind legs, and growl. But Keesh walked right up to the bear."

"Aye," Bim continued the story. "Right up to the bear Keesh walked. And the bear took after him, and Keesh ran away. But as he ran he dropped a little round ball on the ice, and the bear stopped and smelled of it, and then swallowed it up. And Keesh continued to run away and drop little round balls, and the bear continued to swallow them up."

Exclamations and cries of doubt were being made, and Ugh-Gluk expressed open unbelief.

"With our own eyes we saw it," Bim affirmed.

Bawn repeated, "Aye, with our own eyes. And this continued until the bear stood suddenly upright, and cried aloud in pain, and thrashed his forepaws madly about. And Keesh continued to make off over the ice to a safe distance. But the bear gave him no notice, being occupied with the misfortune the little round balls had wrought within him."

"Aye, within him," Bim interrupted. "For he did claw at himself, and leap about over the ice like a playful puppy—save from the way he growled and squealed it was plain it was not play but pain. Never did I see such a sight!"

"Nay, never was such a sight seen," Bawn took up the strain. "Furthermore, it was such a large bear."

"Witchcraft," Ugh-Gluk suggested.

"I know not," Bawn replied. "I tell only of what my eyes beheld. And after a while the bear grew weak and tired, for he was very heavy and he had jumped about with exceeding violence, and he went off along the shore ice, shaking his head slowly from side to side and sitting down ever and again to squeal and cry. And Keesh followed after the bear, and we followed after Keesh, and for that day and three days more we followed. The bear grew weak and never ceased crying from his pain."

"It was a charm!" Ugh-Gluk exclaimed. "Surely it was a charm!"

"It may well be."

Bim relieved Bawn. "The bear wandered, now this way and now that, doubling back and forth and crossing his trail in circles, so that at the end he was near where Keesh had first come upon him. By this time the bear was quite sick and could crawl no farther, so Keesh came up close and speared him to death."

"And what then?" Klosh-Kwan demanded.

"Then we left Keesh skinning the bear and came running that the news of the killing might be told."

In the afternoon of that day, the women hauled in the meat of the bear while the men sat in council assembled. When Keesh arrived, a messenger was sent to him, bidding him come to the council.

Keesh sent reply, saying that he was hungry and tired; also that his igloo was large and comfortable and could hold many men.

Curiosity was so strong on the men that the whole council, Klosh-Kwan to the fore, rose up and went to the igloo of Keesh. He was eating, but he received them with respect and seated them according to their rank. Ikeega was proud and embarrassed by turns, but Keesh was quite composed.

Klosh-Kwan recited the information brought by Bim and Bawn, and at its close he said in a stern voice: "So explanation is wanted, O Keesh, of thy manner of hunting. Is there witchcraft in it?"

Keesh looked up and smiled. "Nay, O Klosh-Kwan. It is not for a boy to know aught of witches, and of witches I know nothing. I have but devised a means whereby I may kill the ice bear with ease, that is all. It be headcraft, not witchcraft."

"And may any man?"

"Any man."

There was a long silence. The men looked in one another's faces, and Keesh went on eating.

"And—and—and wilt thou tell us, O Keesh?" Klosh-Kwan finally asked in a tremulous voice.

"Yea, I will tell thee." Keesh finished sucking a marrowbone and rose to his feet. "It is quite simple. Behold!"

He picked up a thin strip of whalebone and showed it to them. The ends were sharp as needle points. The strip he coiled carefully, till it disappeared in his hand. Then, as he suddenly released it, it sprang straight again. He picked up a piece of blubber.

"So," he said, "one takes a small chunk of blubber, thus, and thus makes it hollow. Then into the hollow goes the whalebone, so, tightly coiled, and another piece of blubber is fitted over the whalebone. After that it is put outside where it freezes into a little round ball. The bear swallows the little round ball, the blubber melts, the whalebone with its sharp ends stands out straight, the bear gets sick, and, when the bear is very sick, why, you kill him with a spear. It is quite simple."

Ugh-Gluk said, "Oh!" and Klosh-Kwan said, "Ah!" and each said something after his own manner, and all understood.

This is the story of Keesh, who lived long ago on the rim of the polar sea. Because he exercised headcraft and not witchcraft, he rose from the meanest igloo to be head man of his village, and, through all the years that he lived, it is related, his tribe was prosperous. Neither widow nor weak one cried aloud in the night because there was no meat.

Two Songs
Uvavnuk

I
The great sea
Has sent me adrift.
It moves me
As the weed in a great river.
Earth and the great weather
Move me,
Have carried me away
And move my inward parts with joy.

II
And I think over again
My small adventures
When with a shore wind I drifted out
In my kayak
And thought I was in danger.
My fears,
Those small ones
That I thought so big
For all vital things
I had to get and to reach.

And yet, there is only
One great thing,
The only thing:
To live and to see in huts and on journeys
The great day that dawns,
And the light that fills the world.

POLAR NIGHT

Norah Burke

As the hot arctic summer drew to a close, till the sun only slid along the horizon to sink again at once, the polar bear knew that a hard time lay ahead for her.

During the months of night, fifty degrees below zero, her cubs would be born. The great task of motherhood was already begun, the time soon coming when she would bury herself deep down under the snow to give birth. From then until the day when she and the cubs burrowed up into daylight again, she would not eat. She and they must live on what she had stored in her body during the summer, and on what she could catch and eat now. She must finish fattening herself up for the ordeal, and there was not much time left.

At the moment she was hunting along the edge of the ice, because where there was water there were seals, also fish, and the chance of a porpoise or walrus. As winter closed the roots and berries and lichen and

seaweed of the polar islands into glass, the bears moved to the ice-edge for their food.

This was the arctic region, the area north of the limit of tree growth. The shores of Greenland, Siberia, Alaska, Canada bordered upon this sea. It was a landscape of snow and old ice and new ice, of drifting pack ice, and berg ice from the glaciers, all in constant motion, lanes and pools of pure cobalt looking glass, opening and closing all the time in the pack. . . . In summer the gulls and other birds made the air raucous with quarrels, but now all that the bear could hear was the wash of blue water against grinding ice.

Under the dark sky, on the white land, in the desolation of the arctic landscape, she was part of its white power, moving with a long swinging walk and huge flat yellow hairy snowman footfalls. Strong and dangerous, the largest of bears, able to swim forty miles out to sea if need be, she stalked her kingdom in which no natural enemy challenged her reign. Her feet, bristled underneath to give grip on the ice, carried her huge weight with a light and silent tread; while the low swinging head searched the ice all the time for food.

She was not clearly aware of what was happening in her body, but the instinct was there to love the unborn cubs, to prepare for them and protect them; she did not risk her body in careless adventures as she would at other times.

But food? Food—

Already the iron of winter was in the clean cold air, though she felt the cold only with her eyes and black nose and black lips, where the air stung her, and on the long pinkish-gray tongue, moving all the time to prevent freezing, that slung in and out of her mouth among the large cruel teeth.

Suddenly, away down the ice field, where a dark blue lead showed in the pack, she saw a blackish slug on the ice—a seal. It was essential to catch him. In a moment she had decided on her approach, and slipped silently into the water to cut off his line of retreat. The ice field rocked as her great weight left it.

The bear was as much at home in the water as on land—swimming like a dog, but on top or submerged—and the water much warmer than the air on her face. Not wet, either. Inside the layer of fat and the shaggy, oily, water-tight coat, she felt as dry as on land.

By a series of cunning dives and approaches, and keeping under the shoulder of ice, she got near to the seal. Breathing carefully, every nerve keyed to the task of silent approach,

ready to spring—to dive—to slaughter, she slid near—near—

Suddenly the seal saw her. Terror convulsed his face. A moment of awful indecision—whether to plunge into the sea, his natural line of escape, and perhaps fall straight into her jaws, or to struggle across the ice to that other hole—

He swung from her, humping madly along. The bear lunged up out of the water, on to the ice, on to the terrified seal.

The water slushed off her everywhere like a tidal wave. There was a flurry of snow and water and fighting seal. His quick struggling body flapped under her as she slew him. Blood spurted on to the snow.

When the seal was dead, the bear attended first to herself, getting rid of the wet from her coat before it could freeze, although oil had kept off the frost so far. She shook, and the drops flew off in rainbows in all directions. She rolled and nosed along in the snow, wiping her flanks, her chin, and soon all was dry. A few hairs crisped up and stuck to each other with frost.

Now for the seal. She ripped up the body, turning back the skin and blubber, letting out a cloud of steam, and ate greedily of the hot crimson meat. Seal meat was her favorite, full of flavor, a hot meal, not like the white icy flakes of cod.

Then, although the bear had no natural enemies, she stopped suddenly as she ate, lifted her head, looked, listened, scented. Blood dripped from her chin on to the snow.

There was nothing.

All the same she trusted her instinct and, leaving the rest of the meal, slipped into the water, where she could keep her cubs safe, where it was warmer, and easier to move.

Presently she saw upright seals coming along the shore. They were rather rare creatures, these, and dangerous for all they were so weak. The places where they lived had light and noise, and smelled full of good food. The she-bear often drew near the places, attracted by those smells. She hunted these land-seals too, and ate them when she could. They were not like the sea-seals, though. They wore seal fur, and their skins were rubbed with seal blubber, but there was a different taste inside.

They in their turn hunted bear, as the she-bear knew well. She had sometimes found the place of the kill, and seen the white empty skins hanging up by the camps, smelled the dark red gamy flesh cooking.

Now as she watched the approaching men, she considered whether to kill them, but the unborn life in her said get away. So she dived and swam and melted out of their radius.

In the next few days the bear gorged on fish and seal. No longer the hot rocks of summer gave forth good-tasting moss and lichens or the sharp-fleshed berries and sweet roots. She dived into the cold blue ocean for her food.

But now the arctic day was over. In the pink twilight a snowy owl was flitting silently across the waste, moving south and south as life was squeezed out of the arctic desert by the polar night.

Then came the freezing of the sea. Crystals formed below the surface and rose, and needles of ice shot across from one to another, joining them together, thickening, hardening, adding more ice to the floes already many years old. The ice talked, grinding its teeth, sending out every now and then a singing crack. Curtains of colored flame rippled in the sky. The polar night began.

Now, the real cold came. Now the food disappeared, and old male bears grew lean and savage.

The she-bear chose her den.

There was a great raw range of decayed ice that had been pushed up into mountains whose hollows were packed with snow. Icicles yards long hung on the south side from the summer, and behind this curtain of ice she found a great purple cave, carved in diamond and full of snow.

This was the place.

Her body was ready now for the ordeal. Thick fat, gathered from seal and halibut, lined her skin.

She burrowed down into the violet snow on the floor of the cave. It was so light that the wind of moving blew it about like feathers, and she could breathe in it. She burrowed deeper and deeper, while the snow sifted and fell soundlessly behind her, till presently she was deep enough.

She curled and rolled herself round and round, pushing the snow, packing it, shaping the den. All the sides of it melted with her heat, then froze again into slippery walls. And the hot breath passed up through the way she had dug, melting the sides of the channel which also froze again and left a tube which would supply her with air until she came up in the spring.

Inside the snow and ice—inside her thick oily fur and the layer of blubber, she was warm, full fed and sleepy. She slept and waited.

In the fullness of time, the first familiar pang of birth trembled in her stomach. Pain fluttered like a butterfly and was gone.

She stirred, lifted her head, rearranged herself.

It came again, stronger, longer.

She moved uneasily.

Then in long strong accomplishing strokes it was there—hard, forcing, contracting, out of her control. She grunted, tensed all her muscles, pressed and gasped. Another spasm, and on the smooth strong river of pain, she felt the first cub come out.

A wave of relief relaxed her.

There he lay mewing, so wet and tiny, hardly alive, and she nuzzled him delightedly, while starting to clean him up.

But now another spasm—the same long final one as before, though easier—and the second cub was born.

It was over now. She felt the diminishing pain, pulsing quieter.

Now to clean them up. She licked and licked them, turning them over, rolling and caressing them; then life strengthened in them as they dried, as they fed. She lay in bliss, feeling her own life flowing from her heart.

Meanwhile in the world above, the sun had returned, first a green glow, then a rosy one, then touching the topmost peaks, days before the first sunrise.

Deep in the snow cave, the bear knew it as the snow grew luminous with the light pressing through.

One day she heard voices. The snow vibrated with footsteps, the ice ceiling cracked.

She rose, shook herself free of the cubs and stood ready in case the land-seals saw the warm yellow air hole that marked her den—in case one of them walked over her and fell in. . . .

She stood fierce, lean, ready, to defend her cubs, her heart pounding hot and loud as fever in her thin body.

Gradually the voices and the footsteps died away.

Presently it was time to come out into the world again. The cubs' eyes were open, their coats grown; they were walking, getting stronger every day. Now they must come out and face the world and swim and fight and catch seals. There was everything to teach them, and while they were still learning—still babies, they had got to be kept safe and fed. All this she had to do alone. Other years she'd had a mate to help her, but this time he was gone—lost—Those white skins hanging by the camps—

She began to tear her way out, the giant paws and black nails breaking open the ice walls of their den. The ice gave; snow fell in.

They climbed out.

Clean frozen air, dazzling with sun, hit them like the stroke of an axe. Light entered the brain in needles through the eyes. Only gradually, as the pupils contracted, did it become possible to see.

The arctic landscape blazed white and navy blue. Everything hit them at once—light, noise, wind—the blast of a new world.

Down there was the water—

The mother bear plunged joyfully into the buoyant cleanness. All the dirt and staleness of winter were washed away. It was like flight. She plunged and rose and shook and plunged again in sheer joy. So fresh, so clean, the salt cold water running through her teeth—

Then she resumed the heavy duties of parenthood, turned to the cubs. They were sitting on the edge, squeaking with fright, and she began urging them to come in. They kept feeling forward, then scrambling back. Suddenly one ventured too far down the ice, and slithered, shrieking, into the sea, where he bobbed up again like a cork.

His brother, seeing this, plucked up courage and plunged in too, in one desperate baby-jump, landing with a painful *smack* and blinking in the spray.

They found they could swim.

Presently she pushed them up on to the ice again where they shook and dried, and the next thing was food. She left them while she killed a seal, and the three of them ate it.

After that there were lessons, how to fish, how to kill. Living was thin at first, for three hunters cannot move as silently as one, but they got along.

Until the day when land-seals approached them unseen from behind an ice ridge. The first they knew of it was an explosion, and one cub gasped and doubled up as he was hit. The bears dived for the water, even the little wounded one. He managed to keep up with them, and his mother and brother would die rather than desert him.

They all swam on, but slowly—slowly. Both cubs were still so small and *slow*, and they must hurry—

Blood ran in the water.

Other shots spattered beside them.

Anxiety roared in the she-bear's blood. Her heart was bursting. She pushed the cubs on, and turned to meet her enemies. Reared up on to the ice and galloped toward them, a charge that nothing could stop—not even death—if they'd stayed to face it, but they broke and ran.

The bear returned to her cubs.

The wounded one was sinking lower and lower in the water, breathing waves, and she managed to push them out at last on to distant ice. Then she licked him as he lay suffering in the snow, and his brother licked him too, whimpering with distress as he worked.

So that presently the blood stopped, and after a long time the suffering too. The cub sniffed the air. In the first real moment of recovery he consented to take food.

Pain went away from her heart.

Before them lay all the arctic lands, the snow in retreat. The floes, soft from solar radiation, were being broken up by the waves. Plant life teemed in the water, the more open sea colored bright green diatoms.

Millions of wild flowers studded the rocky scree. There was everything to eat at once—lichen and moss and roots and halibut and seals. Salmon swam the green water, and cod. Seaweed washed round the rocks. On the land there were hares and young birds.

The summer gathered to almost tropical heat. Snow water dribbled into pools. Icicles glistened with wet, dropped and broke like glass.

And the mother bear in the snow with her cubs did not know why she behaved as she did. There was pain and there was happiness, and these two things drove her according to unfathomable laws. When the summer ended, and the polar night began, she would do the same things over again, and her children after her.

BATTLE BY THE BREADFRUIT TREE

Theodore J. Waldeck

Smith and I were anxious to procure motion pictures of a herd of baboons. We had tried and tried, with no success whatever, though we saw many of these creatures. Our camp was some miles from a little ravine through which a stream ran. Beyond the ravine was a plateau leading back to thick woods. The baboons, scores of them, came out of these woods with their young to play on the plateau, to drink from the stream, and to fight for the favors of the females. Often Smith and I watched them, tried to photograph them, but could never get close enough. The baboons enjoyed what we were doing. They thought it was a game of some sort.

Once we set up the camera at the edge of the plateau, in order to take them when they came through the woods at dawn to greet the sun. We didn't even come close, for when the baboons saw us they charged like a shrieking army of savages. They threw sticks and stones at us, and we fled as though the devil and all his imps were at our heels. A grown bull baboon could have torn either of us to shreds. We didn't even stop to take our camera. We felt sure that our camera would be a wreck when we returned, which could not be until the baboons had retired from the plateau. We went back then, to find it exactly as we had left it. They had not so much as touched it.

"We *must* get those pictures," said Smith, "and I think I know the answer. Those breadfruit trees this side of the ravine. That big one, with the leafy top . . ."

"Yes?"

"We go there now and build a platform, up among the leaves, set up our camera, take blankets, a thermos bottle filled with hot tea, and spend the night. Then, when they come out in the morning, we'll be looking right down on them."

I saw that he was right, and we set about it. The trekkers got boards from the camp and carried them to the tree. Big limbs were cut off and lashed high among the leaves at the top of the breadfruit tree. Then the boards were laid across the limbs, the camera set up. We had supper, took our blankets, and went to the tree to spend an uncomfortable night; but however uncomfortable it might be, it would not matter if we got our pictures.

Night. We sat hunched up with our blankets over us listening to the sounds of the night. Now and again we dozed off. Then we'd waken. I'd have a cigarette; Smith would smoke his pipe. The wind

blew steadily toward us from the plateau, which we could see dimly in the moonlight. The hours wore on.

Finally, animals began to greet the growing morning, though it would be some time, if they stuck to schedule, before the baboons appeared. I sat back on my blanket now—it was already warm enough to do without it—and watched the day break. I never tired of doing that.

The sun comes up in a different way in Africa. First the leaves would be black. Then a grayish haze would outline their shapes. Then the gray would lighten into the green of the leaves. Then the sun itself would strike through and morning would be with us, covering that part of Africa with a mixture of colors that ran through all the spectrum. Sunlight played upon colors like a mighty organist upon the keys, and the keys were everything the sunlight touched; when the dawn was come, it was music made visible. Not just the music that men played, but the music of Nature herself, with all the sounds that Nature used. A great sword of crimson was like a bloodcurdling scream you could not hear, because you came before it sounded, or after the sound had passed—and the sword struck deeply into the ravine, and raised itself to slash across the plateau on which the baboons usually played. The green of the trees was light, and like a touch of agony somehow—not the agony of pain, but the agony of an unexplainable kind of ecstasy. Far away and all around were the mounded hills, with the veldt between them, and some of the hills wore caps of crimson, or orange, or gold, and some were still touched with the mystery of distance, or the night that had not yet left them. Whatever color or combination of colors you cared to mention, you could find there. And they came out of the east in a magical rush, like paint of all colors flung across the world by a painter bigger than all the earth itself.

I sighed and drank it in. Smith was looking out through the leaves, watching for the baboons to appear. Then he nudged me, and I made an end, for the moment, of dreaming. I parted the leaves in utter silence, making sure that my lens was uncovered and aimed at the plateau, and looked through. The baboon herd had not come, but a single baboon and her baby. Smith had not actually seen her coming. One moment he had been watching, seeing nothing. Then he had blinked his eyes and she was there. He signaled me to start the camera. I noted that the wind was toward us. I felt sure that the rest of the baboons would come,

following this one. The mother baboon, while her baby played across the plateau behind her, came down to its edge to peer into the ravine, perhaps to dash down for a drink. I started the camera. It was almost silent, but not quite. And with the first whirring sound, which we ourselves could scarcely hear, though we were right beside it, the mother jumped up and looked around. Her ears had caught the little sound. She looked in all directions, twisting her head swiftly, and even in this her eyes kept darting to her young one. I stilled the whirring. We did not move or make a sound, even a whisper. She was so close we could see her nose wrinkling as she tried to get our scent. But the wind was toward us, and she got nothing. She even looked several times at the breadfruit tree that hid us.

I was about to start grinding again when a terrific squall came from the baby. It caught at my heart, that sound. I know it caught at the heart of Smith, too, for I could see it in his face. The mother baboon whirled around, so fast one could scarcely see the movement. The baby was jumping swiftly to the top of a rock, which was all too low to be of any use to him, as protection against the creature that was close behind him.

That creature was a hunting leopard, and it, like the baboon, had come so softly and silently that we had not seen it. It was simply there, a murderous streak behind the baby baboon. Did the female hesitate for a single moment? Not at all. If the leopard were a streak, so was the mother baboon. She shot toward that leopard and was in the air above him, reaching for his neck, while he was in mid-leap behind the baby, which now sat upon the rock and uttered doleful screams of terror.

The great cat instantly had his work cut out for him. For the baboon, by gripping his neck from behind, beyond reach of those talons, could break it. And that was what she tried, with hands and feet and killing incisors. But while I knew nothing of this fighting combination, the leopard must have, for he did what any cat would instinctively do in such a case. He spun to his back and reached for the baboon with all four of his brutally armed paws. One stroke across the abdomen of the baboon and she would be killed outright. But she knew something of leopards.

Smith did not make a sound, nor did I. I don't think we even breathed. The great cat recovered himself as the baboon jumped free of the leopard and ran toward her baby. The leopard charged the baboon. The baboon waited until the last minute, shot into the air, allowed the cat to go under her, turned in the air, and dropped back for the killing hold on the back of the neck again.

She got some hair in her mouth, which she spat out disgustedly. The baby kept on squalling. As nearly as I could tell—though I probably would not have heard even the trumpeting of elephants or the roaring of lions—there was no sound other than the screaming of the female baboon, the squalling of her baby, and the spitting and snarling of the leopard.

This time, when the leopard whirled to his back to dislodge the baboon, he managed to sink his claws into the baboon. I saw the blood spurt from the baboon's body, dyeing her fur. I knew that the smell of blood would drive the leopard mad, and it did. He would just as soon eat the meat of a grown baboon, if he could not have the baby.

Both stood off for a second, regarding each other, to spit out fur and hair. Then the leopard charged once more. Again the baboon leaped high, started down, reaching for that neck. And this time, when she came down, the leopard had already turned, and she could not entirely avoid landing among those fearful talons. Even a baboon could not jump from a spot in midair. For a brief moment there was a terrific flurry of in-fighting, from which came the snarling of the leopard, the screaming of the she-baboon. Now we could see the leopard, now the baboon, the latter trying with all her strength and agility to escape a disemboweling stroke from one of the four feet of the killer. Then both were so mixed up, and fighting so much all over the plateau, that we could not distinguish them. We could tell they were together, because they formed a ball of fighting fury, and the sounds of the two animals came out of the pinwheel of murderous action.

How long it lasted I do not know. To the she-baboon and her baby it must have seemed ages. It may have been seconds, even a minute. And then they were standing off, catching their breath, spitting out fur, regarding each other again. Both were tired. To my utter amazement the baboon was holding her own with the leopard. At that moment I would not have known which one had the edge, if either. For both were panting, weary, and stained with blood.

Neither gave ground. By common consent they stood for a few seconds, the baboon on her hindlegs, the leopard crouching on all fours. Then the leopard charged. Again the baboon went into the air to let the leopard go under her. She knew better, at this stage of the game, than to run away or jump to either side.

The leopard could overtake her if she ran, could turn instantly and follow her if she jumped to either side. So up and over was her only chance. Again she came down. But this time she was expecting the cat to whip upon his back and present his talons, and was ready. She twisted aside a little, and to the front, perhaps with some idea of reaching for the neck from the underside, now uppermost. The forepaws of the leopard lashed at her. The sun gleamed on the exposed talons, and showed that they were red with baboon blood. I could see long weals across the abdomen of the baboon. She had evaded those slashes at the last moment, each time. Feeling the talons' touch she had got away, just enough to escape disemboweling, not enough to escape deep, parallel gashes that reached inward for her life.

Now I began to see how the fight was going to go, though neither Smith nor I could have done anything about it, because we were spellbound, rooted to our place in the breadfruit tree, watching something that few explorers had ever seen: a battle between a leopard and a baboon! And for the best reason in the world—the baboon to protect her baby.

But now the she-baboon was tiring. It was obvious in all her movements, though I knew and the leopard knew that as long as she stood upright and could see him, she was dynamite—fury incarnate, capable of slaying if she got in the blows she wanted. So far she had not made it.

Now she panted more than the leopard did. She did not entirely evade his rushes, though she jumped over him as before. But she did not go as high or

twist as quickly in the air. She couldn't. Her body was beginning to weigh too much for her tiring muscles. She was like an arm-weary prizefighter who has almost fought himself out. But her little eyes still glared defiance, her screaming still informed him that she was ready for more. Now there were other slashes upon her face, her head, her chest, and her abdomen—clear down even to her hands and feet. She was a bloody mess. But she never even thought of quitting. They drew apart once more, spitting fur. They glared at each other. Several times I saw the orange eyes of the leopard, and there was hell in them—the hell of hate and fury, and thwarted hunger.

Now he charged before the baboon had rested enough. He was getting stronger, the baboon weaker. His second wind came sooner perhaps, and he sorely needed it. Even yet the baboon could break his neck, given the one chance.

Again the baboon went into the air, came down, and was caught in the midst of those four paws. Again the battle raged, the two animals all mixed up together, all over the plateau. The little one squalled from his boulder, and there was despair in his voice. He cried hopeless encouragement to his mother. She heard, I knew she did, and tried to find some reserve with which to meet the attacks of the killer.

That last piece of in-fighting lasted almost too long. There was no relief from it, and the nerves of the two men who watched were strained to the breaking point, though neither was aware of it. How long they had held their breath they did not know.

The two beasts broke apart, and I saw instantly that the leopard had at last succeeded, managing the stroke he had

been trying for since the battle began. He had raked deeply into the abdomen of the baboon. The result may be well imagined. The baboon drew off slowly, and looked down at herself. What she saw told her the truth—that even if the leopard turned and ran away this minute, she was done.

But did she expect mercy? Death did not grant mercy in Africa—certainly not on this particular morning.

The baboon noted the direction of the leopard's glance. The great cat was crouched well back, but facing the rock on which the baby squalled. He licked his chops, looked at the dying she-baboon, and growled, and it was as though he said, "Not much time now. And when you are gone, nothing will keep me from getting him!"

As if the leopard had actually screamed those words, I got the thought which raced through his evil head. And the baboon got it too. For she turned slowly, like a dead thing walking, and moved to turn her back toward the rock, so that now the baby was almost over her head.

Then she looked at the leopard once more, and screamed, as though she answered: "Perhaps, but over my dead body!"

The leopard charged again, for the last time. It would be easy now. And as the she-baboon set herself against that last charge, the strangest, most nearly human cry I ever heard went keening out across the veldt. It bounced against the breadfruit trees, dipped into the ravine; it went back through the forest whence the other baboons usually came to play and drink. It went out in all directions, that cry, across the plain. It rolled across the mounded hills. It was a cry that could never be forgotten by those that heard it.

And then, in the midst of the cry—like none she had uttered while the fight had been so fierce—the leopard struck her down. She sprawled, beaten to a pulp, at the base of the boulder, while that last cry of hers still moved across the veldt.

And now, sure that the she-baboon was dead, the leopard backed away, crouched, lifted his eyes to the baby on the rock.

I came to life then, realizing for the first time what I was seeing. I couldn't have moved before. But now, somehow, my rifle was in my hands, at my shoulder, and I was getting the leopard in my sights. Why had I not done it before, saved the life of the mother? I'll never know. Certainly, and sincerely, I had not allowed the fight to continue simply in order to see which would win out. I had simply become a statue, possessing only eyes and ears.

I got the leopard in my sights as he crouched to spring. I had his head for a target. I'd get him before he moved, before he sprang. The baby—looking down, sorrow in his cries, with a knowledge of doom too—had nowhere to go. I tightened the trigger. And then . . .

On the instant the leopard was blotted out, and for several seconds I could not understand what had happened, what the mother's last cry had meant. But now I did. For living baboons, leaping, screaming, had appeared out of nowhere. They came, the whole herd of them, and the leopard was invisible in their midst. I did not even hear the leopard snarl and spit. I heard nothing save the baboons, saw nothing save the big blur of their bodies, over and around the spot where I had last seen the leopard.

How long that lasted I do not know. But when it was over, another she-baboon jumped to the rock, gathered up the baby, and was gone. After her trailed all the other baboons. Smith and I looked at each other, and if my face was as white and shocked as his, it was white and shocked indeed. Without a word, because we both understood, we slipped down from the tree, crossed the ravine, climbed its far side, crossed the plateau, looked down at the dead she-baboon, then looked away again. One mother had fought to the death for the life of her baby and had saved that life. We looked around for the leopard who had slain her. We couldn't find a piece of it as big as an average man's hand! So the baboons had rallied to the dying cry of the mother baboon.

We went slowly back to the tree, got our camera down, returned with it to our camp. Not until we were back did we realize that neither of us, from the beginning of that fight to its grim and savage end, had thought of the camera, much less touched it.

One of the greatest fights any explorer ever saw was unrecorded.

The Cheyenne Account of How the World Was Made

as told by Mary Little Bear Inkanish

In the beginning there was nothing, and Maheo, the All Spirit, lived in the void. He looked around him, but there was nothing to see. He listened, but there was nothing to hear. There was only Maheo, alone in nothingness.

Because of the greatness of his Power, Maheo was not lonesome. His being was a Universe. But as he moved through the endless time of nothingness, it seemed to Maheo that his Power should be put to use. What good is Power, Maheo asked himself, if it is not used to make a world and people to live in it?

With his Power, Maheo created a great water, like a lake, but salty. Out of this salty water, Maheo knew, he could bring all life that ever was to be. The lake itself was life, if Maheo so commanded it. In the darkness of nothingness, Maheo could feel the coolness of the water and taste on his lips the tang of the salt.

"There should be water beings," Maheo told his Power. And so it was. First the fish, swimming in the deep water, and then the mussels and snails and crawfish, lying on the sand and mud Maheo had formed so his lake should have a bottom.

Let us also create something that lives on the water, Maheo thought to his Power.

And so it was. For now there were snow geese and mallards and teal and coots and terns and loons living and swimming about on the water's surface. Maheo could hear the splashing of their feet and the flapping of their wings in the darkness.

I should like to see the things that have been created, Maheo decided.

And, again, so it was. Light began to grow and spread, first white and bleached in the east, then golden and strong till it filled the middle of the sky and extended all around the horizon. Maheo watched the light, and he saw the birds and fishes, and the shellfish lying on the bottom of the lake as the light showed them to him.

How beautiful it all is, Maheo thought in his heart.

Then the snow goose paddled over to where she thought Maheo was, in the space above the lake. "I do not see You, but I know that You exist," the goose began. "I do not know where You are, but I know You must be everywhere. Listen to me, Maheo. This is good water that You have made, on which we live. But birds are not like fish. Sometimes we get tired swimming. Sometimes we would like to get out of the water."

"Then fly," said Maheo, and he waved his arms, and all the water birds flew, skittering along the surface of the lake until they had speed enough to rise in the air. The skies were darkened with them.

"How beautiful their wings are in the light," Maheo said to his Power, as the birds wheeled and turned, and became living patterns against the sky.

The loon was the first to drop back to the surface of the lake. "Maheo," he said, looking around, for he knew that Maheo was all about him, "You have made us sky and light to fly in, and You have made us water to swim in. It sounds ungrateful to want something else, yet still we do. When we are tired of swimming and tired of flying, we should like a dry solid place where we could walk and rest. Give us a place to build our nests, please, Maheo."

"So be it," answered Maheo, "but to make such a place I must have your help, all of you. By myself, I have made four things: the water, the light, the sky air, and the peoples of the water. Now I must have help if I am to create more, for my Power will only let me make four things by myself."

"Tell us how we can help You," said all the water peoples. "We are ready to do what You say."

Maheo stretched out his hand and beckoned. "Let the biggest and the swiftest try to find land first," he said, and the snow goose came to him.

"I am ready to try," the snow goose said, and she drove herself along the water until the white wake behind her grew and grew to a sharp white point that drove her up into the air as the feathers drive an arrow. She flew high into the sky, until she was only a dark spot against the clearness of the light. Then the goose turned, and down she plunged, faster than any arrow, and dived into the water. She pierced the surface with her beak as if it were the point of a spear.

The snow goose was gone a long time. Maheo counted to four four hundred times before she rose to the surface of the water and lay there floating, her beak half open as she gasped for air.

"What have you brought us?" Maheo asked her, and the snow goose sighed sadly, and answered, "Nothing. I brought nothing back."

Then the loon tried, and after him, the mallard. Each in turn rose until he was a speck against the light, and turned and dived with the speed of a flashing arrow into the water. And each in turn rose wearily, and wearily answered, "Nothing," when Maheo asked him what he had brought.

At last there came the little coot, paddling across the surface of the water very quietly, dipping his head sometimes to catch a tiny fish, and shaking the water beads from his scalp lock whenever he rose.

"Maheo," the little coot said softly, "when I put my head beneath the water, it seems to me that I see something there, far below. Perhaps I can swim down to it—I don't know. I can't fly or dive like my sister and brothers. All I can do is swim, but I will swim down the best I know how, and go as deep as I can. May I try, please, Maheo?"

"Little brother," said Maheo, "no man can do more than his best, and I have asked for the help of all the water peoples. Certainly you shall try. Perhaps swimming will be better than diving, after all. Try, little brother, and see what you can do."

"Hah-ho!" the little coot said. "Thank you, Maheo," and he put his head under the water and swam down and down and down and down, until he was out of sight.

The coot was gone a long, long, long time. Then Maheo and the other birds could see a little dark spot beneath the water's surface, slowly rising toward them. It seemed as if they would never see the coot himself, but at last the spot began to have a shape. Still it rose and rose, and at last Maheo and the water peoples could surely see who it was. The little coot was swimming up from the bottom of the salty lake.

When the coot reached the surface, he stretched his closed beak upward into the light, but he did not open it.

"Give me what you have brought," Maheo said, and the coot let his beak fall open, so a little ball of mud could fall from his tongue into Maheo's hand, for when Maheo wanted to, he could become like a man.

"Go, little brother," Maheo said. "Thank you, and may what you have brought always protect you."

And so it was and so it is, for the coot's flesh still tastes of mud, and neither man nor animal will eat a coot unless there is nothing else to eat.

Maheo rolled the ball of mud between the palms of his hands, and it began to grow larger, until there was almost too much mud for Maheo to hold. He looked around for a place to put the mud, but there was nothing but water or air anywhere around him.

"Come and help me again, water peoples," Maheo called. "I must put this mud somewhere. One of you must let me place it on his back."

All the fish and all the other water creatures came swimming to Maheo, and he tried to find the right one to carry the mud. The mussels and snails and crawfish were too small, although they all had solid backs, and they lived too deep in the water for the mud to rest on them. The fish were too narrow, and their back fins stuck up through the mud and cut it to pieces. Finally only one water person was left.

"Grandmother Turtle," Maheo asked, "do you think that you can help me?"

"I'm very old and very slow, but I will try," the turtle answered. She swam over to Maheo, and he piled the mud on her rounded back, until he had made a hill. Under Maheo's hands the hill grew and spread and flattened out, until the Grandmother Turtle was hidden from sight.

"So be it," Maheo said once again. "Let the earth be known as our Grandmother, and let the Grandmother who carries the earth be the only being who is at home beneath the water, or within the earth, or above the ground; the only one who can go anywhere by swimming or by walking as she chooses."

And so it was, and so it is. Grandmother Turtle and all her descendants must walk very slowly, for they carry the whole weight of the whole world and all its peoples on their backs.

Now there was earth as well as water, but the earth was barren. And Maheo said to his Power, "Our Grandmother Earth is like a woman; she should be fruitful. Let her begin to bear life. Help me, my Power."

When Maheo said that, trees and grass sprang up to become the Grandmother's hair. The flowers became her bright ornaments, and the fruits and the seeds were the gifts that the earth offered back to Maheo. The birds came to rest on her hands when they were tired, and the fish came close to her sides. Maheo looked at the Earth Woman and he thought she was very beautiful; the most beautiful thing he had made so far.

She should not be alone, Maheo thought. Let me give her something of myself, so she will know that I am near her and that I love her.

Maheo reached into his right side, and pulled out a rib bone. He breathed on the bone, and laid it softly on the bosom of the Earth Woman. The bone moved and stirred, stood upright and walked. The first man had come to be.

"He is alone with the Grandmother Earth as I once was alone with the void," said Maheo. "It is not good for anyone to be alone." So Maheo fashioned a human woman from his left rib, and set her with the man. Then there were two persons on the Grandmother Earth, her children and Maheo's. They were happy together, and Maheo was happy as he watched them.

After a year, in the springtime, the first child was born. As the years passed, there were other children. They went their ways, and founded many tribes.

From time to time, after that, Maheo realized that his people walking on the earth had certain needs. At those times, Maheo, with the help of his Power, created animals to feed and care for the people. He gave them deer for clothing and food, porcupines to make their ornaments, the swift antelopes on the open plains, and the prairie dogs that burrowed in the earth.

At last Maheo thought to his Power, Why, one animal can take the place of all the others put together, and then he made the buffalo.

Maheo is still with us. He is everywhere, watching all his people, and all the creation he has made. Maheo is all good and all life; he is the creator, the guardian, and the teacher. We are all here because of Maheo.

The Open Boat

Stephen Crane

None of them knew the color of the sky. Their eyes were on the waves that swept before them. The waves were a dull gray, except for the tops, which were foaming white. The boat wasn't much bigger than a bathtub.

The cook sat at one end, bailing out water. On one side, the oiler handled one of the oars. The reporter, sitting next to him, pulled at the other oar. They both watched the waves and wondered why they were there. They had been rowing for hours.

At the other end was the injured captain. He could not forget seeing his ship sink lower and lower, and finally go down. His voice was deep and sad.

"Steer a little more south," the captain said.

"A little more south, sir," said the oiler.

One thing wrong with the sea is that when you get over one wave, another is right behind it. Each wave is just as eager to swamp your boat as the one before it.

The men were not aware of the dawn. They knew it was morning only because the sea had changed from gray to green.

"It's a good thing the wind is blowing toward shore," the cook said. "Otherwise, we wouldn't have a chance."

The reporter and the oiler agreed. The captain chuckled, but he didn't sound amused.

Gulls flew around them. Sometimes they sat on the sea. The anger of the sea meant nothing to them, and the men envied them.

One gull tried to land on the captain's head. The captain
wanted to knock it away, but a sudden movement would turn
the boat over. So he gently waved his arm over his head. When
the bird flew away, the four men breathed more easily.

All the while, the oiler and the reporter rowed—and rowed
and rowed. Sometimes they had one oar each. Sometimes the
oiler handled both oars. Sometimes the reporter did.

The hardest part was changing places. It's easier to steal
eggs from under a hen than it was to change seats in that boat.

After a while, the captain said he saw a lighthouse. Soon
the cook said he could see it, too. At the oars, the reporter
turned and looked, but he couldn't see it.

At the top of a wave, he turned and looked again. This time, he saw something very small on the horizon.

"Do you think we'll make it, Captain?" the cook asked.

"Yes," said the captain, "if the wind holds and the boat doesn't swamp with water."

The cook bailed faster.

"I wish we had a sail," the captain said. "We could try my coat on the end of an oar. That would give you boys a chance to rest."

So the cook and the reporter made a sail. The oiler steered with the other oar, and the boat made good speed.

Slowly, the lighthouse grew larger. At last, from the top of each wave, the men could see land.

Then the wind died down. So the reporter and the oiler started rowing again.

The reporter wondered how anyone could think of rowing as an amusement. It was not an amusement. It was a horror to the muscles and a crime against the back.

"Easy now, boys," said the captain. "When we reach the surf, we'll have to swim for it. Save your strength."

"They'll see us soon," the cook said. "They'll be out after us."

A quiet cheerfulness surrounded the men. They would probably be ashore in an hour.

After a while, the cook said, "It's funny they don't see us yet."

The cheerfulness faded. Land was within sight, but no one was there to help them.

The men now felt very angry. Each, in his own way, wondered, "If I am going to drown, why was I allowed to come this far? Why didn't it happen at the beginning, before all this suffering?"

When they got near the surf, the oiler said, "We won't last another three minutes. We're about to swamp with water, and we're too far out to swim to shore."

"Take us back out to sea," the captain said sadly.

The reporter and the oiler took turns rowing. Their backs ached so much that they no longer feared the ocean. By now, it looked a lot more comfortable than the boat. It seemed like a great, soft mattress.

"Look!" cried the cook. "There's a man on shore! He's waving at us!"

"Now we're all right," the oiler said. "There will be a boat for us in a half hour."

"Now there are some more people," the cook said. "One of them is waving his coat."

"Why don't they send a boat out after us?" the reporter asked.

"Maybe they think we're out fishing," the captain said. "Maybe they're just waving to be friendly."

The people stood on the shore waving. Soon, it began getting dark. The people on shore blended into the gloom. The oiler and the reporter kept taking turns rowing.

Late at night, it was the reporter's turn. The other three men were asleep. The reporter imagined that he was the only man afloat on all the oceans.

There was a swishing sound near the boat. Then the reporter saw a large fin cut through the water. He stared at it without feeling. He only wished one of the others was awake. He didn't want to be alone with the shark.

Long after the shark swam away, the oiler woke up. The reporter asked him, "Will you take over?"

The oiler took over. The reporter fell asleep as soon as he touched the bottom of the boat.

It seemed only a moment later when the oiler asked, "Will you take over?"

"Sure," the reporter said.

Later, the reporter got some more sleep. When he opened his eyes again, it was dawn. Land was once again in sight. They could see little cottages and a tall windmill on a beach. But no one, not even a dog, appeared on the beach.

"I guess no help is coming," the captain said. "We'd better try to go through the surf anyway. If we stay out much longer, we'll be too weak to swim at all."

The others agreed. The oiler, who was now rowing, turned the boat toward the beach.

The reporter looked at the tall windmill. It was a giant, standing with its back to their struggles, as if they were ants. It seemed neither cruel nor kind. It simply did not care about them.

The captain spoke again. "All we can do is row as far as possible. When she swamps, we'll swim for the beach. We won't get in very close before we turn over."

As they headed toward the shore, the waves tossed the boat higher and higher. The reporter knew he should be afraid. But his mind was ruled by his muscles, and his muscles did not care. His only thought was that if he should drown, it would be a shame.

"When you jump," the captain warned, "get clear of the boat."

The tumbling white water caught the boat and whirled it almost straight up and down. Water poured in from all sides. The reporter went overboard.

The January water was icy. To the reporter, this seemed to be an important fact. It was colder than he had expected to find it off the coast of Florida.

When he came to the surface, he saw the others. The oiler, swimming rapidly, was ahead in the race. The cook paddled nearby him. Behind the reporter, the captain hung on to the overturned boat with his good hand.

The reporter paddled slowly. Suddenly, he felt himself caught in a current. He looked at the shore as if it were a piece of stage scenery. Although he swam, he was not moving forward.

The captain, holding onto the boat, passed the reporter. The reporter stayed in the grip of this new enemy, the strange current.

"Am I going to drown?" he wondered. "Can it be possible?"

Then a wave whirled him out of the current. Now he could make progress toward the shore again.

The captain yelled to him, "Swim for the boat!"

The reporter struggled to reach the boat. He noticed a man running along the shore. The man threw off his coat, shoes, and pants—and ran into the water.

The reporter kept paddling toward the boat. Suddenly, a large wave caught him up and flung him over the boat and far past it.

To the reporter, this seemed to be a miracle. He came down in water that was only up to his waist. But he was too weak to stand. Each time he got up, he was knocked down by a wave.

Then he saw the man who had been running along the shore. The man dragged the cook ashore. Then he waded toward the captain. The captain waved him away and sent him to the reporter.

The man grabbed the reporter's hand and pulled. The reporter thought he saw a halo behind the man's head.

"Thanks, old man," the reporter said.

Then they saw the oiler. He was lying face down in the shallow water.

The reporter wasn't sure of all that happened afterward. When he reached safe ground, he fell. He could feel every part of his body hit the sand.

Now the beach was filled with people, blankets, clothes, and coffee. The land gave a warm and generous welcome to the men from the sea.

One dripping shape, though, was carried slowly up the beach. For the oiler, the only welcome from the land would be a grave.

That night, the white waves moved back and forth in the moonlight. The wind brought the sound of the sea's voice to the three men on shore. Now they felt they could be interpreters of that voice.

Pride of Lion

Margaret Tsuda

I know that the term is
"a pride of lions"
used collectively.
But this lioness is
singular
alone in a dark narrow
cage which causes an
ache behind the eyes
to think of the
wide sun-splendored
land where she
belongs.

The weak
city-pale sunshine
shafts down across
tall buildings to the
very edge of her cage.
To feel its warmth
she must lie against
the steel cage bars.

But it affronts her
lion pride to
be a spectacle for
pointing fingers and
child-shrill comments.
All she presents is a
shapeless sand-tawny
back.

I stand and
love her quietly
until
she turns her head and
topaz eyes meet mine.

Crystal Moment

Robert P. Tristram Coffin

Once or twice this side of death
Things can make one hold his breath.

From my boyhood I remember
A crystal moment of September.

A wooded island rang with sounds
Of church bells in the throats of hounds.

A buck leaped out and took the tide
With jewels flowing past each side.

With his high head like a tree
He swam within a yard of me.

I saw the golden drop of light
In his eyes turned dark with fright.

I saw the forest's holiness
On him like a fierce caress.

Fear made him lovely past belief,
My heart was trembling like a leaf.

He leaned towards the land and life
With need upon him like a knife.

In his wake the hot hounds churned,
They stretched their muzzles out and yearned.

They bayed no more, but swam and throbbed,
Hunger drove them till they sobbed.

Pursued, pursuers reached the shore
And vanished. I saw nothing more.

So they passed, a pageant such
As only gods could witness much,

Life and death upon one tether
And running beautiful together.

What we frankly give,
forever is our own.

I Remember Mama

John Van Druten

Act 1

SCENE: *The period of the play is around 1910. On either side of the stage, down front, are two small turntables, left and right, on which the shorter front scenes are played against very simplified backgrounds. As each scene finishes, the lights dim and the table revolves out, leaving an unobstructed view of the main stage. The main stage is raised by two steps, above which traveler curtains open and close.*

When the curtain rises, KATRIN, *in a spotlight, is seated at a desk on the right turntable, facing the audience. She is writing and smoking a cigarette.* KATRIN *is somewhere in her early twenties. She should be played by an actress who is small in stature, and capable of looking sufficiently a child not to break the illusion in subsequent scenes. She is a blonde. Her hair, when we see her first, is in a modern "up" style, capable of being easily loosened to fall to shoulder length for the childhood scenes. She wears a very short dress, the skirt of which is concealed for the prologue by the desk behind which she is seated.*

KATRIN *writes in silence for a few moments, then puts down her pen, takes up her manuscript, and begins to read aloud what she has written.*

KATRIN (*reading*). "For as long as I could remember, the house on Steiner Street had been home. Papa and Mama had both been born in Norway, but they came to San Francisco because Mama's sisters were here. All of us were born here. Nels, the oldest and the only boy—my sister Christine—and the littlest sister, Dagmar." (*She puts down her manuscript and looks out front.*) It's funny, but when I look back, I always see Nels and Christine and myself looking almost as we do today. I guess that's because the people you see all the time stay the same age in your head. Dagmar's different. She was always the baby—so I see her as a baby. Even Mama—it's funny, but I always see Mama as around forty. She couldn't always have been forty. (*She puts out her cigarette, picks up her manuscript, and starts to read again.*) "Besides us, there was our boarder, Mr. Hyde. Mr. Hyde was an Englishman who had once been an actor, and Mama

206

was very impressed by his flowery talk and courtly manners. He used to read aloud to us in the evenings. But first and foremost, I remember Mama."

(The light dims down, leaving KATRIN *only faintly visible. Lights come up on the main stage, revealing the house on Steiner Street—a kitchen room. It has a black flat, with a dresser* C., *holding china. On either side of the dresser is a door, the one to the* R. *leads to the pantry, the one to the* L. *to the rest of the house. The* L. *wall is a short one. It is the wall of the house, and contains a door upstage leading into the street, being presumably the back door of the house, but the one most commonly used as the entry-door. Beyond it the street is visible, with a single lamppost* L., *just outside the house. Behind the room rises the house itself with upper windows lighted, and behind it a painted backdrop of the San Francisco hills, houses, and telegraph posts. The furniture of the kitchen is simple. A table* C., *with two chairs above it, armchairs at either end, and a low bench below it. Against the* R. *wall upstage, a large stove, below it another armchair. The window is below the door in the* L. *wall and has a low Norwegian chest under it.* KATRIN'S VOICE *continuing in the half-dark, as the scene is revealed.)*

"I remember that every Saturday night Mama would sit down by the kitchen table and count out the money Papa had brought home in the little envelope."

(By now the tableau is revealed in full, and the light on KATRIN *dwindles further. The picture is as she described.* MAMA—*looking around forty—is in the armchair* R. *of the table, emptying the envelope of its silver dollars and smaller coins.* PAPA—*looking a little older than* MAMA—*stands above her. His English throughout is better than hers, with less accent.)*

MAMA. You call the children, Lars. Is good they should know about money.

(PAPA goes to door back L., and calls.)

PAPA. Children! Nels—Christine—Katrin!
CHILDREN'S VOICES *(off, answering).* Coming, Papa!
MAMA. You call loud for Katrin. She is in her study, maybe.
PAPA. She is where?
MAMA. Katrin make the old attic under the roof into a study.
PAPA *(amused).* So? *(Shouting.)* Katrin! Katrin!
KATRIN *(still at her desk, down front).* Yes, Papa. I heard.
PAPA *(returning to the room).* A study now, huh? What does Katrin study?
MAMA. I think Katrin wants to be author.

PAPA. Author?

MAMA. Stories she will write. For the magazines. And books, too, maybe, one day.

PAPA (*taking out his pipe*). Is good pay to be author?

MAMA. I don't know. For magazines, I think maybe yes. For books, I think no.

PAPA. Then she become writer for magazines.

MAMA. Maybe. But I like she writes books. Like the ones Mr. Hyde reads us. (DAGMAR *enters from the pantry. She is a plump child of about eight and carries an alley cat in her arms.*) Dagmar, you bring that cat in again?

DAGMAR. Sure, she's my Elizabeth—my beautiful Elizabeth! (*She crosses to the chest under the window, and sits, nursing the cat.*)

PAPA. Poor Elizabeth looks as if she had been in fight again.

DAGMAR. Not poor Elizabeth. *Brave* Elizabeth. Elizabeth's a
Viking cat. She fights for her honor!

PAPA (*exchanging an amused glance with* MAMA). And just what is a
cat's honor, little one?

DAGMAR. The honor of being the bravest cat in San Francisco.
(CHRISTINE *comes in back* L. *She, like* KATRIN, *should be played
by a small young actress, but not a child. Her hair is to her
shoulders—her dress short—her age indeterminate. Actually, she
is about 13 at this time. She is the cool, aloof, matter-of-fact one of
the family. She carries a box of crayons, scissors, and a picture
book.*) Aren't you, Elizabeth?

CHRISTINE (*sitting above the table and starting to color the picture book
with the crayons*). That disgusting cat!

DAGMAR. She's not disgusting. She's beautiful. Beautiful as the
dawn!

CHRISTINE. And when have *you* ever seen the dawn?

DAGMAR. I haven't seen it, but Mr. Hyde read to us about it.
(MR. HYDE *comes in from door back* L. *He is a slightly seedy,
long-haired man in his fifties. Rather of the old-fashioned English
"laddie" actor type. He wears a very shabby long overcoat, with a
deplorable fur collar, and carries his hat. His accent is English.*)
Didn't you, Mr. Hyde? Didn't you read to us about the
dawn?

MR. HYDE. I did, my child of joy. The dawn, the rosy-finger-
tipped Aurora . . .

DAGMAR. When can I get to *see* the dawn, Mama?

MAMA. Any morning you get up early.

DAGMAR. Is there a dawn every morning?

MAMA. Sure.

DAGMAR (*incredulous*). It's all that beautiful, and it happens every
morning? Why didn't anyone *tell* me?

MR. HYDE. My child, that is what the poets are for. To tell you
of *all* the beautiful things that are happening every day, and
that no one sees until they tell them. (*He starts for the door* L.)

MAMA. You go out, Mr. Hyde?

MR. HYDE. For a few moments only, dear Madam. To buy myself
a modicum of that tawny weed, tobacco, that I lust after, as
Ben Jonson says. I shall be back in time for our nightly
reading. (*He goes out and disappears down the street, into the
wings, off* L.)

MAMA (*who has gone to the door back* L., *calls with a good deal of
sharpness and firmness*). Nels! Katrin! You do not hear Papa
call you?

NELS (*from off, upstairs*). Coming, Mama!

KATRIN (*at her desk*). Yes, Mama. I'm coming. (*She rises. In her few moments in the dark, she has loosened her hair to her shoulders, and we see that her skirt is short as she walks from her desk, and up the steps into the set. As soon as she has left it, the turntable revolves out. Immediately after her, NELS comes in back L. He is a tall, strapping young fellow—old enough to look 18 or 19, or 15 or 16, according to his dress, or demeanor. Now, he is about 15. KATRIN, to CHRISTINE.*) Move over. (*She shares CHRISTINE's chair at the table with her.*)

PAPA. So now all are here.

MAMA. Come, then. (*CHRISTINE, NELS, and KATRIN gather around the table. DAGMAR remains crooning to ELIZABETH, but rises and stands behind PAPA. Sorting coins.*) First, for the landlord. (*She makes a pile of silver dollars. It gets pushed down the table from one member of the family to the next, each speaking as he passes it. PAPA comes last.*)

NELS (*passing it on*). For the landlord.

KATRIN (*doing likewise*). For the landlord.

CHRISTINE (*passing it to PAPA*). The landlord.

PAPA. For the landlord. (*He dumps the pile at his end of the table, writing on a piece of paper, which he wraps around the pile.*)

MAMA (*who has been sorting*). For the grocer.

(*The business is repeated. During this repeat, DAGMAR's crooning to the cat becomes audible, contrapuntally to the repetitions of "For the grocer."*)

DAGMAR (*in a crescendo*). In all the United States no cat was as brave as Elizabeth. (*Fortissimo.*) In all the *world* no cat was as brave as Elizabeth!

MAMA (*gently*). Hush, Dagmar. Quietly. You put Elizabeth back into the pantry.

DAGMAR (*in a loud stage whisper, as she crosses to pantry*). In Heaven or Hell no cat was as brave as Elizabeth! (*She goes out with the cat.*)

MAMA. For Katrin's shoes to be half-soled. (*She passes a half dollar.*)

NELS. Katrin's shoes.

KATRIN (*proudly*). My shoes!

CHRISTINE (*contemptuously*). Katrin's old shoes.

PAPA. Katrin's shoes.

CHRISTINE (*rising and coming R. of MAMA*). Mama, Teacher says this week I'll need a new notebook.

MAMA. How much it will be?

CHRISTINE. A dime.

MAMA (*giving her a dime*). For the notebook. You don't lose it.

CHRISTINE. I won't lose it. (*She wraps it in her handkerchief.*)

MAMA. You take care when you blow your nose.

CHRISTINE. I'll take care. (*She returns to her seat.*)

PAPA. Is all, Mama?

MAMA. Is all for this week. Is good. We do not have to go to the Bank. (*She starts to gather up the few remaining coins.* KATRIN *leaves the group, comes and sits on steps, front.*)

NELS (*rising*). Mama. . . . (*She looks up, catching an urgency in his tone.* PAPA *suspends smoking for a moment.*) Mama, I'll be graduating from grammar school next month. Could I . . . could I go on to High, do you think?

MAMA (*pleased*). You want to go to High School?

NELS. I'd like to . . . if you think I could.

MAMA. Is good.

(PAPA *nods approvingly.*)

NELS (*awkwardly*). It . . . it'll cost a little money. I've got it all written down. (*Producing a piece of paper from his pocket.*) Carfare, clothes, notebooks, things I'll really need. I figured it out with Cy Nichols. He went to High last year.

(PAPA *rises and comes behind* MAMA *to look at the paper* NELS *puts before them.*)

MAMA. Get the *Little* Bank, Christine.

(CHRISTINE *gets a small box from the dresser.*)

KATRIN (*from the steps—herself again, in the present—looking out front*). The Little Bank! That was the most important thing in the whole house. It was a box we used to keep for emergencies—like the time when Dagmar had croup and Papa had to go and get medicine to put in the steam kettle. I can *smell* that medicine now! The things that came out of the Little Bank! Mama was always going to buy herself a warm coat out of it, when there was enough; only there never was.

(*Meanwhile,* MAMA *has been counting the contents.*)

NELS (*anxiously*). Is there enough, Mama?

MAMA (*shaking her head*). Is not much in the Little Bank right now. We give to the dentist, you remember? And for your roller skates?

NELS (*his face falling*). I know. And there's your warm coat you've been saving for.

MAMA. The coat I can get another time. But even so . . . (*She shakes her head.*)

CHRISTINE. You mean Nels can't go to High?

MAMA. Is not enough here. We do not want to have to go to the Bank, do we?

NELS. No, Mama, no. I'll work in Dillon's grocery after school.

(MAMA *writes a figure on the paper and starts to count on her fingers.* PAPA *looks over, and does the sum in his head.*)

PAPA. Is not enough.

MAMA (*finishing on her fingers against her collarbone*). No, is not enough.

PAPA (*taking his pipe out of his mouth and looking at it a long time*). I give up tobacco.

(MAMA *looks at him, almost speaks, then just touches his sleeve, writes another figure, and starts on her fingers again.*)

CHRISTINE. I'll mind the Maxwell children Friday nights. Katrin can help me.

(MAMA *writes another figure.* PAPA *looks over—calculates again, nods with satisfaction.*)

MAMA (*triumphantly*). Is good! Is enough!

NELS. Gee! (*He moves beside* PAPA *down* R. *and starts to play with a wire puzzle.*)

MAMA. We do not have to go to the Bank.

(DAGMAR *returns, without the cat.*)

DAGMAR (*hearing the last line*). Where is the Bank?

CHRISTINE (*leaving the table, moving down* L., *cutting out the picture which she colored*). Downtown.

DAGMAR. What's it look like?

CHRISTINE. Just a building.

DAGMAR (*sitting on the bench, below the table*). Like a prison?

CHRISTINE (*sharply*). No, nothing like a prison.

DAGMAR. Well, then, why does Mama always say "We don't want to go to the Bank"?

CHRISTINE. Because . . . well, because no one ever wants to go to the Bank.

DAGMAR. Why not?

CHRISTINE. Because if we went to the Bank all the time, there'd be no money left there. And then if we couldn't pay our rent, they'd turn us out like Mrs. Jensen down the street.

DAGMAR. You mean, it's like saving some of your candy for tomorrow?

MAMA (*busy with coffee and cups at the stove and the dresser*). Yes, my Dagmar. Is exactly like saving your candy.

DAGMAR. But if . . . if all the other people go to the Bank, then there won't be any money left for us, either.

NELS (*kindly*). It isn't like that, Dagmar. Everyone can only get so much.

DAGMAR. How much?

NELS. However much you've got there . . . put away. You see, it's *our* money that we put there, to keep safe.

DAGMAR. When did we put it there?

NELS. I . . . I don't know when. A long time back, I guess. Wasn't it, Mama?

MAMA. Is enough about the Bank.

DAGMAR. How much money have we got in the Bank?

NELS. I don't know. How much, Mama?

MAMA. Enough. (*During the last speeches* AUNT TRINA *appears from the wings down front* L. *She is a timid, mouselike little woman of about 40, with some prettiness about her. She wears her hat and coat, and a pathetic feather boa. She comes up the street and knocks on the house door.* MAMA, *hearing the knock.*) Was the door?

CHRISTINE (*quickly moving*). If it's the aunts, I'm going to my boodwar.

KATRIN (*rising, entering the scene*). And I'm going to my study.

MAMA (*stopping them*). You cannot run away. We must be polite to the aunts. (*She opens the door.*) Why, is Trina!

PAPA. Trina, and all by herself!

MAMA. Say good evening to Aunt Trina, children.

CHILDREN (*together*). Good evening, Aunt Trina.

TRINA. Good evening, children. How well they all look. (*She comes above the table* L.)

MAMA. You have a feather boa. Is new. (*Inspecting it.*) Beautiful.

TRINA (*simpering a little*). It was a present.

MAMA (*smiling*). A present! Look, Lars. Trina has a present.

PAPA (*feeling it*). Is fine. (*He puts* TRINA'S *hat, coat, and boa on the chest under the window.*)

MAMA. Jenny and Sigrid don't come with you, Trina?

TRINA (*embarrassed*). No, I . . . I didn't tell them I was coming. I want to talk to you, Marta.

MAMA (*smiling*). So? Sit then, and we talk. (*She puts her in* PAPA'S *chair,* L. *of the table.*)

TRINA (*nervously agitated*). Could we talk alone?

MAMA. Alone?

TRINA. If you wouldn't mind.

MAMA. Children, you leave us alone a little. I call you. Dagmar, you go with Katrin.

KATRIN (*protesting*). Oh, but, Mama . . .

MAMA (*firmly*). Katrin, you take Dagmar!

KATRIN. Yes, Mama. (*Pushing* DAGMAR, *resentfully.*) Come on.

(*The* CHILDREN *go out back* L.)

MAMA. Now—what is it, Trina?

TRINA (*looking down, embarrassed*). Marta . . .

MAMA (*helpfully*). Yes?

TRINA. Oh, no, I can't say it.

MAMA (*anxiously*). Trina, what is it?

TRINA. It's . . . something very personal.

MAMA. You want Lars should go outside?

TRINA. Would you mind, Lars? Just for a minute?

PAPA (*good-humoredly*). No, I go. I know what women's secrets are. (*Teasing.*) As your Uncle Chris say—"Vomen! Pff!"

MAMA. You have your pipe, Lars? Is fine night. (PAPA *takes out his pipe—then lays it down.*) What is it?

PAPA. I forget. I give up tobacco.

MAMA. Is still some tobacco in your pouch? (PAPA *nods.*) Then you do not give up tobacco till you have finish. You give up *more* tobacco—not the tobacco you already have.

PAPA. Is not right, Marta. (*He pats her, takes his pipe, and goes out* L., *standing outside the house, under the lamppost, and looking up at the stars, smoking.*)

MAMA (R. *of table*). So, Trina. Now. What is it?

TRINA (L. *of table*). Marta . . . I want to get married.

MAMA. You mean . . . you want to get married, or there is someone you want to marry?

TRINA. There's someone I want to marry.

MAMA. Does *he* want to marry *you*?

TRINA (*sitting on bench*). He says he does.

MAMA (*delighted*). Trina! Is wonderful! (*She sits beside her.*)

TRINA (*crying a little*). I think it is.

MAMA. Who is?

TRINA. Mr. Thorkelson.

MAMA. From the Funeral Parlor? (TRINA *nods.* MAMA *nods, speculatively, but with less enthusiasm.*)

TRINA. I know he isn't very handsome or . . . or tall. I know it isn't what most people would think a very nice profession, but . . .

MAMA. You love him, Trina. (TRINA *nods ecstatically.*) Then is good. (*She pats* TRINA'S *hand.*)

TRINA. Marta, will you . . . will you help me tell the others?

MAMA. Oh . . . Jenny and Sigrid . . . they do not know?

TRINA. No. I was afraid they'd laugh at me. But if *you* tell them . . .

MAMA. Jenny will not like you tell me first.

TRINA (*desperately*). I can't help that. You've got to tell them not to laugh at me. If they laugh at me, I'll . . . I'll kill myself.

MAMA (*with decision*). Jenny and Sigrid will not laugh. I promise you, Trina.

TRINA. Oh, thank you, Marta, and . . . Uncle Chris?

MAMA (*with some seriousness*). Ah!

TRINA. Will you talk to him?

MAMA. It is Mr. Thorkelson who must talk to Uncle Chris. Always it is the husband who must talk to the head of the family.

TRINA. Yes. I know, but . . . well, Uncle Chris is so very frightening. He's so big and black, and he shouts so. And Mr. Thorkelson is (*gesturing a very small man*) . . . well, kind of timid, really.

MAMA (*gently*). But Trina, if he is to be your husband, he must learn not to be timid. You do not want husband should be timid. *You* are timid. It is not good when *both* are timid. (*Then firmly.*) No! Jenny and Sigrid I speak to, but Mr. Thorkelson must go to Uncle Chris.

PAPA (*re-enters the house*). Marta, Trina, I do not want to interrupt your talk, but Jenny and Sigrid are coming.

TRINA (*alarmed*). Oh, dear! (*She rises, quickly.*)

PAPA. I see them get off the cable car. They came up the hill.

TRINA (*in a flurry*). I'd better go to your room for a minute. (*She starts for the door, turns back, gets her things from the chest, and runs out, carrying them, back* L. *Meanwhile,* MAMA *has been whispering the news to* PAPA.)

MAMA. The coffee is ready—I get more cups.

(During the above, AUNTS JENNY *and* SIGRID *have entered from the wings* L., *front.* JENNY *is a domineering woman in her fifties,* SIGRID, *whining and complaining.)*

SIGRID *(in the street).* Wait, Jenny, I must get my breath. This hill
    kills me every time I climb it.
JENNY. You climbed bigger hills than that in the old country.
SIGRID. I was a *girl* in the old country.

*(They march to the door and knock—*SIGRID *following* JENNY.*)*

MAMA *(opening the door to them).* Jenny. Sigrid. Is surprise. *(To*
    SIGRID.*)* Where's Ole?
SIGRID. Working. He's always working. I never see anything of
    him at all.
MAMA *(crossing to the stove for coffeepot).* Is good to work.
SIGRID. It's good to see your husband once in a while, too. *(Sits*
    above table L.*)*
JENNY *(no nonsense about her).* Has Trina been here? *(L. of table.)*
MAMA *(R. of table).* Trina?
JENNY. She's gone somewhere. And she doesn't know anyone
    but *you.* . . .
MAMA. That is what *you* think.
JENNY. What do you mean by that?
MAMA. Give Lars your coat. I give you some coffee. Then we
    talk about Trina.
SIGRID *(as* PAPA *helps with coats).* She *has* been here?
MAMA. Yes, she has been here. *(Pouring coffee and passing cups.)*
JENNY. What did Trina want?
MAMA. She want to talk to me.
JENNY. What about?
MAMA. Marriage.
SIGRID. What?
MAMA *(pouring calmly).* Marriage. *(Passing* SIGRID'S *cup.)* Trina
    wants to get married.
JENNY *(seated* L. *of table).* That's no news. Of course she wants to
    get married. Every old maid wants to get married. *(She rolls*
    up her veil.)
MAMA. There is someone who wants to marry Trina.
JENNY. Who'd want to marry Trina?
MAMA. Mr. Thorkelson.
SIGRID. Peter Thorkelson? Little Peter? *(She gestures a midget.)*

MAMA. He is not so little.

SIGRID. He's hardly bigger than my Arne—and Arne is not ten yet.

MAMA. So he is hardly bigger than your Arne. Does every husband have to be big man?

JENNY. Trina's making it up. That happens with old maids when they get to Trina's age.

MAMA (*firmly*). No, Jenny—it is true. Mr. Thorkelson wants to marry Trina.

JENNY (*changing her tactics slightly*). Mr. Thorkelson. She'd be the laughing stock. (*She laughs, rising and moving* L.)

MAMA (*moving to her*). Jenny, Trina is here. She will come in in a minute. This is serious for her. You will not laugh at her.

JENNY. I shall do what I please.

MAMA. No, Jenny, you will not.

JENNY. And why won't I?

MAMA. Because I will not let you.

JENNY. And how will you stop me?

MAMA. If you laugh at Trina, I will tell her of the time before your wedding when your husband try to run away.

SIGRID (*rising, intrigued*). What is that?

JENNY. Who told you that?

MAMA. I know.

SIGRID (*intrigued—stealing around and below the table*). Erik . . . tried to run away?

JENNY. It's not true.

MAMA. Then you do not mind if I tell Trina.

JENNY. Uncle Chris told you.

SIGRID (*tenaciously*). Tried to run away?

MAMA. It does not matter, Sigrid. Jenny will not laugh at Trina now. Nor will you! For if *you* laugh at her, I will tell her of your wedding night with Ole, when you cry all the time, and he send you back to Mother.

PAPA (*with sudden enjoyment*). This I do *not* know!

MAMA (*reprovingly*). Is no need you should know. I do not tell these stories for spite—only so they do not laugh at Trina. Call her, Lars. You like more coffee, Jenny? Sigrid?

(PAPA *goes to the door back* L., *calls "Trina."* MAMA *pours coffee for* JENNY. MR. HYDE *reappears down front* L., *and lets himself into the house. The* AUNTS *rise, standing in line with* MAMA.)

MR. HYDE (*seeing company*). Oh, I beg your pardon. I was not aware . . .

MAMA. Mr. Hyde, these are my sisters.

MR. HYDE. Enchanted, ladies, Madame, Madame. The Three Graces. (*He bows.* SIGRID *giggles coyly. He goes to the door back* L.) You will excuse me?

MAMA. Sure, Mr. Hyde.

MR. HYDE. I shall be in my room. (*He goes out.*)

JENNY (*moving* L. *of table again*). So *that's* your famous boarder. Has he paid you his rent yet? Three months he's been here, hasn't he?

MAMA (R. *of table*). Is hard to ask. Surely he will pay soon.

JENNY (*with a snort*). Surely he won't! If I ran my boarding house the way you run this place . . .

PAPA. Maybe your boarders wouldn't always leave you.

JENNY. If Marta thinks she's going to get the warm coat she's always talking about out of *that* one . . .

MAMA. Jenny, Mr. Hyde is a gentleman. He reads to us aloud. Wonderful books . . . Longfellow, and Charles Dickens, and Fenimore Kipling. (TRINA *steals back.* MAMA, *seeing her hesitant in the doorway.*) Come in, Trina. The coffee is getting cold. (*She pours a cup. There is a silence.*) I tell them.

JENNY. Why did you come to Marta first?

PAPA (*beside her* L.). She thought Marta would understand.

JENNY. Aren't Sigrid and I married women, too?

PAPA. You have been married longer than Marta. She think maybe you forget.

JENNY. What sort of a living does Mr. Thorkelson make?

TRINA (*on bench below table*). I . . . I haven't asked.

SIGRID (R. *of table*). Can he keep you?

TRINA. I don't think he would have asked me to marry him if he couldn't.

JENNY. Maybe he thinks you are going to keep *him.*

MAMA (*warningly*). Jenny!

SIGRID. Maybe he thinks Trina will have a dowry like the girls at home.

TRINA. Well, why shouldn't I? You all had dowries . . .

JENNY. We were married in Norway. And our parents were alive. Where would your dowry come from, I'd like to know?

TRINA. Uncle Chris. He's head of the family.

JENNY. And who will ask him?

TRINA. He won't need asking. When Mr. Thorkelson goes to see him . . .

JENNY. Uncle Chris will eat him!

SIGRID (*giggling maliciously*). Little Peter and Uncle Chris!
MAMA (*with meaning*). Maybe Uncle Chris will tell him some family stories. He knows many, does Uncle Chris.

(*The* AUNTS *put down their cups, discomfited.*)

JENNY (*to change the subject*). Where are the children? Aren't we going to see them before we go?
PAPA. Of course. I'll call them. (*He goes to the door and does so, shouting.*) Children! Your aunts are *leaving!*
CHILDREN'S VOICES (*eagerly shouting back*). Coming, Papa!
JENNY. You come with us, Trina?
MAMA. I think maybe Trina like to stay here and listen to Mr. Hyde read to us. You like, Trina?
TRINA. Well, if I wouldn't be in the way. I asked Mr. Thorkelson to call for me here. He'll see me home. I'll help you with the coffee things. (*She takes the tray of coffee cups and goes into the pantry.*)

(KATRIN *returns back* L. *She carries her diary.* DAGMAR *follows her, and behind them,* CHRISTINE.)

KATRIN *and* DAGMAR (*curtseying*). Good evening, Aunt Sigrid. Good evening, Aunt Jenny.

(CHRISTINE *sketches a perfunctory curtsey without speaking.*)

JENNY. Where have *you* all been hiding yourselves?
DAGMAR (*going into the pantry*). We've been in Christine's boodwar.
JENNY. Her *what?*
MAMA. Christine makes the little closet into a boudoir. I give her those bead portieres, Jenny, that you lend us when we come from the old country.
SIGRID. And what does she do there?
CHRISTINE (*impertinently*). What people usually do in boudoirs.
MAMA. Christine, that is rude. It is her little place to herself.

(NELS *enters, back* L.)

NELS. Hello, Aunt Sigrid. Hello, Aunt Jenny.
SIGRID (*shaking hands*). Good evening, Nels! My, how tall he is getting!

MAMA (*proudly*). Yes, is almost as tall as his Papa.

(NELS *sits on the chest under the windows.*)

SIGRID. He looks to me as if he was outgrowing his strength. Dagmar was looking pale, too. (DAGMAR *returns now, carrying the cat again.* SIGRID, *jumping.*) Goodness, what a horrid-looking cat.

DAGMAR. She's not. She's beautiful.

PAPA. Is her new friend. She goes with Dagmar everywhere.

CHRISTINE (*seated, above table*). She does. First thing you know, she'll have the cat sleeping with her.

DAGMAR (*eagerly*). Oh, Mama, can I? Can I, Mama? (*She comes to the bench and sits.*)

JENNY. Certainly not. Don't you know a cat draws breath from a sleeping child? You wouldn't want to wake up some morning *smothered,* would you?

DAGMAR. I wouldn't care. Elizabeth can have *all* my breath! (*She blows into the cat's face.*) There!

JENNY (*putting on gloves*). Elizabeth—what a very silly name for a cat.

NELS (*rising*). It's a very silly name for *that* cat. It's a Tom.

MAMA. Nels, how you know?

NELS. I looked!

DAGMAR. How can you tell?

NELS. You can.

DAGMAR. But how?

MAMA (*quickly warning*). Nels, you do not say how!

NELS (*to* DAGMAR). So you'd better think up another name for him.

DAGMAR. I won't. He's Elizabeth. And he's going to *stay* Elizabeth.

PAPA. We could call him *Uncle* Elizabeth!

DAGMAR (*laughing delightedly*). Uncle Elizabeth! Do you hear, Elizabeth? You're called *Uncle* Elizabeth now!

JENNY. Such foolishness! Well, goodbye, all. Marta. Lars.

(*Goodbyes are exchanged all around, the* CHILDREN *curtseying formally.*)

MAMA. Goodbye, Jenny. Goodbye, Sigrid. Nels, you go tell Mr. Hyde we are ready for the reading.

(NELS *goes off, back* L. *The* AUNTS *leave and walk down* L. MAMA *stands in the doorway, waving goodbye.*)

SIGRID (*as they go*). Well, I never thought we'd live to see Trina get married.

JENNY. She's not married yet. She's got Uncle Chris to deal with first.

(*They disappear into wings* L.)

MAMA (*returning to the room and calling into the pantry*). Trina, they have gone. Dagmar, you put Elizabeth out for the night now.

DAGMAR (*correcting her*). Uncle Elizabeth!

MAMA. Uncle Elizabeth. (DAGMAR *goes out into the pantry with the cat.* TRINA *comes in as* MR. HYDE *and* NELS *return back* L.) Mr. Hyde, this is my sister Trina.

MR. HYDE (*bowing*). Enchanted!

MAMA (*seating herself* R. *of the table*). Mr. Hyde reads to us *The Tales from Two Cities.* Is beautiful story. But sad.

TRINA (*brightly*). I like sad stories. (*She gets out her handkerchief.*)

(*The whole family group themselves around the table,* MAMA R. *of table in her old chair*—PAPA *above her.* TRINA R. *above table,* NELS L. *above the table.* DAGMAR *returning and seating herself on the floor below* MAMA. MR. HYDE *takes the armchair* L. *of table.* CHRISTINE *sits on the floor below the table.* KATRIN *is on the steps* R. *front.*)

MR. HYDE. Tonight, I would like to finish it.

MAMA. Is good.

MR. HYDE. Are you ready?

CHILDREN. Yes, please, Mr. Hyde.

MR. HYDE. I will go on from where we left off. (*He starts to read.*) "In the black prison of the Conciergerie, the doomed of the day awaited their fate. They were in number as the weeks of the year. Fifty-two were to roll that afternoon on the life-tide of the City to the boundless, everlasting sea. . . ."

(*The lights dim down slowly, leaving spots on* KATRIN *and* MR. HYDE *only.*)

KATRIN. I don't think I shall ever forget that night. It was almost midnight when he came to the end, and none of us had noticed.

MR. HYDE (*reading from the last page*). "It is a far, far better thing that I do than I have ever done; it is a far, far better rest that I go to than I have ever known." (*He closes the book.*) "The End."

(*The* R. *turntable revolves in again.* KATRIN *rises from the step and crosses to her desk on the turntable.*)

KATRIN. I wrote in my diary that night before I went to bed. (*She reads aloud from it.*) "Tonight Mr. Hyde finished *The Tale of Two Cities*. The closing chapters are indeed superb. How beautiful a thing is self-sacrifice. I wish there were someone I could die for." (*She sits looking out front.*) Mr. Hyde read us all kinds of books. He thrilled us with *Treasure Island*, and terrified us with "The Hound of the Baskervilles." I can still remember the horror in his voice as he read. . . .

MR. HYDE (*still on the main stage in his spot, reading*). "Dr. Mortimer looked strangely at us for an instant, and his voice sank almost to a whisper as he answered, 'Mr. Holmes, they were the footprints of a gigantic *hound!*' " (*He closes the book.*) We will continue tomorrow night. If you are interested.

KATRIN (*looking out front*). If we were interested! You couldn't have kept us from it. It meant a lot to Mama, too, because Nels stopped going nights to the street corner to hang about with the neighborhood boys. The night they got into trouble for breaking into Mr. Dillon's store, Nels was home with us. And sometimes Mr. Hyde read us poetry. "The Lady of the Lake" . . . and the "Rime of the Ancient Mariner."

MR. HYDE (*reading*).
> "About, about, in reel and rout
> The death-fires danced at night.
> The water, like a witch's oils,
> Burnt green and blue and white."

(*His spot goes out, and the traveler curtains close on the kitchen scene.*)

KATRIN. There were many nights I couldn't sleep for the way he had set my imagination dancing. (*Reading from her diary again.*) "What a wonderful thing is literature, transporting us to realms unknown." (*To herself.*) And all the time my school teacher kept telling me that I ought to write about things I knew. I did write a piece for her once about Uncle Chris, and she said it wasn't nice to write like that about a member of one's own family. Papa called Mama's Uncle Chris a black Norwegian, because of his dark hair and fierce mustache, but there were others in the family who claimed that he was black in a different way. The aunts, for example.

(Spot goes up on L. *front turntable, representing* JENNY'S *kitchen.* JENNY *and* TRINA *are discovered.* JENNY *is rolling pastry.* TRINA *is crocheting.)*

JENNY. Black! I'll say he's black. Black in his heart. Cursing and swearing. . . .

TRINA. Marta says that's only because it hurts him to walk.

JENNY. Rubbish. I know all about his limp and the accident back in the old country—but has anyone ever heard him complain? Marta's always making excuses for him.

TRINA. I know . . . but he *is* good to the children. All those oranges he's always sending them. . . .

JENNY. Oranges! What good is oranges? Turn 'em yellow. They're the only things he's ever been known to give away, anyway. He's got other uses for his money.

TRINA. What you mean?

JENNY. That woman he lives with!

TRINA. He says she's his housekeeper.

(SIGRID comes through the curtains C. *She crosses to* JENNY *and* TRINA.*)*

SIGRID. Jenny. Trina. What do you think? What do you think Uncle Chris has done now?

TRINA. What?

JENNY. Tell us.

SIGRID. You know my little Arne's knee—that fall he had two months ago? The man at the drugstore said it was only a bruise, but today it was hurting him again, so I left him home when I went to do the marketing. I asked Mrs. Schultz next door to keep an eye on him, and who should turn up, not ten minutes after I'd gone, but Uncle Chris. And what do you think?

JENNY. Well, tell us, if you're going to. Don't keep *asking* us.

SIGRID. He took one look at Arne's knee, bundled him into that rattletrap old automobile of his, and rushed him straight off to the hospital. I've just come from there . . . and what do you think? They've operated! They've got him in Plaster of Paris!

223

JENNY. Without consulting you?

SIGRID. It seems the doctor is a friend of his . . . that's why he did it. No, this time he's gone too far. To put a child of Arne's age through all that pain. They wouldn't even let me *see* Arne. I'm going to tell Uncle Chris exactly what I think of him . . .

JENNY. That's right.

SIGRID. I'm going to tell him right now. *(Weakening a little.)* Come with me, Jenny.

JENNY. Well, I . . . No, I can't leave my baking.

SIGRID. You must, Jenny. We must stand together. You come, too, Trina, and ask about your dowry. *Make* him give it to you.

TRINA. Oh, but . . . Marta said Mr. Thorkelson should do that . . .

JENNY. Well, then, go and get Mr. Thorkelson. Go down to the mortuary and get him now. Sigrid is right. We girls have got to stand together!

(Blackout. Turntable revolves out.)

KATRIN *(at her desk)*. Nobody knew where Uncle Chris lived. That was part of the mystery about him. He used to roam up and down the state buying up farms and ranches that had gone to pieces, and bullying them back into prosperity. Then he'd sell at a profit and move on again. Two or three times a year he'd descend on the city in his automobile and come roaring and stamping into our house.

(Her light dims. The sound of a very old and noisy Ford car changing gears is heard off L. A grinding and screaming as it comes to a standstill. Then UNCLE CHRIS'S VOICE, shouting.)

UNCLE CHRIS'S VOICE. Marta! Lars! Children—vere are you?

(The curtains part on the kitchen again. Outside in the street is UNCLE CHRIS'S car—an antique model. A woman is seated beside the empty driver's seat. UNCLE CHRIS is knocking on the house door. He is an elderly, powerful, swarthy man with a limp. In the kitchen, NELS and CHRISTINE are cowering.)

UNCLE CHRIS. Marta! Lars!

CHRISTINE *(scared)*. It's Uncle Chris.

NELS *(equally so)*. I know.

CHRISTINE. What'll we do?

UNCLE CHRIS. Is nobody home? Hey, there—is nobody home? (Banging on the door.) Hey—someone—answer the door. (He tries the door handle, it opens and he strides, limpingly in. He has a strong accent, and uses the Norwegian pronunciation of the children's names.) So, vat is—you do not answer the door? You do not hear me calling? (The CHILDREN cower silently.) I say, you do not hear me calling? I do not call loud enough?

CHRISTINE. Y-yes, Uncle Chris.

UNCLE CHRIS. Which yes? Yes, you do not hear me—or yes I do not call loud enough?

NELS. We heard you, Uncle Chris.

UNCLE CHRIS. Then why you do not come?

NELS. We . . . we were just going to.

(KATRIN has left her desk and come up the steps.)

UNCLE CHRIS. Let me look at you. You too, Katrinë, do not stand there—come and let me look at you. (They line up as though for inspection. He thumps NELS between the shoulderblades.) Stand tall! (They all straighten up.) Um-hum. By the dresser, where the marks are. (NELS goes to the wall by the dresser back R. UNCLE CHRIS compares his mark with the previous one—and makes a new one on the wall, writing by it.) Two inches. Two inches in . . . (Examining the date.) Six months. Is good. Christinë. (CHRISTINE replaces NELS.) Show me your teeth. (She does so.) You brush them goot? (She nods.) Nils, there is a box of oranges in the automobile. You fetch them in. (NELS goes out L. UNCLE CHRIS measures CHRISTINE.) Where is the little von? Dagmar?

KATRIN. She's sick, Uncle Chris.

UNCLE CHRIS (arrested). Sick? What is the matter with her?

KATRIN. It's her ear. She's had an earache for two days. Bad earache. Mama sent for the doctor.

UNCLE CHRIS. Goot doctor? What he say?

KATRIN. He's in there now. (She points off, back L. Meanwhile CHRISTINE has remained standing by the wall, afraid to move.)

UNCLE CHRIS. I go in. (He starts to the door back L., but MAMA and DR. JOHNSON come into the room as he does so. During this, NELS has gone to the car, and with nervous smiles at the woman seated by the driver's seat, has heaved out a huge box of oranges. He returns with the oranges during the ensuing scene.)

MAMA (greeting him). Uncle Chris.

UNCLE CHRIS. How is with Dagmar?

MAMA. Is bad. Doctor, this is my uncle, Mr. Halvorsen.

DOCTOR. How do you do, sir? *(He goes for his hat and bag which are on the bench below the window.)*

UNCLE CHRIS. What is with the child?

DOCTOR. We must get her to a hospital. At once. We'll have to operate.

MAMA. Operate?

DOCTOR. I'm afraid so.

MAMA. Can wait? Until my husband comes home from work?

DOCTOR. I'm afraid not. Her best chance is for us to operate immediately.

MAMA *(after a second)*. We go. *(She goes to the dresser for the Little Bank.)*

UNCLE CHRIS *(who has watched her decision with approval, turns to the doctor, moving to him down L)*. What is with the child?

DOCTOR. I'm afraid it's a mastoid.

UNCLE CHRIS. Ah . . . then you operate immediately.

DOCTOR *(resenting this)*. That's what I said.

UNCLE CHRIS. Immediately!

MAMA *(who has poured the contents of the Little Bank onto the table)*. Doctor . . . is enough?

DOCTOR *(L. of table)*. I was thinking of the County Hospital.

MAMA. No. No. We pay. Is enough?

KATRIN. If there isn't, we can go to the Bank.

CHRISTINE. We've got a bank account.

MAMA. Is enough without we go to the Bank, Doctor? My husband is carpenter. Make good money.

UNCLE CHRIS. If there is need of money, *I* pay.

DOCTOR *(mainly in dislike of UNCLE CHRIS)*. It'll be all right. We'll take her to the Clinic. You pay what you can afford.

UNCLE CHRIS. Goot. Goot. I have a patient there already. My nephew, Arne. They operate this morning on his knee.

DOCTOR. Are you a physician, sir?

UNCLE CHRIS. I am better physician than most doctors. Nils, there, my other nephew, he become doctor when he grow up.

(NELS, who has just returned, looks up, surprised.)

DOCTOR *(chilly)*. Oh, indeed . . . very interesting. Well, now, if you will have the child at the Clinic in . . . shall we say an hour's time . . .

UNCLE CHRIS *(striding across below table)*. The child will be at the Clinic in *ten minutes'* time. I haf my automobile.

DOCTOR. I can hardly make arrangements in ten minutes.

UNCLE CHRIS (R. *of table*). *I* make arrangements. I know doctors.

MAMA. Uncle Chris, Dr. Johnson arrange. He is good doctor.

DOCTOR (*ironically*). Thank you, Madam.

MAMA. You go, Doctor. We come.

DOCTOR. Very well, in an hour, then. And Dagmar will be well taken care of, I promise you. I will do the operation myself.

UNCLE CHRIS. I watch.

DOCTOR. You will do no such thing, sir.

UNCLE CHRIS. Always I watch operations. I am head of family.

DOCTOR. I allow no one to attend my operations.

UNCLE CHRIS. Are so bad?

DOCTOR (*to* MAMA). Mrs. Hanson, if I am to undertake this operation and the care of your child, it must be on the strict understanding that this gentleman does not come near either me or my patient.

MAMA. Yes, Doctor, I talk to him. . . . You go to hospital now, please.

DOCTOR. Very well. But you understand . . . nowhere near me, or I withdraw from the case. (*He goes.*)

UNCLE CHRIS. I go see Dagmar.

MAMA (*stopping him above table*). Wait. Uncle Chris, is kind of you, but Dagmar is sick. You frighten her.

UNCLE CHRIS. I frighten her?

MAMA. Yes, Uncle Chris. You frighten everyone. . . .

UNCLE CHRIS (*amazed*). I??

MAMA. Everyone but me. Even the girls. . . . Jenny, Sigrid, Trina . . . they are frightened of you.

UNCLE CHRIS. The girls! Vomen! Pff!

MAMA. And the children, too. So Nels and I get Dagmar. You drive us to hospital in your automobile, but you do not frighten Dagmar. And you leave doctor alone. Dr. Johnson is *fine* doctor. You come with me, Nels. You carry Dagmar.

(NELS *and* MAMA *go out back* L. UNCLE CHRIS *stands in amazement and puzzlement. The* TWO GIRLS *watch him, hardly daring to move.*)

UNCLE CHRIS (*coming down* L. *of table*). Is true? I frighten you? Christinë . . . Katrinë . . . you are frightened of me? Come, I ask you. Tell me the truth. You are frightened of me?

KATRIN (*tremulously*). A . . . a little, Uncle Chris.

UNCLE CHRIS (*on bench*). No? And you, Christinë?

CHRISTINE. Y . . . yes, Uncle Chris.

UNCLE CHRIS. But Nils . . . Nils is a boy . . . he is not frightened?

CHRISTINE. Not . . . not as much as we are. . . .

UNCLE CHRIS. But he is frightened?

CHRISTINE. Yes, Uncle Chris.

UNCLE CHRIS (with a roar). But why? What is there to be frightened of? I am your Uncle Chris . . . why do I frighten you?

CHRISTINE. I don't know.

UNCLE CHRIS. But that is bad. Very bad. The aunts, yes, I like to frighten them. (The GIRLS giggle.) That makes you laugh. (He crosses to them.) You do not like the aunts? Come, tell me. You do not like the aunts. Say!

KATRIN. Not . . . very much, Uncle Chris.

UNCLE CHRIS. And which do you not like the most? Jenny . . . Sigrid . . . Trina. . . . Tell me—huh?

KATRIN. I think I like Aunt Jenny least. She's so . . . so bossy.

CHRISTINE. I can't stand Aunt Sigrid. Always whining and complaining.

UNCLE CHRIS (with a great roar of laughter). Is good. Jenny, bossy. Sigrid, whining. Is true! But your Mama, she is different. And she cook goot. The aunts, they cannot cook at all. Only you do not tell your Mama we have talked of them so. It is a secret, for us. Then you cannot be frightened of me any more . . . when we have secret. I tell you my secret, too. *I* do not like the aunts. And so that they do not bother me, I frighten them and shout at them. You I do not shout at if you are goot children, and clean your teeth goot, and eat your oranges. (He takes out a snuffbox and partakes of its contents.)

(On the cue "You I do not shout at" the posse of AUNTS appears, in outdoor clothes, accompanied by MR. THORKELSON, a terrified little man. They come in down L. and start up to the house.)

JENNY (striding to the front door and entering the house, with the others following). Uncle Chris, Sigrid has something to say to you.

SIGRID (with false bravery). Uncle Chris, you took Arne to the hospital. . . .

UNCLE CHRIS (R. of table). Yes, I take Arne to the hospital. And now we take Dagmar to the hospital, so you do not clutter up the place.

JENNY (L. of table). What's the matter with Dagmar?

CHRISTINE. It's her ear. Dr. Johnson's going to operate.

SIGRID (*catching her favorite word*). Operate? This is some more of
  Uncle Chris's doing. Did you hear what he did to Arne?
UNCLE CHRIS (*turning on her*). Sigrid, you are a whining old fool,
  and you get out of here. . . .
SIGRID (*deflating*). We'd better go, Jenny. . . .
JENNY (*stoutly*). No . . . there has been enough of these
  highhanded goings-on. . . .
UNCLE CHRIS. And you, Jenny . . . you are a bossy old fool, and
  you get out of here, too, and we take Dagmar to hospital.
  (NELS *enters, back* L., *carrying* DAGMAR *in his arms, wrapped in
  a blanket.*) You got her goot, Nils?
NELS. Sure, Uncle Chris.
UNCLE CHRIS. We go.

JENNY (*getting between him and the door*). No! You are going to hear me out. (*Weakening.*) That is, you are going to hear *Sigrid* out. . . .

UNCLE CHRIS. If you do not get out of the way of the door before I count three, I trow you out. And Sigrid, too, as big as she is. Von. . . . (SIGRID *moves.*) Two. . . . (JENNY *moves. He looks back at the children with a wink and a smile.*) Is goot! You put her in back of the car, Nils.

(NELS *goes out,* L., *carrying* DAGMAR, *and lifts her into the car.* UNCLE CHRIS *follows and starts cranking.*)

TRINA (*running to the door after him, with* MR. THORKELSON). But, Uncle Chris, I want to introduce Mr. Thorkelson. . . . (*But* UNCLE CHRIS *ignores her, continuing to crank. She returns crestfallen into the room with* MR. THORKELSON. MAMA *re-enters back* L, *wearing hat and coat and carrying a cheap little overnight case.*)

MAMA. Jenny . . . Trina, we go to hospital. (*She goes to* KATRIN *and* CHRISTINE.) You will be good children until Mama comes home?

THE GIRLS. Sure, Mama.

UNCLE CHRIS (*calling from the car*). Marta, we go!

MAMA (*calling back*). I come! (*She turns to the children again.*) There is milk in the cooler, and fruit and cookies for your lunch.

CHRISTINE. We'll be all right, Mama. Don't worry.

MAMA. I go now. (*She starts for the door.*)

SIGRID (*stopping her*). Marta!

MAMA. What is it?

SIGRID. You *can't* go in his automobile.

MAMA. Why not?

UNCLE CHRIS (*calling again*). Marta, we go!

MAMA. I come!

SIGRID. Because . . . because *she's* in it. The . . . the woman!

MAMA. So it will kill me, or Dagmar, if we sit in the automobile with her? I have see her. She looks nice woman. (*Calling off, as she goes.*) I come!

UNCLE CHRIS. We go! (MAMA *climbs into the rear of the car, which backs noisily off during the next speeches.*)

MR. THORKELSON (*in a low whisper to* TRINA). Is that woman his wife?

TRINA (*nervously*). Yes. . . .

MR. THORKELSON. Yes?

TRINA (*whispering back, loudly*). No!

230

JENNY (to the GIRLS). Don't stand there gaping like that, girls. (She shoos them into the pantry.) Go away! Go away! (The GIRLS go. JENNY turns and sees the disappearing car through the open door.) Oh! They've gone! We go after them! Sigrid, you lead the way! (She gives SIGRID a push and the four go out, with JENNY dragging MR. THORKELSON, and TRINA following. Blackout. The travelers close.)

(Spot on R. turntable, representing a kind of closet-room. Roller skates hanging on the wall. KATRIN is seated on the floor and CHRISTINE on a small kitchen stepladder with glasses of milk, and cookies on plates.)

KATRIN. How long have they been gone now?

CHRISTINE. About three hours. And I wish you wouldn't keep asking that.

KATRIN. How long do operations take? I heard Aunt Sigrid telling about Mrs. Bergman who was five hours on the table.

CHRISTINE. Aunt Sigrid's friends always have everything worse than anyone else. And it gets worse each time she tells it, too.

(KATRIN smiles—drinks some milk and eats a cookie.)

KATRIN (with a certain melancholy enjoyment). The house feels lonesome, doesn't it—without Mama? It's like in a book. "The sisters sat huddled in the empty house, waiting for the verdict that was to spell life or death to the little family."

CHRISTINE. Oh, don't talk such nonsense.

KATRIN. It's not nonsense.

CHRISTINE. It is, too. In the first place, we're not a little family. We're a big one. And who said anything about life or death, anyway? Always trying to make everything so dramatic!

KATRIN. Well, it *is* dramatic.

CHRISTINE. It's not. It's just . . . well, worrying. But you don't have to make a tragedy out of it.

(Pause.)

KATRIN. You're not eating anything.

CHRISTINE. I know that.

KATRIN. You're not drinking your milk, either. Aren't you hungry?

231

CHRISTINE. No. And you wouldn't be, either, if you'd any feeling for Mama and Dagmar, instead of just heartlessly sitting there eating and enjoying making a story out of it.

KATRIN. Oh, Chris, I'm not heartless. I do have feeling for them. I can't help it if it goes into words like that. Everything always does with me. But it doesn't mean I don't feel it. And I think we *ought* to eat. I think Mama would want us to.

(Pause. CHRISTINE *hesitates a moment, then takes a bite of a cookie. They both eat in silence. The light dims on them, and the turntable revolves out. The travelers part on the hospital corridor. A main back flat representing the wall, running diagonally up from the front of the main stage* L. *towards the back. Down front* L. *is a bench, on which* MAMA *and* NELS *are sitting, holding hands, looking off. Below the bench is the elevator, and above the bench, set back a little, is a closet for brooms and mops, etc. The reception desk, at which a nurse is sitting, is* R. C., *towards the front. The wall goes up into darkness, and behind the nurse's desk is darkness. As the curtains open, there is a hubbub down front by the nurse's desk, where the* AUNTS *are haranguing* UNCLE CHRIS. MR. THORKELSON *stands slightly in back of them.*)

SIGRID. But, Uncle Chris, I tell you I must see him!

UNCLE CHRIS (*storming*). You don't understand English? No visitors for twenty-four hours.

SIGRID. But *you've* seen him.

UNCLE CHRIS. I am not visitor. I am exception.

SIGRID. Well, then, his mother should be an exception, too. I'll see the doctor.

UNCLE CHRIS. *I* have seen doctor. I have told him you are not goot for Arne.

SIGRID. Not good for my own son. . . .

UNCLE CHRIS. Not goot at all. You cry over him. I go now. (*He starts to do so, but* JENNY *pushes* TRINA *forward.*)

TRINA (*with desperate courage*). Uncle Chris . . . Uncle Chris . . . I *must* speak to you.

UNCLE CHRIS. I have business.

TRINA. But, Uncle Chris . . . I want to get married.

UNCLE CHRIS. Well, then, *get* married. (*He starts off again.*)

TRINA. No, wait, I . . . I want to marry Mr. Thorkelson. Here. (*She produces him from behind her.*) Peter, this is Uncle Chris. Uncle Chris, this is Mr. Thorkelson.

UNCLE CHRIS (*staring at him*). So?

MR. THORKELSON. How are you, sir?

UNCLE CHRIS. Busy. *(He turns again.)*

TRINA. Please, Uncle Chris . . .

UNCLE CHRIS. What is? You want to marry him? All right, marry him. I have other things to think about.

TRINA *(eagerly)*. Then . . . then you give your permission?

UNCLE CHRIS. Yes, I give my permission. If you want to be a fool, I cannot stop you.

TRINA *(gratefully)*. Oh, thank you, Uncle Chris.

UNCLE CHRIS. So. Is all?

TRINA *(anxious to escape)*. Yes, I think is all.

JENNY *(firmly)*. No!!

UNCLE CHRIS. No? *(MR. THORKELSON is pushed forward again.)*

MR. THORKELSON. Well, there . . . there was a little something else. You see, Trina mentioned . . . well, in the old country it was always usual . . . and after all, we do all come from the old country. . . .

UNCLE CHRIS. What is it? What you want?

MR. THORKELSON. Well, it's a question of Trina's . . . well, not to mince matters . . . her dowry.

UNCLE CHRIS *(shouting)*. Her what?

MR. THORKELSON *(very faintly)*. Her dowry . . .

UNCLE CHRIS. Ah. Her dowry. Trina wants a dowry. She is forty-two years old. . . .

TRINA *(interrupting)*. No, Uncle Chris. . . .

UNCLE CHRIS *(without pausing)*. And it is not enough she gets husband. She must have dowry.

NURSE *(who has been trying to interrupt, now bangs on her desk and moves down R.)*. Please! Would you mind going and discussing your family matters somewhere else? This is a hospital, not a marriage bureau.

UNCLE CHRIS *(after glaring at the NURSE, turns to MR. THORKELSON)*. You come into waiting room. I talk to you about dowry. *(He strides off into the darkness behind the NURSE's desk. MR. THORKELSON, with an appealing look back at TRINA, follows him. The AUNTS now remember MAMA, sitting on the bench, and cross to her.)*

JENNY. Did you hear that, Marta?

MAMA *(out of a trance)*. What?

JENNY. Uncle Chris.

MAMA. No, I do not hear. I wait for doctor. Is two hours since they take Dagmar to operating room. More.

SIGRID. Two hours? That's nothing! When Mrs. Bergman had her gall bladder removed she was *six* hours on the table.

MAMA. Sigrid, I do not want to hear about Mrs. Bergman. I do not want to hear about anything. I wait for doctor. Please, you go away now. You come this evening.

TRINA. But, Marta, you can't stay here all by yourself.

MAMA. I have Nels. Please, Trina . . . I wait for doctor . . . you go now.

JENNY. We go.

TRINA. Oh, but I must wait for Peter and Uncle Chris. . . .

JENNY. We'll go next door and have some coffee. Sigrid, do you have money?

SIGRID. Yes, I . . . I have a little.

JENNY. Good. Then I treat you. We'll be next door if you want us, Marta.

(MAMA *nods without looking at them, her eyes still fixed on the elevator door. The* AUNTS *leave, going down the steps from the stage as though they were the hospital steps, and off* L. *For a moment, the stage is quiet. Then a* SCRUBWOMAN *enters from down* R., *carrying a mop and pail which she puts into the closet, and then leaves. The elevator door opens and a doctor in white coat comes out, followed by an orderly, carrying a tray of dressings. They disappear up* R. *behind the desk.* MAMA *rises, agitatedly, looking after them. Then* DR. JOHNSON *returns from* R. *front, carrying his hat and bag. He sees* MAMA *and crosses to her,* C.)

DOCTOR. Oh, Mrs. Hanson. . . .

MAMA. Doctor. . . .

DOCTOR. Well, Dagmar's fine. She came through it beautifully. She's back in bed now, sleeping off the anesthetic.

MAMA. Thank you, Doctor. (*She shakes hands with him.*)

DOCTOR. You're very welcome.

MAMA. Is good of you, Doctor. (*She shakes hands with him again.*) Where is she? I go to her now.

DOCTOR. Oh, I'm sorry, but I'm afraid that's against the rules. You shall see her tomorrow.

MAMA. Tomorrow? But, Doctor, she is so little. When she wakes up she will be frightened.

DOCTOR. The nurse will take care of her. Excellent care. You needn't worry. You see, for the first twenty-four hours, clinic patients aren't allowed to see visitors. The wards must be kept quiet.

MAMA. I will not make a sound.

DOCTOR. I'm very sorry. Tomorrow. And now . . . (*He looks at his watch.*) Good afternoon. (*He puts on his hat and goes* L.,

234

down the steps and off. MAMA *stands still a moment, looking after him.)*

MAMA. Come, Nels. We go find Dagmar.

NELS. But, Mama, the doctor said . . .

MAMA. We find Dagmar. *(She looks vaguely around her. She goes to the* NURSE'S *desk.)* You tell me, please, where I can find my daughter?

NURSE. What name?

MAMA. Dagmar.

NELS. Dagmar Hanson.

NURSE *(looking at her record book).* Hanson, Ward A. Along there. *(She points upstage.* MAMA *starts to go up.)* Oh, just a moment. *(*MAMA *returns.)* When did she come in?

MAMA. This morning. They just finish operation.

NURSE. Oh, well, then, I'm afraid you can't see her today. No visitors for the first twenty-four hours.

MAMA. Am not visitor. I am her Mama.

NURSE. I'm sorry, but it's against the rules.

MAMA. Just for one minute. Please.

NURSE. I'm sorry, but it's against the rules.

*(*MAMA *stands staring.* NELS *touches her arm. She looks at him, nods, trying to smile, then turns and walks with him to* L. *and down the steps.)*

MAMA. We must think of some way.

NELS. Mama, they'll let you see her tomorrow. They said so.

MAMA. If I don't see her today, how will I know that all is well with her? What can I tell Papa when he comes home from work?

NELS. The nurses will look after her, Mama. Would you like to come next door for some coffee?

MAMA *(shaking her head).* We go home. We have coffee at home. But I must see Dagmar today. *(She plods off* L. *with* NELS.*)*

(The travelers close. Spot goes up on R. *turntable.* UNCLE CHRIS *and* MR. THORKELSON *are seated on a bench and chair, as in a waiting room. A table with a potted plant is between them. A clock on the wall points to 2:30.)*

UNCLE CHRIS *(on bench,* R.*).* Well, it comes then to this. You love my niece, Trina? *(*MR. THORKELSON, *very scared, gulps and nods.)* You want to marry her? *(*MR. THORKELSON *nods again.)*

You are in position to support her? (MR. THORKELSON *nods again.*) Why, then, you want dowry? (*No answer. He shouts.*) What for you want dowry?

MR. THORKELSON. Well . . . well, it would be a nice help. And it is customary.

UNCLE CHRIS. Is not customary. Who give dowries? Parents. Why? Because they are so glad they will not have to support their daughters any more, they pay money. I do not support Trina. I do not care if Trina gets married. Why then should I pay to have her married?

MR. THORKELSON. I never thought of it like that.

UNCLE CHRIS. Is insult to girl to pay dowry. If I do not give dowry, will you still marry Trina?

MR. THORKELSON. I . . . I don't know.

UNCLE CHRIS. You don't know? You don't know? You think I let Trina marry a man who will not take her without dowry?

MR. THORKELSON. No, I suppose you wouldn't.

UNCLE CHRIS. What kind of man would that be? I ask you, what kind of man would that be?

MR. THORKELSON (*fascinated—helpless*). Well, not a very nice kind of man.

UNCLE CHRIS. And are you that kind of man?

MR. THORKELSON. I . . . I don't think so.

UNCLE CHRIS (*conclusively*). Then you don't want dowry!!

MR. THORKELSON (*giving up*). No, I . . . I guess I don't.

UNCLE CHRIS (*slapping his back*). Goot. Goot. You are goot man. I like you. I give you my blessing. And I send you vedding present. I send you box of oranges!

(*While he is boisterously shaking* MR. THORKELSON'S *hand, blackout. Turntable revolves out. The curtain opens on the kitchen. It is empty.* MAMA *and* NELS *come up the hill from the* L. *and let themselves into the house. There is silence as they take off their hats and coats.*)

MAMA (*after a moment*). Where are the girls?

NELS. I guess they're upstairs. (*Goes to door back* L. *and calls.*) Chris! Katrin!

GIRLS' VOICES. Coming!

NELS. Shall I make you some coffee? (MAMA *shakes her head.*) You said you'd have coffee when you got home.

MAMA. Later. First I must think.

NELS. Mama, please don't worry like that. Dagmar's all right. You know she's all right.

(The GIRLS *come in back* L.*)*

CHRISTINE *(trying to be casual,* R. *of table).* Well, Mama, everything
all right?

MAMA *(nodding).* Is all right. You have eaten?

KATRIN *(*L. *of table).* Yes, Mama.

MAMA. You drink your milk?

CHRISTINE. Yes, Mama.

MAMA. Is good.

CHRISTINE *(seeing her face).* Mama, something's the matter.

KATRIN *(over-dramatically).* Mama, Dagmar's not——? She
isn't——? Mama!

MAMA. No, Dagmar is fine. The doctor say she is fine. *(She
rises.)* What is time?

NELS. It's three o'clock.

MAMA. Three hours till Papa come home. *(She looks around, and
then goes slowly into the pantry, back* R.*)*

KATRIN. Nels, what is it? There *is* something the matter.

NELS. They wouldn't let Mama see Dagmar. It's a rule of the
hospital.

CHRISTINE. But Dagmar's all right?

NELS. Oh, yes, she's all right.

CHRISTINE *(impatiently).* Well, then . . . !

NELS. But Mama's very upset. She started talking to me in
Norwegian in the streetcar.

KATRIN *(emotionally).* What can we do?

CHRISTINE *(coldly).* You can't do anything. When *will* they let her
see Dagmar?

NELS. Tomorrow.

CHRISTINE. Well, then, we'll just have to wait till tomorrow.

KATRIN. Chris, how can you be so callous? Can't you see that
Mama's heart is breaking?

CHRISTINE. No. I can't. And you can't, either. People's hearts
don't break.

KATRIN. They do, too.

CHRISTINE. Only in books. (MAMA *comes back; she wears an apron,
and carries a scrub brush and a bucket of hot water.)* Why,
Mama, what are you going to do?

MAMA *(coming down front,* R. *of table).* I scrub the floor. *(She gets
down on her knees, facing front.)*

CHRISTINE. But you scrubbed it yesterday.

MAMA. I scrub it again. *(She starts to do so.)*

KATRIN. But, Mama . . .

MAMA (*bending low*). Comes a time when you've got to get down
    on your knees.
KATRIN (*to* CHRISTINE). Now do you believe me?

(CHRISTINE, *suddenly unendurably moved, turns and rushes from the
room.*)

NELS. Mama, don't. Please don't. You must be tired.
KATRIN (*strangely*). Let her alone, Nels. (*They stand in silence
    watching* MAMA *scrub. Suddenly she stops.*) What is it, Mama?
    What is it?
MAMA (*sitting back on her haunches*). I tink of something! (*Slowly.*)
    I tink I tink of something!

(*The lights dim and the curtains close on the kitchen. From down front
L.* UNCLE CHRIS'S VOICE *singing. The lights slowly come up on the* L.
turntable, showing ARNE [*a child of about eight*] *in a hospital bed, with*
UNCLE CHRIS *beside him.*)

UNCLE CHRIS (*singing*).
"Ten t'ousand Svedes vent t'rough de veeds
  At de battle of Coppen-hagen.
Ten t'ousand Svedes went t'rough de veeds
  Chasing vun Nor-ve-gan!"
ARNE. Uncle Chris!
UNCLE CHRIS. Yes, Arne?
ARNE. Uncle Chris, does it *have* to hurt like this?
UNCLE CHRIS. If you vant it to be vell, and not to valk alvays like
    Uncle Chris, it does . . . for a little. Is very bad?
ARNE. It is . . . kinda. . . .
    Oo—oo . . . !
UNCLE CHRIS. You sleep some now, maybe?
ARNE. I'll try. Will . . . will you stay here, Uncle Chris?
UNCLE CHRIS. Sure. Sure. I stay here. You are not frightened of
    Uncle Chris?
ARNE. No. Not any more.
UNCLE CHRIS. Goot. Goot. You like I sing some more?
ARNE. If you wouldn't mind. But maybe something a little . . .
    well, quieter.
UNCLE CHRIS (*tenderly*). Sure. Sure. (*He begins quietly to sing a
    Norwegian lullaby; in the midst,* ARNE *cries out.*)
ARNE. Oo—oo.
UNCLE CHRIS. Now you sleep some! (*He fixes* ARNE'S *pillows for
    him, and resumes the lullaby, seated on his chair beside the bed.*

After another verse, he leans over, assuring himself that the child is asleep, as the light dims. The table revolves out.)

(The curtains part on the hospital corridor again. There is a different NURSE *now at the reception desk, talking on the telephone as* MAMA *and* KATRIN *come in from* L. *and up the steps.)*

MAMA *(as they come up, in an undertone).* Is not the same nurse. Katrin, you take my hat and coat. *(She takes them off, revealing that she still wears her apron.)*
KATRIN. But, Mama, won't they . . .
MAMA *(interrupting, finger to her lips).* Ssh! You let me go ahead. You wait on bench for me. *(She goes to the closet door above*

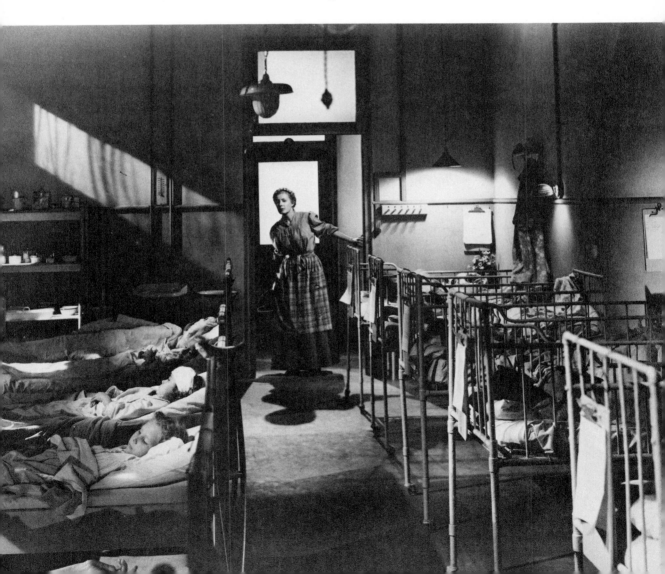

the bench and opens it. KATRIN *stares after her in trepidation.*
MAMA *takes out a damp mop and pail, and gets down on her
knees by the nurse's desk, starting to clean the floor. The* NURSE
looks up. MAMA *catches her eye, brightly.)* Very dirty floors.

NURSE. Yes, I'm glad they've finally decided to clean them.
Aren't you working late?

MAMA *(quickly, lowering her head).* Floors need cleaning. *(She
pushes her way, crawling on hands and knees, up behind the desk,
and disappears up the corridor, still scrubbing.* KATRIN *steals to
the bench, where she sits, still clutching* MAMA'S *hat and coat,
looking interestedly around her. The light dims, leaving her in a
single spot, as she starts to talk to herself.)*

KATRIN *(to herself).* "The Hospital" . . . A poem by Katrin
Hanson. *(She starts to improvise.)*

"She waited, fearful, in the hall,
And held her bated breath."
Breath—yes, that'll rhyme with death.

(She repeats the first two lines.)

"She waited fearful in the hall
And held her bated breath.
She trembled at the least footfall,
And kept her mind on death."

*(She gets a piece of paper and pencil from her pocket and begins to
scribble, as a* NURSE *comes out of the elevator, carrying some charts,
which she takes to the desk, and then goes out down* R. KATRIN *goes
on with her poem.)*

"Ah, God, 'twas agony to wait.
To wait and watch and wonder. . . . "
Wonder—under—bunder—funder—sunder. Sunder! *(Nods
to herself and goes on again.)*
"To wait and watch and wonder,
About her infant sister's fate.
If Death life's bonds would sunder."

(Then to herself again, looking front.) That's beautiful. Yes, but it
isn't true. Dagmar isn't dying. It's funny—I don't want her to
die—and yet when Mama said she was all right I was
almost—well, almost disappointed. It wasn't exciting any
more. Maybe Christine's right, and I haven't any heart. How
awful! "The girl without a heart." That'd be a nice title

for a story. "The girl without a heart sat in the hospital corridor. . . ."

(The lights come up again as UNCLE CHRIS *appears, up* R. *behind the desk. He wears his hat. He sees* KATRIN.)

UNCLE CHRIS. Katrinë! What you do here? *(He sits on the bench beside her.)*
KATRIN *(nervously).* I'm waiting for Mama.
UNCLE CHRIS. Where is she?
KATRIN *(scared).* I . . . don't know.
UNCLE CHRIS. What you mean . . . you don't know?
KATRIN *(whispering).* I think . . . I think she's seeing Dagmar.
UNCLE CHRIS *(shaking his head).* Is first day. They do not allow visitors first day.
KATRIN *(trying to make him aware of the* NURSE). I know. But I think that's where she is.
UNCLE CHRIS. Where *is* Dagmar?
KATRIN. I don't know.

*(*UNCLE CHRIS *rises and goes to the* NURSE *at the desk.)*

UNCLE CHRIS. In what room is my great-niece, Dagmar Hanson?
NURSE *(looking at her book).* Hanson . . . Hanson . . . when did she come in?
UNCLE CHRIS. This morning.
NURSE. Oh, yes. Were you wanting to see her?
UNCLE CHRIS. What room is she in?
NURSE. I asked were you wanting to see her.
UNCLE CHRIS. And *I* ask what room she is in.
NURSE. We don't allow visitors the first day.
UNCLE CHRIS. Have I said I vant to visit her? I ask what room she is in.
NURSE. Are you by any chance, Mr. . . . *(Looking at her book.)* Halvorsen?
UNCLE CHRIS *(proudly, and correcting her pronunciation).* Christopher Halvorsen.
NURSE. Did you say you were her uncle?
UNCLE CHRIS. Her great-uncle.
NURSE. Well, then, I'm afraid I can't tell you anything about her.
UNCLE CHRIS. Why not?
NURSE. Orders.
UNCLE CHRIS. Whose orders?

NURSE. Dr. Johnson's. There's a special note here. Patient's uncle, Mr. Halvorsen, not to be admitted or given information under any circumstances.

UNCLE CHRIS (*after a moment's angry stupefaction*). Vomen! Pff! (*He strides away down* L.)

(MAMA *returns from up* R., *carrying the mop and pail, walking now and smiling triumphantly.*)

MAMA (*to the* NURSE). Thank you. (*She replaces the mop and pail in the closet, and then sees* UNCLE CHRIS. *Crossing to him.*) Uncle Chris, Dagmar is fine!

UNCLE CHRIS (*amazed*). You see her?

MAMA. Sure, Uncle Chris, I see her.

UNCLE CHRIS (*reiterating, incredulous*). You see Dagmar?!

MAMA. Sure. (*She takes her hat from* KATRIN *and starts to put it on.*) Is fine hospital. But such floors! A mop is never good. Floors should be scrubbed with a brush. We go home. Uncle Chris, you come with us? I make coffee.

UNCLE CHRIS (*joining them in a little group on the steps down* L.). Pah! Vot good is coffee? I go get drink.

MAMA (*reprovingly*). Uncle Chris!

UNCLE CHRIS. Marta, you are fine woman. Fine. But I go get drink.

MAMA (*quickly aside to* KATRIN). His leg hurts him.

UNCLE CHRIS. And you do not make excuses for me! I get drink because I like it.

MAMA (*conciliating him*). Sure, Uncle Chris.

UNCLE CHRIS (*shouting*). I like it! (*Then, with a change.*) No, is not true. You know is not true. I do not like to drink at all. But I do not like to come home with you, either. (*Growing slightly maudlin.*) You have family. Is fine thing. You do not know how fine. Katrinë, one day when you grow up, maybe you know what a fine thing family is. I haf no family.

KATRIN (*on the lower step*). But, Uncle Chris, Mama's always said you were the *head* of the family.

UNCLE CHRIS. Sure. Sure. I am head of the family, but I haf no family. So I go get drink. You understand, Marta?

MAMA. Sure, Uncle Chris. You go get drink. (*Sharply.*) But don't you feel sorry for yourself! (UNCLE CHRIS *glares at her a moment, then strides down the steps and off* R., *boisterously singing his song of "Ten Thousand Swedes."* MAMA *watches him go, then takes her coat from* KATRIN.) Is fine man. Has fine

242

ideas about family. (KATRIN *helps her on with her coat.*) I can tell Papa now that Dagmar is fine. She wake while I am with her. I explain rules to her. She will not expect us now until tomorrow afternoon.

KATRIN. You won't try and see her again before that?

MAMA (*gravely*). No. That would be against the rules! Come. We go home.

(They go off L.)

Act 2

SCENE: *Opening, exactly as in Act One.* KATRIN *at her desk.*

KATRIN (*reading*). "It wasn't very often that I could get Mama to talk—about herself, or her life in the old country, or what she felt about things. You had to catch her unawares, or when she had nothing to do, which was very, very seldom. I don't think I can ever remember seeing Mama unoccupied." (*Laying down the manuscript and looking out front.*) I do remember one occasion, though. It was the day before Dagmar came home from the hospital. And as we left, Mama suggested treating me to an ice-cream soda. (*She rises, gets her hat from beside her—a schoolgirl hat—puts it on and crosses C. while she speaks the next lines.*) She had never done such a thing before, and I remember how proud it made me feel—just to sit and talk to her quietly like a grown-up person. It was a kind of special *treat*-moment in my life that I'll always remember—quite apart from the soda, which was *wonderful.* (*She has reached C. stage now.* MAMA *has come from between the curtains, and starts down the steps.*)

MAMA. Katrin, you like we go next door, and I treat you to an ice-cream soda?

KATRIN (*young now, and overcome*). Mama—do you mean it?

MAMA. Sure. We celebrate. We celebrate that Dagmar is well, and coming home again. (*They cross to the L., where the turntable represents a drugstore, with a table and two chairs at which they seat themselves.* MAMA *is L. of table.*) What you like to have, Katrin?

KATRIN (*with desperate earnestness*). I think a chocolate . . . no, a strawberry . . . no, a chocolate soda.

MAMA (*smiling*). You are sure?

243

KATRIN (*gravely*). I think so. But, Mama, can we *afford* it?

MAMA. I think this once we can afford it.

(*The* SODA CLERK *appears from* L.)

SODA CLERK. What's it going to be, ladies?

MAMA. A chocolate ice-cream soda, please—and a cup of coffee.

(*The* SODA CLERK *goes.*)

KATRIN. Mama, he called us "ladies"! (MAMA *smiles.*) Why aren't you having a soda, too?

MAMA. Better I like coffee.

KATRIN. When can I drink coffee?

MAMA. When you are grown up.

KATRIN. When I'm eighteen?

MAMA. Maybe before that.

KATRIN. When I graduate?

MAMA. Maybe. I don't know. Comes the day you are grown up. Papa and I will know.

KATRIN. Is coffee really nicer than a soda?

MAMA. When you are grown up, it is.

KATRIN. Did you used to like sodas better . . . before you were grown up?

MAMA. We didn't have sodas before I was grown up. It was in the old country.

KATRIN (*incredulous*). You mean they don't have sodas in Norway?

MAMA. Now, maybe. Now I think they have many things from America. But not when I was a little girl.

(*The* SODA CLERK *brings the soda and the coffee.*)

SODA CLERK. There you are, folks. (*He sets them down and departs.*)

KATRIN (*after a good pull at the soda*). Mama, do you ever want to go back to the old country?

MAMA. I like to go back once to look, maybe. To see the mountains and the fjords. I like to show them once to you all. When Dagmar is big, maybe we all go back once . . . one summer . . . like tourists. But that is how it would be. I would be tourist there now. There is no one I would know any more. And maybe we see the little house where Papa and I live when we first marry. And . . . (*Her eyes grow misty and reminiscent.*) something else I would look at.

KATRIN. What is that? (MAMA *does not answer.*) What would you look at, Mama?

MAMA. Katrin, you do not know you have brother? Besides Nels?

KATRIN. No! A brother? In Norway? Mama. . . .

MAMA. He is my first baby. I am eighteen when he is born.

KATRIN. Is he there now?

MAMA (*simply*). He is dead.

KATRIN (*disappointed*). Oh. I thought you meant . . . I thought you meant a real brother. A long-lost one, like in stories. When did he die?

MAMA. When he is two years old. It is his grave I would like to see again. (*She is suddenly near tears, biting her lip and stirring her coffee violently, spilling some. She gets her handkerchief from her pocketbook, dabs at her skirt, then briefly at her nose, then she returns the handkerchief and turns to* KATRIN *again. Matter-of-factly.*) Is good, your ice-cream soda?

KATRIN (*more interested now in* MAMA *than in it*). Yes. Mama . . . have you had a very *hard* life?

MAMA (*surprised*). Hard? No. No life is easy all the time. It is not meant to be. (*She pours the spilled coffee back from the saucer into her cup.*)

KATRIN. But . . . rich people . . . aren't *their* lives easy?

MAMA. I don't know, Katrin. I have never known rich people. But I see them sometimes in stores and in the streets, and they do not *look* as if they were easy.

KATRIN. Wouldn't you like to be rich?

MAMA. I would like to be rich the way I would like to be ten feet high. Would be good for some things—bad for others.

KATRIN. But didn't you come to America to *get* rich?

MAMA (*shocked*). No. We come to America because they are all here—all the others. Is good for families to be together.

KATRIN. And did you like it right away?

MAMA. Right away. When we get off the ferry boat and I see San Francisco and all the family, I say, "Is like Norway," only it is better than Norway. And then you are all born here, and I become American citizen. But not to get rich.

KATRIN. *I* want to be rich. Rich and famous. I'd buy you your warm coat. When are you going to get that coat, Mama?

MAMA. Soon now, maybe—when we pay doctor, and Mr. Hyde pay his rent. I think now I *must* ask him. I ask him tomorrow, after Dagmar comes home.

KATRIN. When I'm rich and famous, I'll buy you lovely clothes.

White satin gowns with long trains to them. And jewelry. I'll buy you a pearl necklace.

MAMA. We talk too much! (*She signs to the* SODA CLERK.) Come, finish your soda. We must go home. (*The* SODA CLERK *comes.*) How much it is, please?

SODA CLERK. Fifteen cents.

MAMA. Here are two dimes. You keep the nickel. And thank you. Was good coffee. (*They start out and up the steps towards the curtains* C.) Tomorrow Dagmar will be home again. And, Katrin, you see Uncle Elizabeth is there. This afternoon again she was asking for him. You keep Uncle Elizabeth in the house all day until she comes home.

(*They disappear behind the curtains. After a second, the howls of a cat in pain are heard from behind the curtains—low at first, then rising to a heart-rending volume, and then diminishing again as the curtains part on the kitchen once more.* MAMA, PAPA, *and* DAGMAR *are entering the house.*)

DAGMAR (*standing on threshold, transfixed*). It's Uncle Elizabeth, welcoming me home! That's his song of welcome. Where is he, Mama? (*She looks around for the source of the howls.*)

MAMA. He is in the pantry. . . . (*As* DAGMAR *starts to rush thither.*) But wait . . . wait a minute, Dagmar. I must tell you. Uncle Elizabeth is . . . sick.

DAGMAR. Sick? What's the matter with him?

PAPA. He has been in fight. Last night. He come home this morning very sick indeed.

(DAGMAR *starts for the pantry door, back* R., *as* NELS *comes out.*)

MAMA. Nels, how is Uncle Elizabeth? Nels has been doctoring him.

NELS. He's pretty bad, Mama. I've dressed all his wounds again with boric acid, but . . . (*As* DAGMAR *tries to get past him.*) I wouldn't go and see him now, baby.

DAGMAR. I've got to. He's my cat. I haven't seen him in a whole month. More. (*She runs into the pantry and disappears.*)

MAMA. Nels, what you think?

NELS. I think we ought to have had him put away before she came home.

MAMA. But she would have been so unhappy if he was not here *at all.*

NELS. She'll be unhappier still if he dies.

(Another howl is heard from the pantry, and then DAGMAR *comes rushing back.)*

DAGMAR. Mama, what happened to him? What happened to him? Oh, Mama . . . when I tried to pick him up, his bandage slipped over his eye. It was bleeding. Oh, Mama, it looked awful. Oh . . . *(She starts to cry.)*

MAMA *(fondling her).* He looks like that all over. Nels, you go see to his eye again. *(Wearily,* NELS *returns to the pantry.)* Listen, Dagmar . . . *Lille Ven* . . . would it not be better for the poor thing to go quietly to sleep?

DAGMAR. You mean—go to sleep and never wake up again? *(*MAMA *nods gently.)* No.

PAPA. I think he die, anyway. Nels try to make him well. But I do not think he can.

DAGMAR. Mama can. Mama can do everything. *(Another howl from offstage. She clutches* MAMA *agonizedly.)* Make him live, Mama. Make him well again. *Please!*

MAMA. We see. Let us see how he gets through the night. And now, Dagmar, you must go to bed. l bring you your supper.

DAGMAR. But you will fix Uncle Elizabeth? You promise, Mama?

MAMA. I promise I try. Go now. *(*DAGMAR *goes out, back* L.*)* I must fix her supper. *(She starts for the pantry. Howls again. She and* PAPA *stand and look at each other.* NELS *comes out.)*

NELS. Mama, it's just cruelty, keeping that cat alive.

MAMA. I know.

PAPA *(as another howl, the loudest yet, emerges).* You say we see how the cat get through the night. I ask you how do *we* get through the night? Is no use, Marta. We must put the cat to sleep. Nels, you go to the drugstore, and get something. Some chloroform, maybe. *(He gives him a coin.)*

NELS. How much shall I get?

PAPA. You ask the man. You tell him it is for a cat. He knows. *(*NELS *goes out* L. *and down the street into the wings. Looking at* MAMA'S *face.)* Is best. Is the only thing.

MAMA. I know. But poor Dagmar. It is sad homecoming for her. And she has been so good in hospital. Never once she cry. *(She pulls herself together.)* I get her supper. *(Another howl from off stage.)* And I take the cat outside. Right outside, where we . . . where *Dagmar* cannot hear him. *(She goes into the pantry.* PAPA *takes a folded newspaper from his pocket, puts on his glasses and starts to read. The door, back* L.*, opens gently and*

MR. HYDE *peeps out. He wears his hat and coat and carries his suitcase and a letter.* PAPA *has his back to him.* MR. HYDE *lays the letter on the dresser and then starts to tiptoe across to the door. Then* PAPA *sees him.)*

PAPA. You go out, Mr. Hyde?

MR. HYDE *(pretending surprise).* Oh. . . . Oh, I did not see you, Mr. Hanson. *(He puts down the suitcase.)* I did not know you were back. As a matter of fact, I . . . I was about to leave this letter for you. *(He fetches it.)* The fact is . . . I . . . I have been called away.

PAPA. So?

MR. HYDE. A letter I received this morning necessitates my departure. My immediate departure.

PAPA. I am sorry. *(MAMA returns with a tray, on which are milk, bread, butter, and jelly.)* Mama, Mr. Hyde says he goes away.

MAMA *(coming to the table with the tray).* Is true?

MR. HYDE. Alas, dear Madam, yes. 'Tis true, 'tis pity. And pity 'tis, 'tis true. You will find here . . . *(He presents the letter.)* my check for all I owe you, and a note expressing my profoundest thanks for all your most kind hospitality. You will say goodbye to the children for me? *(He bows, as* MAMA *takes the letter.)*

MAMA *(distressed).* Sure. Sure.

MR. HYDE *(bowing again).* Madam, my deepest gratitude. *(He kisses her hand.* MAMA *looks astonished. He bows to* PAPA.*)* Sir— my sincerest admiration! *(He opens the street door.)* It has been a privilege. *Ave Atque Vale!* Hail and farewell! *(He makes a gesture and goes.)*

MAMA. Was wonderful man! Is too bad. *(She opens the letter, takes out the check.)*

PAPA. How much is check for?

MAMA. Hundred ten dollar! Is four months.

PAPA. Good. Good.

MAMA. Is wonderful. Now we pay doctor everything.

PAPA. And you buy your warm coat. With fur now, maybe.

MAMA *(sadly).* But there will be no more reading. You take the check, Lars. You get the money?

PAPA *(taking it).* Sure. I get it. What does he say in his letter?

MAMA. You read it while I fix supper for Dagmar. *(She starts to butter the bread, and spread jelly, while* PAPA *reads.)*

PAPA *(reading).* "Dear Friends, I find myself compelled to take a somewhat hasty departure from this house of happiness. . . ."

MAMA. Is beautiful letter.
PAPA *(continuing)*. "I am leaving you my library for the children. . . ."
MAMA. He leaves his books?
PAPA. He says so.
MAMA. But is wonderful. Go see, Lars. See if they are in his room.

(PAPA *lays down the letter and goes out back* L. NELS *and* CHRISTINE *appear down* L., *coming up to the house.* CHRISTINE *carries school-books.*)

CHRISTINE. I'm sure it was him, Nels. Carrying his suitcase, and getting on the cable car. I'm sure he's going away.
NELS. Well, I hope he's paid Mama.

(They open the street door.)

CHRISTINE *(bursting in)*. Mama, I saw Mr. Hyde getting on the cable car.
MAMA. I know. He leave.
CHRISTINE. Did he pay you?
MAMA. Sure, he pay me. Hundred ten dollar. . . .
NELS. Gee. . . .
MAMA *(smiling)*. Is good.
CHRISTINE. Are you going to put it in the Bank?
MAMA. We need it right away. (PAPA *returns, staggering under an armload of books.)* Mr. Hyde leaves his books, too. For you.
NELS. Say! (PAPA *stacks them on the table.* NELS *and* CHRISTINE *rush to them, reading the titles.)* The Pickwick Papers, The Complete Shakespeare . . .
CHRISTINE. *Alice in Wonderland, The Oxford Book of Verse* . . .
NELS. *The Last of the Mohicans, Ivanhoe* . . .
CHRISTINE. We were right in the middle of that.
MAMA. Nels can finish it. He can read to us now in the evenings. He has fine voice, too, like Mr. Hyde. (NELS *flushes with pleasure.)* Is wonderful. So much we can learn. *(She finishes the supper-making.)* Christine, you take the butter back to the cooler for me, and the yelly, too. (CHRISTINE *does so.)* I go up to Dagmar now. *(She lifts the tray, then pauses.)* You get it, Nels?
NELS. What? . . . Oh. . . . *(Taking a druggist's small bottle from his pocket.)* Here.

MAMA. You put it down. After I come back, we do it. You know how?

NELS. Why, no, Mama, I . . .

MAMA. You do not ask?

NELS. No, I . . . I thought Papa . . .

MAMA. You know, Lars?

PAPA. No, I don't *know* . . . but it cannot be difficult. If you *hold* the cat . . .

MAMA. And watch him die? No! I think better you get rags . . . and a big sponge, to soak up the chloroform. You put it in the box with him, and cover him over. You get them ready out there.

NELS. Sure, Mama.

MAMA. I bring some blankets.

(NELS *goes off to the pantry, as* CHRISTINE *comes back. Again* MAMA *lifts the tray and starts for the door back* L. *But there is a knock on the street door from* AUNT JENNY, *who has come to the house from down* L. *in a state of some excitement.*)

MAMA (*agitated*). So much goes on! See who it is, Christine.

CHRISTINE (*peeping*). It's Aunt Jenny. (*She opens the door.*)

MAMA. Jenny. . . .

JENNY (*breathless*). Marta . . . has he gone?

MAMA (*above table*). Who?

JENNY (L. *of table*). Your boarder . . . Mr. Hyde. . . .

MAMA. Yes, he has gone. Why?

JENNY. Did he pay you?

MAMA. Sure he pay me.

JENNY. How?

MAMA. He give me a check. Lars has it right there.

JENNY (*with meaning*). A check!

MAMA. Jenny, what is it? Christine, you give Dagmar her supper. I come soon. (CHRISTINE *takes the tray from her and goes out back* L.) What is it, Jenny? How do you know that Mr. Hyde has gone?

JENNY. I was at Mr. Kruper's down the street . . . you know, the restaurant and bakery . . . and he told me Mr. Hyde was there today having his lunch, and when he left he asked if he would cash a check for him. For fifty dollars. (*She pauses.*)

PAPA. Well, go on.

JENNY. Your fine Mr. Hyde didn't expect Mr. Kruper to take it to the bank until tomorrow, but he did. And what do you think? Mr. Hyde hasn't even an *account* at that bank! (NELS *returns and stands in the pantry doorway.*)

MAMA. I don't understand.

PAPA (*taking the check from his pocket*). You mean the check is no good?

JENNY. No good at all. (*Triumphantly.*) Your Mr. Hyde was a crook, just as I always thought he was, for all his reading and fine ways. Mr. Kruper said he'd been cashing them all over the neighborhood. (MAMA *stands quite still, without answering.*) How much did he owe you? Plenty, I'll bet. (*Still no answer.*) Eh? Marta, I said I bet he owed you plenty. Didn't he?

MAMA (*looks around, first at* NELS *and then down at the books on the table; she touches them*). No. No, he owed us nothing. (*She takes the check from* PAPA, *tearing it.*) Nothing.

JENNY (*persistently*). How much was that check for? (*She reaches her hand for it.*)

MAMA (*evading her*). It does not matter. He pay with better things than money. (*She goes to the stove, where she throws the check, watching it burn.*)

JENNY. I told you right in the beginning that you shouldn't trust him. But you were so sure . . . just like you always are. Mr. Hyde was a gentleman. A gentleman! I bet it must have been a hundred dollars that he rooked you of. Wasn't it?

MAMA (*returning to the table*). Jenny, I cannot talk now. Maybe you don't have things to do. I have.

JENNY (*sneeringly*). What? What have you got to do that's so important?

MAMA (*taking up the medicine bottle, fiercely*). I have to chloroform a cat!

(JENNY *steps back in momentary alarm, almost as though* MAMA *were referring to her, as she goes out into the pantry with the medicine bottle, not so very unlike Lady Macbeth with the daggers. Blackout and curtains close. After a moment, the curtains part again on the kitchen, the next morning. The books have been taken off the table, and* MAMA *is setting the breakfast dishes, with* PAPA *helping her.* DAGMAR *comes bursting into the room, back* L.)

DAGMAR. Good morning, Mama, 'Morning, Papa. Is Uncle Elizabeth all better?

MAMA. Dagmar, there is something I must tell you.

DAGMAR. I want to see Uncle Elizabeth first. (*She runs into the pantry.* MAMA *turns helplessly to* PAPA.)

MAMA. Do something! Tell her!

PAPA. If we just let her think the cat die . . . by itself. . . .

MAMA. No. We cannot tell her lies.

(PAPA goes to the pantry door, opening it.)

DAGMAR *(heard in pantry, off)*. What a funny, funny smell. Good
    morning, my darling, my darling Elizabeth. *(MAMA and PAPA
    stand stricken. DAGMAR comes in, carrying the cat, wrapped in an
    old shirt, with its head covered. She comes down R. of table.)* My
    goodness, you put enough blankets on him! Did you think
    he'd catch cold?

MAMA *(horror-stricken)*. Dagmar, you must not. . . . *(She stops at
    the sight of the cat, whose tail is twitching, quite obviously alive.)*
    Dagmar, let me see . . . Let me see the cat! *(She goes over to
    her, below table front, and uncovers the cat's head.)*

DAGMAR *(overjoyed)*. He's well. Oh, Mama, I *knew* you'd fix him.

MAMA *(appalled)*. But, Dagmar, I didn't. I . . .

DAGMAR *(ignoring her)*. I'm going to take him right up and show
    him to Nels. *(She runs off back L., calling.)* Nels! Nels! Uncle
    Elizabeth's well again!

MAMA *(turning to PAPA)*. Is a miracle! *(She sits, dumbfounded, on
    the bench in front of the table.)*

PAPA *(beside her, shrugging)*. You cannot have used enough
    chloroform. You just give him good sleep, and that cures
    him. We rechristen the cat, Lazarus!

MAMA. But, Lars, we must tell her. Is not *good* to let her grow
    up believing I can fix *everything!*

PAPA. Is best thing in the world for her to believe. *(He chuckles.)*
    Besides, I know *exactly* how she feels. *(He lays his hand on
    hers.)*

MAMA *(turning with embarrassment from his demonstrativeness and
    slapping his hand)*. We finish getting breakfast. *(She turns back
    to the table.)*

*(The curtains close. Lights up down front R. KATRIN and CHRISTINE
enter from the wings, in school clothes, wearing hats. CHRISTINE
carries schoolbooks in a strap. KATRIN is reciting.)*

KATRIN. "The quality of mercy is not strained,
         It droppeth as the gentle rain from heaven
         Upon the place beneath: it is twice blest;
         It blesseth him that gives, and him that takes. . . ."
(She dries up.) ". . . him that takes. It blesseth him that gives

and him that takes . . ." (*She turns to* CHRISTINE.) What comes after that?

CHRISTINE. I don't know. And I don't care.

KATRIN. Why, Chris!

CHRISTINE. I don't. It's all I've heard for weeks. The school play, and your graduation, and going on to High. And never a thought of what's happening at home.

KATRIN. What do you mean?

CHRISTINE. You see—you don't even know!

KATRIN. Oh, you mean the strike?

CHRISTINE. Yes, I mean the strike. Papa hasn't worked for four whole weeks, and a lot you care. Why, I don't believe you even know what they're striking *for*. Do you? All you and your friends can talk about is the presents you're going to get. You make me ashamed of being a girl.

(*Two girls,* MADELINE *and* DOROTHY, *come through the curtains,* C., *talking.*)

MADELINE (*to* DOROTHY). Thyra Walsh's family's going to add seven pearls to the necklace they started for her when she was a baby. Oh, hello, Katrin! Did you hear about Thyra's graduation present?

KATRIN (*not very happily*). Yes, I heard.

MADELINE. I'm getting an onyx ring, with a diamond in it.

KATRIN. A real diamond?

MADELINE. Yes, of course. A *small* diamond.

DOROTHY. What are *you* getting?

KATRIN. Well . . . well, they haven't actually told me, but I think . . . I think I'm going to get that pink celluloid dresser set in your father's drugstore.

DOROTHY. You mean that one in the window?

KATRIN (*to* MADELINE). It's got a brush and comb and mirror . . . and a hair-receiver. It's genuine celluloid!

DOROTHY. I wanted Father to give it to me, out of stock, but he said it was too expensive. Father's an awful tightwad. They're giving me a bangle.

MADELINE. Oh, there's the streetcar. We've got to fly. 'Bye, Katrin. 'Bye, Christine. See you tomorrow. Come on, Dorothy.

(*The* TWO GIRLS *rush off* L.)

CHRISTINE. Who said you were going to get the dresser set?

KATRIN. Nobody's said so . . . for certain. But I've sort of hinted, and . . .

CHRISTINE (*going up the steps*). Well, you're not going to get it.

KATRIN. How do you know?

CHRISTINE (*turning up back, still on steps*). Because I know what you *are* getting. I heard Mama tell Aunt Jenny. Aunt Jenny said you were too young to appreciate it.

KATRIN. What is it?

CHRISTINE. Mama's giving you her brooch. Her *solje*.

KATRIN. You mean that old silver thing she wears that belonged to Grandmother? What would I want an old thing like that for?

CHRISTINE. It's an heirloom. Mama thinks a lot of it.

KATRIN. Well, then, she ought to keep it. You don't really mean that's *all* they're going to give me?

CHRISTINE. What more do you want?

KATRIN. I want the dresser set. My goodness, if Mama doesn't realize what's a suitable present . . . why, it's practically the most important time in a girl's life, when she graduates.

CHRISTINE. And you say you're not selfish!

KATRIN. It's not selfishness.

CHRISTINE. Well, I don't know what else you'd call it. With Papa not working, we need every penny we can lay our hands on. Even the Little Bank's empty. But you'll devil Mama into giving you the dresser set somehow. So why talk about it? I'm going home. (*She turns and goes through the curtains.*)

(KATRIN *stands alone with a set and stubborn mouth, and then sits on the steps.*)

KATRIN. Christine was right. I got the dresser set. They gave it to me just before supper on graduation night. Papa could not attend the exercises because there was a strike meeting to decide about going back to work. I was so excited that night I could hardly eat, and the present took the last remnants of my appetite clean away.

(*The curtains part on the kitchen.* PAPA, MAMA, *and* DAGMAR *at table, with coffee.* CHRISTINE *is clearing dishes.*)

CHRISTINE. I'll just stack the dishes now, Mama. We'll wash them when we come home. (*She carries them into the pantry.*)

PAPA (R. *of table, holding up a cube of sugar*). Who wants coffee sugar? (*He dips it in his coffee.*) Dagmar? (*He hands it to her.*)

Katrin? (*She rises from the steps, coming into the scene for the sugar.*)

MAMA (L. *of table*). You get your coat, Katrin; you need it.

(KATRIN *goes out back* L.)

DAGMAR (*above table*). Aunt Jenny says if we drank black coffee like you do at our age, it would turn our complexions dark. I'd like to be a black Norwegian. Like Uncle Chris. Can I, Papa?

PAPA. I like you better blonde. Like Mama.

DAGMAR. When do you get old enough for your complexion *not* to turn dark? When can we drink coffee?

PAPA. One day, when you are grown up.

(JENNY *and* TRINA *have come to the street door* L. JENNY *knocks.*)

MAMA. There are Jenny and Trina. (*She goes to the door.*) Is good. We can start now. (*She opens the door.*) JENNY *and* TRINA *come in.*)

JENNY. Well, are you all ready? Is Katrin very excited?

PAPA (*nodding*). She ate no supper.

(MAMA *has started to put on her hat, and to put on* DAGMAR'S *hat and coat for her down* L. CHRISTINE *comes back from the pantry.* PAPA *gives her a dipped cube of sugar.*)

JENNY. Is that *black* coffee you dipped that sugar in? Lars, you shouldn't. It's not good for them. It'll . . .

PAPA (*finishing for her*). Turn their complexions dark. I know. Well, maybe it is all right if we have *one* dark Norwegian.

JENNY. Lars, really!

(KATRIN *returns with her coat.*)

KATRIN. Aunt Jenny, did you see my graduation present? (*She gets it from a chair.* CHRISTINE *gives her a disgusted look, and goes out back* L. KATRIN *displays the dresser set above the table.*) Look! It's got a hair-receiver.

JENNY (L. *of table*). But I thought . . . Marta, I thought you were going to give her . . .

MAMA (L.). No, you were right, Jenny. She is too young to appreciate that. She like something more gay . . . more modern.

255

JENNY. H'm. Well, it's very pretty, I suppose, but . . . (She looks up as MAMA puts on her coat.) You're not wearing your solje!

MAMA (quickly). No. I do not wear it tonight. Come, Trina, we shall be late.

TRINA (above table R.). Oh, but Peter isn't here yet.

MAMA. Katrin has her costume to put on. He can follow. Or do you like to wait for Peter?

TRINA. I think . . . if you don't mind . . .

MAMA. You can stay with Lars. He does not have to go yet.

JENNY. I hope Katrin knows her part.

PAPA. Sure she knows it. I know it, too.

TRINA. It's too bad he can't see Katrin's debut as an actress.

MAMA. You will be back before us, Lars?

PAPA (nodding). I think the meeting will not last long.

MAMA. Is good. We go now. (She goes out with JENNY and DAGMAR. CHRISTINE and NELS return from back L., and follow, waiting outside for KATRIN, while the others go ahead. KATRIN puts on her hat and coat and picks up the dresser set.)

PAPA (to TRINA). You like we play a game of checkers while we wait?

TRINA (sitting R. of table). Oh, I haven't played checkers in years.

PAPA. Then I beat you. (He rises to get the checker set. KATRIN kisses him.)

KATRIN. Goodbye, Papa.

PAPA. Goodbye, daughter. I think of you.

KATRIN. I'll see you there, Aunt Trina.

TRINA. Good luck!

PAPA. I get the checkers.

(KATRIN goes out L., PAPA gets the checker set from a cupboard under the dresser, brings it to the table and sets it up during the ensuing scene, which is played outside in the street.)

CHRISTINE (contemptuously). Oh, bringing your cheap trash with you to show off?

KATRIN. It's not trash. It's beautiful. You're just jealous.

CHRISTINE. I told you you'd devil Mama into giving it to you.

KATRIN. I didn't. I didn't devil her at all. I just showed it to her in Mr. Schiller's window . . .

CHRISTINE. And made her go and sell her brooch that her very own mother gave her.

KATRIN. What?

NELS. Chris . . . you weren't supposed to tell that!

CHRISTINE. I don't care. I think she ought to know.

KATRIN. Is that true? Did Mama—Nels——?

NELS. Well, yes, as a matter of fact, she did. Now, come on.

KATRIN. No, no, I don't believe it. I'm going to ask Papa.

NELS. You haven't time.

KATRIN. I don't care. *(She rushes back to the house and dashes into the kitchen.* CHRISTINE *goes off down* L., NELS *follows her.)* Papa—Papa—Christine says——Papa, did Mama sell her brooch to give me this?

PAPA *(above table)*. Christine should not have told you that.

KATRIN. It's true, then?

PAPA. She did not sell it. She traded it to Mr. Schiller for your present.

KATRIN *(near tears)*. Oh, but she shouldn't. . . . I never meant . . .

PAPA *(taking her by the shoulders)*. Look, Katrin. You wanted the present. Mama wanted your happiness; she wanted it more than she wanted the brooch.

KATRIN. But I never meant her to do *that*. *(Crying.)* She *loved* it so. It was all she had of Grandmother's.

PAPA. She always meant it for you, Katrin. And you must not cry. You have your play to act.

KATRIN *(sobbing)*. I don't want to act in it now.

PAPA. But you must. Your audience is waiting.

KATRIN *(as before)*. I don't care.

PAPA. But you must care. Tonight you are not Katrin any longer. You are an actress. And an actress must act, whatever she is feeling. There is a saying—what is it——

TRINA *(brightly)*. The mails must go through!

PAPA. No, no. The show must go on. So stop your crying, and go and act your play. We talk of this later. Afterwards.

KATRIN *(putting herself together)*. All right, I'll go. *(Sniffing a good deal, she picks up the dresser set and goes back to the street and off down* L. PAPA *and* TRINA *exchange glances, and then settle down to their checkers.)*

PAPA. Now we play.

(The lights fade and the curtains close. Spot up on stage R. *turntable. The two girls from the earlier scene are dressing in costumes for* The Merchant of Venice *before a plank dressing table.)*

DOROTHY. I'm getting worried about Katrin. If anything's happened to *her* . . .

MADELINE *(pulling up her tights)*. I'll forget my lines. I know I will. I'll look out and see Miss Forrester sitting there, and forget every single line. (KATRIN *rushes in from the* L. *She carries the dresser set, places it on the dressing table.*) We thought you'd had an accident, or something. . . .

KATRIN. Dorothy, is your father here tonight?

DOROTHY. He's going to be. Why?

KATRIN. I want to speak to him. (*As she pulls off her hat and coat.*) Will you tell him . . . please . . . not to go away without speaking to me? After. After the exercises.

DOROTHY. What on earth do you want to speak to Father for?

KATRIN. I've got something to say to him. Something to ask him. It's important. *Very* important.

MADELINE. Is that the dresser set? (*Picking it up.*) Can I look at it a minute?

KATRIN (*snatching it from her, violently*). No!

MADELINE. Why, what's the matter? I only wanted to look at it.

KATRIN (*emotionally*). You can't. You're not to touch it. Dorothy, you take it and put it where I can't see it. (*She thrusts it at her.*) Go on. . . . Take it! Take it! Take it!!

(*Blackout. Curtains part on the kitchen.* MAMA *and* PAPA *in conclave at the table with cups of coffee.*)

MAMA (*above table*). I am worried about her, Lars. When it is over, I see her talking with Mr. Schiller—and then she goes to take off her costume and Nels tells me that he will bring her home. But it is long time, and is late for her to be out. And in the play, Lars, she was not good. I have heard her practice it here, and she was good, but tonight, no. It was as if . . . as if she was thinking of something else all the time.

PAPA (R. *of table*). I think maybe she was.

MAMA. But what? What can be worrying her?

PAPA. Marta . . . tonight, after you leave, Katrin found out about your brooch.

MAMA. My brooch? But how? Who told her?

PAPA. Christine.

MAMA (*angry*). Why?

PAPA. I do not know.

MAMA (*rising with a sternness we have not seen before, and calling*). Christine! Christine!

CHRISTINE (*emerging from the pantry, wiping a dish*). Were you calling me, Mama?

MAMA. Yes. Christine, did you tell Katrin tonight about my brooch?

CHRISTINE (*frightened, but firm, R.*). Yes.

MAMA (*level with her, L. of table*). Why did you?

CHRISTINE. Because I hated the smug way she was acting over that dresser set.

MAMA. Is no excuse. You make her unhappy. You make her not good in the play.

CHRISTINE. Well, she made *you* unhappy, giving up your brooch for her selfishness.

MAMA (*moving towards her, above table*). Is not your business. I choose to give my brooch. Is not for you to judge. And you know I do not want you to tell. I am angry with you, Christine.

CHRISTINE. I'm sorry. But I'm not sorry I told. (*She goes back to the pantry with a set, obstinate face.*)

PAPA. Christine is the stubborn one.

(NELS *and* KATRIN *have approached the house outside L. They stop and look at each other in the lamplight.* KATRIN *looks scared. Then* NELS *pats her, and she goes in,* NELS *following.* MAMA *looks up inquiringly and searchingly into* KATRIN'S *face.* KATRIN *turns away, taking off her hat and coat, and taking something from her pocket.*)

NELS. What happened at the meeting, Papa?

PAPA. We go back to work tomorrow.

NELS. Gee, that's bully. Isn't it, Mama?

MAMA (*seated again L. of table, absently*). Yes, is good.

KATRIN (*coming to* MAMA). Mama . . . here's your brooch. (*She gives it to her.*) I'm sorry I was so bad in the play. I'll go and help Christine with the dishes. (*She turns and goes into the pantry.*)

MAMA (*unwrapping the brooch from tissue paper*). Mr. Schiller give it back to her?

NELS (*above table*). We went to his house to get it. He didn't want to. He was planning to give it to his wife for her birthday. But Katrin begged and begged him. She even offered to go and work in his store during her vacation if he'd give it back.

PAPA (*impressed*). So? So?

MAMA. And what did Mr. Schiller say?

NELS. He said that wasn't necessary. But he gave her a job all the same. She's going to work for him, afternoons, for three dollars a week.

MAMA. And the dresser set—she gave that back?

NELS. Yes. She was awful upset, Mama. It was kinda hard for

her to do. She's a good kid. Well, I'll say good night. I've got to be up early.

PAPA. Good night, Nels.

NELS. Good night, Papa. (*He goes out back* L.)

MAMA. Good night, Nels.

PAPA. Nels is the kind one. (*He starts to refill* MAMA'S *coffee cup. She stops him, putting her hand over her cup.*) No?

MAMA (*rising, crossing* R. *and calling*). Katrin! Katrin!

KATRIN (*coming to the pantry door*). Yes, Mama?

MAMA (*sitting* R. *of table*). Come here. (KATRIN *comes to her.* MAMA *holds out the brooch.*) You put this on.

KATRIN. No . . . it's yours.

MAMA. It is your graduation present. I put it on for you. (*She pins the brooch on* KATRIN'S *dress.*)

KATRIN (*near tears*). I'll wear it always. I'll keep it forever.

MAMA. Christine should not have told you.

KATRIN (*moving away down* R.). I'm glad she did. Now.

PAPA. And I am glad, too. (*He dips a lump of sugar and holds it out to her.*) Katrin?

KATRIN (*tearful again, shakes her head*). I'm sorry, Papa. I . . . I don't feel like it. (*She crosses below the table and sits on the chest under the window, with her back to the room.*)

PAPA. So? So? (*He goes to the dresser.*)

MAMA. What you want, Lars? (*He does not answer, but takes a cup and saucer, comes to the table and pours a cup of coffee, indicating* KATRIN *with his head.* MAMA *nods, pleased, then checks his pouring and fills up the cup from the cream pitcher, which she empties in so doing.* PAPA *puts in sugar, and moves to* KATRIN.)

PAPA. Katrin. (*She turns. He holds out the cup.*)

KATRIN (*incredulous*). For me?

PAPA. For our grown-up daughter. (MAMA *nods, standing arm in arm with* PAPA. KATRIN *takes the cup, lifts it—then her emotion overcomes her. She thrusts it at* PAPA *and rushes from the room.*) Katrin is the dramatic one! Is too bad. Her first cup of coffee, and she does not drink it.

MAMA. It would not have been good for her, so late at night.

PAPA (*smiling*). And you, Marta, you are the practical one.

MAMA. You drink the coffee, Lars. We do not want to waste it. (*She pushes it across to him.*)

(*Lights dim. Curtains close. Light up on* L. *turntable, representing the parlor of* JENNY'S *house. A telephone on a table, at which* TRINA *is discovered, talking.*)

TRINA (*into phone*). Yes, Peter. Yes, Peter. I know, Peter, but we don't know where he is. It's so long since we heard from him. He's sure to turn up soon. Yes, I know, Peter. I know, but . . . (*Subsiding obediently.*) Yes, Peter. Yes, Peter. (*Sentimentally.*) Oh, Peter, you know I do. Goodbye, Peter. (*She hangs up, and turns, to see* JENNY, *who has come in behind her, eating a piece of toast and jam.*)

JENNY. What was all that about?

TRINA. Peter says we shouldn't wait any longer to hear from Uncle Chris. He says we should send the wedding invitations out right away. He was quite insistent about it. Peter can be very masterful sometimes . . . when he's alone with *me!*

(*The telephone rings again.* JENNY *answers it, putting down the toast, which* TRINA *takes up and nibbles at during the scene.*)

JENNY. This is Mrs. Stenborg's boarding house. Mrs. Stenborg speaking. Oh, yes, Marta . . . what is it? (*She listens.*)

(*Spot up on* R. *turntable, disclosing* MAMA *standing at a wall telephone booth. She wears hat and coat, and has an opened telegram in her hand.*)

MAMA. Jenny, is Uncle Chris. I have a telegram. It says if we want to see him again we should come without delay.

JENNY. Where is he?

MAMA (*consulting the telegram*). It comes from a place called Ukiah. Nels says it is up north from San Francisco.

JENNY. Who is the telegram from?

MAMA. It does not say.

JENNY. That . . . woman?

MAMA. I don't know, Jenny. I think maybe.

JENNY. I won't go. (SIGRID *comes in through the curtains* C., *dressed in hat and coat, carrying string marketing bags, full of vegetables.* JENNY *speaks to her, whisperingly, aside.*) It's Uncle Chris. Marta says he's dying. (*Then, back into phone.*) Why was the telegram sent to *you?* I'm the eldest.

MAMA. Jenny, is not the time to think of who is eldest. Uncle Chris is dying.

JENNY. *I* don't believe it. He's too mean to die. Ever. (NELS *comes to booth from wings* R., *and hands* MAMA *a slip of paper.*) I'm not going.

MAMA. Jenny, I cannot stop to argue. There is a train at eleven
o'clock. It takes four hours. You call Sigrid.

JENNY. Sigrid is here now.

MAMA. Good. Then you tell her.

JENNY. What do you say the name of the place is?

MAMA. Ukiah. (Spelling in Norwegian.) U-K-I-A-H.

JENNY. I won't go.

MAMA. That *you* decide. (She hangs up. Her spot goes out.)

SIGRID. Uncle Chris dying!

JENNY. The wages of sin.

TRINA. Oh, he's old. Maybe it is time for him to go.

JENNY. Four hours by train, and maybe have to stay all night.
All that expense to watch a wicked old man die.

SIGRID. I know, but . . . there is his will. . . .

JENNY. Huh, even supposing he's anything to leave—you know
who he'd leave it *to*, don't you?

SIGRID. Yes. But all the same he's dying now, and blood is
thicker than water. Especially when it's Norwegian. I'm
going. I shall take Arne with me. Uncle Chris was always
fond of children.

TRINA. I agree with Sigrid. I think we *should* go.

JENNY. Well, *you* can't go, anyway.

TRINA. Why not?

JENNY. Because of that woman. You can't meet that woman.

TRINA. Why not? If you two can . . .

SIGRID. We're married women.

TRINA. I'm engaged!

JENNY. That's not the same thing.

SIGRID. Not the same thing at all!

TRINA. Nonsense. I've never met a woman like that. Maybe I'll
never get another chance. Besides, if he's going to change
his will, there's still my dowry, remember. Do you think we
should take Peter?

JENNY. Peter Thorkelson? Whatever for?

TRINA. Well, after all, I mean . . . I mean, his profession . . .

JENNY. Trina, you always were a fool. Anyone would know the
last person a dying man wants to see is an undertaker!

(Blackout. Turntable revolves out. Spot up on KATRIN, standing down
from R. C. She wears her schoolgirl hat.)

KATRIN. When Mama said I was to go with her, I was excited
and I was frightened. It was exciting to take sandwiches for
the train, almost as though we were going on a picnic. But I

was scared at the idea of seeing death, though I told myself that if I was going to be a writer, I had to experience everything. But all the same, I hoped it would be all over when we got there. *(She starts to walk toward* C. *and up the steps.)* It was afternoon when we arrived. We asked at the station for the Halvorsen ranch, and it seemed to me that the man looked at us strangely. Uncle Chris was obviously considered an odd character. The ranch was about three miles from the town; a derelict, rambling old place. There was long grass, and tall trees, and a smell of honeysuckle. We made quite a cavalcade, walking up from the gate. *(The procession comes from the* R., *behind* KATRIN. MAMA, JENNY, TRINA, SIGRID, *and* ARNE.) The woman came out on the steps to meet us.

(The procession starts towards the C., *moving upwards. The* WOMAN *comes through the curtains, down one step. The* AUNTS *freeze in their tracks.* MAMA *goes forward to her.)*

MAMA. How is he? Is he——?
WOMAN *(with grave self-possession).* Come in, won't you? *(She holds the curtains slightly aside.* MAMA *goes in.* KATRIN *follows, looking curiously at the* WOMAN. *The* AUNTS *walk stiffly past her,* SIGRID *clutching* ARNE. *They disappear behind the curtains. The* WOMAN *stands a moment, looking off into the distance. Then she goes in behind the curtains, too.)*

(The curtains draw apart, revealing UNCLE CHRIS'S *bedroom. It is simple, and shabby. The door to the room is at the back,* L. *In the* L. *wall is a window, with curtains, drawn aside now. In front of it, a washstand. The afternoon sunlight comes through the window, falling onto the big double bed, in which* UNCLE CHRIS *is propped up on pillows. Beside him,* R., *on a small table, is a pitcher of water. He has a glass in his hand.* MAMA *stands to the* R. *of him,* JENNY *to the* L. *The others are ranged below the window. The* WOMAN *is not present.)*

UNCLE CHRIS *(handing* MAMA *the empty glass).* I want more. You give me more.
MAMA. Uncle Chris, that will not help now.
UNCLE CHRIS. It always help. *(With a glance at* JENNY.) Now especially.
JENNY *(firmly).* Uncle Chris, I don't think you realize . . .
UNCLE CHRIS. What I don't realize? That I am dying? Why else do I think you come here? Why else do I think you stand

there, watching me? (*He sits upright.*) Get out. Get out. I don't want you here. Get out!

JENNY. Oh, very well. Very well. We'll be outside on the porch, if you want us. (*She starts towards the door.*)

UNCLE CHRIS. That is where I want you—on the porch! (JENNY *goes out.* TRINA *follows.* SIGRID *is about to go, too, when* UNCLE CHRIS *stops her.*) Wait. That is Arne. Come here, Arne. (ARNE, *propelled by* SIGRID, *advances toward the bed.*) How is your knee?

ARNE. It's fine, Uncle Chris.

UNCLE CHRIS. Not hurt any more?

ARNE. N-no, Uncle Chris.

UNCLE CHRIS. You walk goot? Quite goot? Let me see you walk. Walk around the room. (ARNE *does so.*) Fast. Fast. Run! Run! (ARNE *does so.*) Is goot.

SIGRID (*encouraged and advancing*). Uncle Chris, Arne has always been so fond of you. . . .

UNCLE CHRIS (*shouting*). I tell you all to get out. Except Marta. (*As* KATRIN *edges with the* AUNTS *to the door.*) And Katrinë. Katrinë and I haf secret. You remember, Katrinë?

KATRIN. Yes, Uncle Chris.

MAMA. Uncle Chris, you must lie down again.

UNCLE CHRIS. Then you give me drink.

MAMA. No, Uncle Chris.

UNCLE CHRIS. We cannot waste what is left. You do not drink it . . . who will drink it when I am gone? What harm can it do . . . now? I die, anyway. . . . You give it to me. (MAMA *goes to the washstand, pours him a drink and takes it to him, sitting on the bed beside him to the* L. *of him. He drinks, then turns to her, leaning back against her arm and the pillows.*) Marta, I haf never made a will. Was never enough money. But you sell this ranch. It will not bring moch. I have not had it long enough. And there is mortgage. Big mortgage. But it leave a little. Maybe two, tree hundred dollars. You give to Yessie.

MAMA. Yessie?

UNCLE CHRIS. Yessie Brown. My housekeeper. She was trained nurse, but she get sick, and I bring her to the country to get well again. There will be no money for *you*, Marta. Always I wanted there should be money to make Nils doctor. But there were other things . . . quick things. And now there is no time to make more. There is no money, but you make Nils doctor, all the same. You like?

MAMA. Sure, Uncle Chris. It is what Lars and I have always

wanted for him. To help people who suffer. . . .

UNCLE CHRIS. Is the greatest thing in the world. It is to have a little of God in you. Always I wanted to be doctor myself. Is the only thing I have ever wanted. Nils must do it for me.

MAMA. He will, Uncle Chris.

UNCLE CHRIS. Is goot. (*He strokes her hand.*) You are the goot one. I am glad you come, *Lille Ven.* (*He moves his head restlessly.*) Where is Yessie?

MAMA. I think she wait outside.

UNCLE CHRIS. You do not mind if she is here?

MAMA. Of course not, Uncle Chris.

UNCLE CHRIS. You call her. I like you both be here. (MAMA *goes, with a quick glance at* KATRIN, *who has been standing, forgotten, down* L. *listening intently.* UNCLE CHRIS *signs to* KATRIN *to come closer. She sits on the chair beside the bed.*) Katrinë, your Mama write me you drink coffee now? (*She nods. He looks at her affectionately.*) Katrinë, who will be writer. . . . You are not frightened of me now?

KATRIN. No, Uncle Chris.

UNCLE CHRIS. One day maybe you write story about Uncle Chris. If you remember.

KATRIN (*whispering*). I'll remember.

(MAMA *returns with the* WOMAN. *They come to his bed, standing on either side of it—*MAMA *to the* L.)

UNCLE CHRIS (*obviously exhausted and in pain*). I like you both stay with me . . . now. I think best now maybe Katrinë go away. Goodbye, Katrinë. (*Then he repeats it in Norwegian.*) Farvell, Katrinë.

KATRIN. Goodbye, Uncle Chris.

UNCLE CHRIS. You say it in Norwegian, like I do.

KATRIN (*in Norwegian*). Farvell, Onkel Chris. (*She slips out, in tears.*)

UNCLE CHRIS. Yessie! Maybe I should introduce you to each other. Yessie, this is my niece, Marta. The only von of my nieces I can stand. Marta, this is Yessie, who have give me much happiness. . . .

(*The* TWO WOMEN *shake hands across the bed.*)

MAMA. I am very glad to meet you.

JESSIE. I am, too.

UNCLE CHRIS (*as they shake*). Is goot. And now you give me von more drink. You have drink with me . . . both of you.

(JESSIE *and* MAMA *look at each other.*)

MAMA. Sure, Uncle Chris.

UNCLE CHRIS. Goot. Yessie, you get best glasses. (*With a chuckle to* MAMA.) Yessie does not like to drink, but this is special occasion. (JESSIE *gets three glasses from a wall shelf.*) What is the time?

MAMA. It is about half-past four, Uncle Chris.

UNCLE CHRIS. The sun come around this side the house in afternoon. You draw the curtain a little maybe. Is strong for my eyes. (MAMA *goes over and draws the curtain over the window. The stage darkens.* JESSIE *pours three drinks, filling the glasses with water. She sits on the bed beside him, about to feed his drink to him, but he pushes her aside.*) No. No, I do not need you feed it to me. I can drink myself. (*He takes the glass from her.*) Give Marta her glass. (JESSIE *hands a glass to* MAMA. *The* TWO WOMEN *stand on either side of the bed, holding their glasses.*) So. . . . Skoal!

JESSIE (*clinking glasses with him*). Skoal.

MAMA (*doing likewise*). Skoal.

(*They all three drink. Slow dim to blackout. Curtains close. Spot up on* R. *turntable. A porch with a bench, and a chair, on which the three* AUNTS *are sitting.* JENNY *is dozing in the chair.*)

SIGRID (*flicking her handkerchief*). These gnats are awful. I'm being simply eaten alive.

TRINA. Gnats are always worse around sunset. (*She catches one.*)

JENNY (*rousing herself*). I should never have let you talk me into coming. To be insulted like that . . . turned out of his room . . . and then expected to sit here hour after hour without as much as a cup of coffee. . . .

SIGRID. I'd make coffee if I knew where the kitchen was.

JENNY (*rising*). No, I'm going home. Are you coming, Trina?

TRINA. Oh, I think we ought to wait a little longer. After all, you can't *hurry* these things. . . . I mean . . . (*She breaks off in confusion at what she has said.*)

JENNY (*to* SIGRID). And all your talk about his will. A lot of chance we got to say a word!

TRINA. Maybe Marta's been talking to him.

(MAMA *comes from between the curtains* C.)

JENNY. Well?

MAMA. Uncle Chris has . . . gone.

(*There is a silence.*)

JENNY (*more gently than is her wont*). Did he . . . say anything
about a will?

MAMA. There is no will.

JENNY. Well, then, that means . . . we're his nearest
relatives. . . .

MAMA. There is no money, either.

SIGRID. How do you know?

MAMA. He told me. (*She brings out a small notebook that she is
carrying.*)

JENNY. What's that?

MAMA. Is an account of how he spent the money. I read it to
you. (JENNY *sits again.*) You know how Uncle Chris was
lame . . . how he walked always with limp. It was his one
thought . . . lame people. He would have liked to be doctor
and help them. Instead, he help them other ways. I read
you the last page. . . . (*She reads from the notebook.*) "Joseph
Spinelli. Four years old. Tubercular left leg. Three hundred
thirty-seven dollars, eighteen cents." (*Pause.*) "Walks now.
Esta Jensen. Nine years. Club-foot. Two hundred seventeen
dollars, fifty cents. Walks now." (*Then, reading very slowly.*)
"Arne Solfeldt. . . ."

SIGRID (*startled*). My Arne?

MAMA (*reading on*). "Nine years. Fractured kneecap. Four
hundred forty-two dollars, sixteen cents."

(KATRIN *and* ARNE *come running in from the* L. *across the stage.*)

ARNE (*calling as he comes running across*). Mother . . . Mother . . .
Are we going to eat soon? (*He stops, awed by the solemnity of
the group, and by* MAMA, *who puts out her hand gently, to
silence him.*) What is it? Is Uncle Chris . . .?

MAMA (*to the* AUNTS). It does not tell the end about Arne. I like
to write "Walks now." Yes?

SIGRID (*very subdued*). Yes.

MAMA (*taking a pencil from the book*). Maybe even . . . "runs"?
(SIGRID *nods, moist-eyed.* TRINA *is crying.* MAMA *writes in the*

book, and then closes it.) So. Is finished. Is all. *(She touches* JENNY *on the shoulder.)* It was good.

JENNY *(after a gulping movement).* I go and make some coffee.

(The woman, JESSIE, *appears from between the curtains on the steps.)*

JESSIE. You can go in and see him now if you want. *(*JENNY *looks back, half-hesitant, at the others. Then she nods and goes in.* TRINA *follows her, mopping her eyes.* SIGRID *puts her arm suddenly around* ARNE *in a spasm of maternal affection, and they, too, go in.* MAMA, KATRIN, *and* JESSIE *are left alone.* KATRIN *stands* L. C., MAMA *and* JESSIE *are in front of the curtains.)* I'm moving down to the hotel for tonight . . . so that you can all stay. *(She is about to go back, when* MAMA *stops her.)*

MAMA. Wait. What will you do now . . . after he is buried? You have money? *(*JESSIE *shakes her head.)* Where you live?

JESSIE. I'll find a room somewhere. I'll probably go back to nursing.

MAMA. You like to come to San Francisco for a little? To our house? We have room. Plenty room.

JESSIE *(touched, moving to* MAMA*).* That's very kind of you, but . . .

MAMA. I like to have you. You come for a little as our guest. When you get work you can be our boarder.

JESSIE *(awkwardly grateful).* I don't know why you should bother. . . .

MAMA *(touching her).* You were good to Uncle Chris. *(*JESSIE *grasps her hand, deeply moved, then turns and goes quickly back through the curtains.* MAMA *turns to* KATRIN.*)* Katrin, you come and see him?

KATRIN *(scared).* See him? You mean . . .

MAMA. I like you see him. You need not be frightened. He looks . . . happy and at peace. I like you to know what death looks like. Then you are not frightened of it, ever.

KATRIN. Will you come with me?

MAMA. Sure. *(She stretches out her hand, puts her arm around her, and then leads her gently in through the curtains.)*

(Spot up on L. *turntable, representing a park bench against a hedge.* TRINA *and* MR. THORKELSON, *in outdoor clothes, are seated together.* TRINA *is cooing over a baby carriage.)*

TRINA. Who's the most beautiful Norwegian baby in San Francisco? Who's going to be three months old tomorrow?

Little Christopher Thorkelson! *(To* MR. THORKELSON.*)* Do you know, Peter, I think he's even beginning to *look* a little like Uncle Chris! Quite apart from his black curls—and those, of course, he gets from *you. (To baby again.)* He's going to grow up to be a black Norwegian, isn't he, just like his daddy and his Uncle Chris? *(Settling down beside* MR. THORKELSON.*)* I think there's something about his mouth . . . a sort of . . . well . . . *firmness.* Of course, it's *your* mouth, too. But then, I've always thought you had quite a lot of Uncle Chris about you. *(She looks back at the baby.)* Look—he's asleep!

MR. THORKELSON. Trina, do you know what next Thursday is?

TRINA *(nodding, smilingly).* Our anniversary.

MR. THORKELSON. What would you think of our giving a little party?

TRINA. A party?

MR. THORKELSON. Oh, quite a modest one. Nothing showy or ostentatious—but, after all, we have been married a year, and with your having been in mourning and the baby coming so soon and everything, we've not been able to entertain. I think it's time you . . . took your place in society.

TRINA *(scared).* What . . . sort of a party?

MR. THORKELSON. An evening party. *(Proudly.)* A soirée! I should say about ten people . . . some of the Norwegian colony . . . and Lars and Marta, of course. . . .

TRINA *(beginning to count on her fingers).* And Jenny and Sigrid. . . .

MR. THORKELSON. Oh . . . I . . . I hadn't thought of asking Jenny and Sigrid.

TRINA. Oh, we'd have to. We couldn't leave them out.

MR. THORKELSON. Trina, I hope you won't be offended if I say that I have never really felt . . . well, altogether comfortable with Jenny and Sigrid. They have always made me feel that they didn't think I was . . . well . . . *worthy* of you. Of course, I know I'm not, but . . . well . . . one doesn't like to be reminded of it . . . *all* the time.

TRINA *(taking his hand).* Oh, Peter.

MR. THORKELSON. But you're quite right. We must ask them. Now, as to the matter of refreshments . . . what would you suggest?

TRINA *(flustered).* Oh, I don't know. I . . . what would you say to . . . ice cream and cookies for the ladies . . . and coffee, of course . . . and . . . perhaps port wine for the gentlemen?

MR. THORKELSON *(anxiously).* Port wine?

TRINA. Just a little. You could bring it in already poured out, in *little* glasses. Jenny and Sigrid can help me serve the ice cream.

MR. THORKELSON (*firmly*). No. If Jenny and Sigrid come, they come as guests, like everybody else. You shall have someone in to help you in the kitchen.

TRINA. You mean a waitress? (MR. THORKELSON *nods, beaming.*) Oh, but none of us have *ever* . . . do you really think . . . I mean . . . you did say we shouldn't be ostentatious. . . .

MR. THORKELSON (*nervously, rising and starting to pace up and down*). Trina, there's something I would like to say. I've never been very good at expressing myself or my . . . well . . . *deeper* feelings—but I want you to know that I'm not only very fond of you, but very . . . well . . . very *proud* of you as well, and I want you to have the best of everything, as far as it's in my power to give it to you. (*He sits again— then, as a climax.*) I want you to have a waitress!

TRINA (*overcome*). Yes, Peter. (*They hold hands.*)

(*The lights fade and the turntable revolves out. Curtains part on kitchen, slightly changed, smartened and refurnished now.* MAMA *and* PAPA *seated as usual.* MAMA *is darning.* DAGMAR, *looking a little older, is seated on the chest, reading a solid-looking book.* NELS *enters from back* L. *door, carrying a newspaper. He wears long trousers now, and looks about seventeen.*)

NELS (*hitting* PAPA *playfully on the head with the paper*). Hello! Here's your evening paper, Papa.

(PAPA *puts down the morning paper he is reading, and takes the evening one from* NELS.)

PAPA (R. *of table*). Is there any news?

NELS. No. (*He takes out a package of cigarettes with elaborate unconcern.* MAMA *watches with disapproval. Then, as he is about to light his cigarette, he stops, remembering something.*) Oh, I forgot. There's a letter for Katrin. I picked it up on the mat as I came in. (*Going to door back* L., *and calling.*) Katrin! Katrin! There's a letter for you.

KATRIN (*answering from off stage*). Coming!

MAMA (L. *of table*). Nels, you know who the letter is from?

NELS. Why, no, Mama. (*Hands it to her.*) It looks like her own handwriting.

MAMA (*gravely inspecting it*). Is bad.

PAPA. Why is bad?

MAMA. She gets too many like that. I think they are stories she send to the magazines.

DAGMAR (closing her book loudly, rising). Well, I'll go and see if I have any puppies yet. (Crosses below the table and then turns.) Mama, I've just decided something.

MAMA. What have you decided?

DAGMAR. If Nels is going to be a doctor, when I grow up, I'm going to be a—(Looking at the book-title, and stumbling over the word.) —vet-vet-veterinarian.

MAMA. And what is that?

DAGMAR. A doctor for animals.

MAMA. Is good. Is good.

DAGMAR. There are far more animals in the world than there are human beings, and far more human doctors than animal ones. It isn't fair. (She goes to the pantry door.) I suppose we couldn't have a horse, could we? (This only produces a concerted laugh from the family. She turns, sadly.) No. . . . I was afraid we couldn't. (She goes into the pantry.)

(KATRIN comes in, back L. She wears a slightly more adult dress than before. Her hair is up, and she looks about eighteen.)

KATRIN. Where's the letter?

MAMA (handing it to her). Here.

(KATRIN takes it, nervously. She looks at the envelope, and her face falls. She opens it, pulls out a manuscript and a rejection slip, looks at it a moment, and then replaces both in the envelope. The others watch her covertly. Then she looks up, with determination.)

KATRIN (above table). Mama . . . Papa . . . I want to say something.

PAPA. What is it?

KATRIN. I'm not going to go to college.

PAPA. Why not?

KATRIN. Because it would be a waste of time and money. The only point in my going to college was to be a writer. Well, I'm not going to be one, so . . .

MAMA. Katrin, is it your letter that makes you say this? It is a story come back again?

KATRIN. Again is right. This is the tenth time. I made this one a test. It's the best I've ever written, or ever shall write. I know that. Well, it's no good.

NELS (R. *of her*). What kind of a story is it?

KATRIN. Oh . . . it's a story about a painter, who's a genius, and he goes blind.

NELS. Sounds like *The Light That Failed.*

KATRIN. Well, what's wrong with that?

NELS (*quickly*). Nothing. Nothing!

KATRIN (*moving down* L.). Besides, it's not like that. My painter gets better. He has an operation and recovers his sight, and paints better than ever before.

MAMA. Is good.

KATRIN (*bitterly unhappy*). No, it isn't. It's rotten. But it's the best I can do.

MAMA. You have asked your teachers about this?

KATRIN. Teachers don't know anything about writing. They just know about literature. (*She crosses* R.)

MAMA. If there was someone we could ask . . . for advice . . . to tell us . . . tell us if your stories are good.

KATRIN. Yes. Well, there isn't. And they're *not.*

PAPA (*looking at the evening paper*). There is something here in the paper about a lady writer. I just noticed the headline. Wait. (*He looks back for it and reads.*) "Woman writer tells key to literary success."

KATRIN. Who?

PAPA. A lady called Florence Dana Moorhead. It gives her picture. A fat lady. You have heard of her?

KATRIN. Yes, of course. Everyone has. She's terribly successful. She's here on a lecture tour.

MAMA. What does she say is the secret?

PAPA. You read it, Katrin. (*He hands her the paper.*)

KATRIN (*grabbing the first part*). "Florence Dana Moorhead, celebrated novelist and short story writer . . . blah-blah-blah . . . interviewed today in her suite at the Fairmont . . . blah-blah-blah . . . pronounced sincerity the one essential quality for success as a writer." (*Throwing aside the paper.*) A lot of help that is.

MAMA. Katrin, this lady . . . maybe if you sent her your stories, *she* could tell you what is wrong with them?

KATRIN (*wearily*). Oh, Mama, don't be silly.

MAMA. Why is silly?

KATRIN (*above table*). Well, in the first place because she's a very important person . . . a celebrity . . . and she'd never read them. And in the second, because . . . you seem to think writing's like . . . well, like cooking, or something. That all

272

you have to have is the recipe. It takes a lot more than that. You have to have a gift for it.

MAMA. You have to have a gift for cooking, too. But there are things you can learn, if you have the gift.

KATRIN. Well, that's the whole point. I haven't. I *know* . . . now. So, if you've finished with the morning paper Papa, I'll take the want ad section, and see if I can find myself a job. (*She takes the morning paper and goes out back* L.)

MAMA. Is bad. Nels, what you think?

NELS. I don't know, Mama. Her stories seem all right to me, but I don't know.

MAMA. It would be good to know. Nels, this lady in the paper . . . what else does she say?

NELS (*taking up the paper*). Not much. The rest seems to be about *her* and her home. Let's see. . . . (*He reads—walking down* L.) "Apart from literature, Mrs. Moorhead's main interest in life is gastronomy."

MAMA. The stars?

NELS. No—eating. "A brilliant cook herself, she says that she would as soon turn out a good soufflé as a short story, or find a new recipe as she would a first edition."

MAMA (*reaching for the paper*). I see her picture? (*She looks at it.*) Is kind face. (*Pause while she reads a moment. Then she looks up and asks.*) What is first edition?

(*Blackout. Lights up on* L. *turntable, representing the lobby of the Fairmont Hotel. A couch against a column with a palm behind it. An orchestra plays softly in the background.* MAMA *is discovered seated on the couch, waiting patiently. She wears a hat and suit, and clutches a newspaper and a bundle of manuscripts. A couple of guests come through the curtains and cross, disappearing into the wings* L. MAMA *watches them. Then* FLORENCE DANA MOORHEAD *enters through the curtains. She is a stout, dressy, good-natured, middle-aged woman. A* BELLBOY *comes from the* R., *paging her.*)

BELLBOY. Miss Moorhead?

F. D. MOORHEAD. Yes?

BELLBOY. Telegram.

F. D. MOORHEAD. Oh . . . Thank you. (*She tips him, and he goes.* MAMA *rises and moves towards her.*)

MAMA. Please . . . Please . . . Miss Moorhead . . . Miss Moorhead.

F. D. MOORHEAD (*looking up from her telegram, on the steps*). Were you calling me?

MAMA. Yes. You are . . . Miss Florence Dana Moorhead?

F. D. MOORHEAD. Yes.

MAMA. Please . . . might I speak to you for a moment?

F. D. MOORHEAD. Yes—what's it about?

MAMA. I read in the paper what you say about writing.

F. D. MOORHEAD (*with a vague social smile*). Oh, yes?

MAMA. My daughter, Katrin, wants to be writer.

F. D. MOORHEAD (*who has heard that one before*). Oh, really? (*She glances at her watch on her bosom.*)

MAMA. I bring her stories.

F. D. MOORHEAD. Look, I'm afraid I'm in rather a hurry. I'm leaving San Francisco this evening. . . .

MAMA. I wait two hours here for you to come in. Please, if I may talk to you for one, two minutes. That is all.

F. D. MOORHEAD (*kindly*). Of course, but I think I'd better tell you that if you want me to read your daughter's stories, it's no use. I'm very sorry, but I've had to make it a rule never to read anyone's unpublished material.

MAMA (*nods—then after a pause*). It said in the paper you like to collect recipes . . . for eating.

F. D. MOORHEAD. Yes, I do. I've written several books on cooking.

MAMA. I, too, am interested in gastronomy. I am good cook. Norwegian. I make good Norwegian dishes. Lutefisk. And Kjodboller. That is meat-balls with cream sauce.

F. D. MOORHEAD. Yes, I know. I've eaten them in Christiania.

MAMA. I have a special recipe for Kjodboller . . . my mother give me. She was best cook I ever knew. Never have I told this recipe, not even to my own sisters, because they are not good cooks.

F. D. MOORHEAD (*amused*). Oh?

MAMA. But . . . if you let me talk to you . . . I give it to you. I promise it is good recipe.

F. D. MOORHEAD (*vastly tickled now*). Well, that seems fair enough. Let's sit down. (*They move to the couch and sit.*) Now, your daughter wants to write, you say? How old is she?

MAMA. She is eighteen. Just.

F. D. MOORHEAD. *Does* she write, or does she just . . . *want* to write?

MAMA. Oh, she write all the time. Maybe she should not be author, but it is hard to give up something that has meant so much.

F. D. MOORHEAD. I agree, but . . .

MAMA. I bring her stories. I bring twelve.

F. D. MOORHEAD *(aghast)*. Twelve!

MAMA. But if you could read maybe just one . . . To know if someone is good cook, you do not need to eat a whole dinner.

F. D. MOORHEAD. You're very persuasive. How is it your daughter did not come herself?

MAMA. She was too unhappy. And too scared . . . of you. Because you are celebrity. But I see your picture in the paper . . .

F. D. MOORHEAD. That frightful picture!

MAMA. Is the picture of woman who like to eat good. . . .

F. D. MOORHEAD *(with a rueful smile)*. It certainly is. Now, tell me about the Kjodboller.

MAMA. When you make the meat-balls you drop them in boiling stock. Not water. That is one of the secrets.

F. D. MOORHEAD. Ah!

MAMA. And the cream sauce. That is another secret. It is half *sour* cream, added at the last.

F. D. MOORHEAD. That sounds marvelous.

MAMA. You must grind the meat six times. I could write it out for you. And . . . (*tentatively.*) while I write, you could read?

F. D. MOORHEAD (*with a laugh*). All right. You win. Come upstairs to my apartment. (*She rises.*)

MAMA. Is kind of you. (*They start out* L.) Maybe if you would read *two* stories, I could write the recipe for Lutefisk as well. You know Lutefisk . . .?

(*They have disappeared into the wings, and the turntable revolves out. Spot up,* R. *turntable.* KATRIN *at her desk.*)

KATRIN. When Mama came back, I was sitting with my diary, which I called my Journal now, writing a Tragic Farewell to my Art. It was very seldom that Mama came to the attic, thinking that a writer needed privacy, and I was surprised to see her standing in the doorway. (*She looks up.* MAMA *is standing on the steps,* C.) Mama!

MAMA. You are busy, Katrin?

KATRIN (*jumping up*). No, of course not. Come in.

MAMA (*coming down*). I like to talk to you.

KATRIN. Yes, of course.

MAMA (*seating herself at the desk*). You are writing?

KATRIN (*on the steps*). No. I told you, that's all over.

MAMA. That is what I want to talk to you about.

KATRIN. It's all right, Mama. Really, it's all right. I was planning to tear up all my stories this afternoon, only I couldn't find half of them.

MAMA. They are here.

KATRIN. Did *you* take them? What for?

MAMA. Katrin, I have been to see Miss Moorhead.

KATRIN. Who's Miss . . . ? You don't mean Florence Dana Moorhead? (MAMA *nods.*) You don't mean . . . (*She comes down to her.*) Mama, you don't mean you took her my stories?

MAMA. She read five of them. I was two hours with her. We have glass of sherry. Two glass of sherry.

KATRIN. What . . . what did she say about them?

MAMA (*quietly*). She say they are not good.

KATRIN (*turning away*). Well, I knew that. It was hardly worth your going to all that trouble just to be told that.

MAMA. She say more. Will you listen, Katrin?

KATRIN (*trying to be gracious*). Sure. Sure. I'll listen.

MAMA. I will try and remember. She say you write now only because of what you have read in other books, and that no one can write good until they have felt what they write about. That for years she write bad stories about people in the olden times, until one day she remember something that happen in her own town . . . something that only she could know and understand . . . and she feels she must tell it . . . and that is how she write her first good story. She say you must write more of things you know. . . .

KATRIN. That's what my teacher always told me at school.

MAMA. Maybe your teacher was right. I do not know if I explain good what Miss Moorhead means, but while she talks I think I understand. Your story about the painter who is blind . . . that is because . . . forgive me if I speak plain, my Katrin, but it is important to you . . . because you are the dramatic one, as Papa has said . . . and you think it would feel good to be a painter and be blind and not complain. But never have you imagined how it would really be. Is true?

KATRIN (*subdued*). Yes, I . . . guess it's true.

MAMA. But she say you are to go on writing. That you have the gift. (KATRIN *turns back to her, suddenly aglow.*) And that when you have written story that is real and true . . . then you send it to someone whose name she give me. (*She fumbles for a piece of paper.*) It is her . . . agent . . . and say she recommend you. Here. No, that is recipe she give me for goulash as her grandmother make it . . . here . . . (*She hands over the paper.*) It helps, Katrin, what I have told you?

KATRIN (*subdued again*). Yes, I . . . I guess it helps. Some. But what have *I* got to write about? I haven't seen anything, or been anywhere.

MAMA. Could you write about San Francisco, maybe? Is fine city. Miss Moorhead write about her home town.

KATRIN. Yes, I know. But you've got to have a central character or something. She writes about her grandfather . . . he was a wonderful old man.

MAMA. Could you maybe write about Papa?

KATRIN. Papa?

MAMA. Papa is fine man. Is wonderful man.

KATRIN. Yes, I know, but . . .

MAMA (*rising*). I must go fix supper. Is late. Papa will be home. (*She goes up the steps to the curtains, and then turns back.*) I like you should write about Papa. (*She goes inside.*)

KATRIN (*going back to her seat behind the desk*). Papa. Yes, but
what's he ever done? What's ever happened to him? What's
ever happened to *any* of us? Except always being poor and
having illness, like the time when Dagmar went to hospital
and Mama . . . (*The idea hits her like a flash.*) Oh. . . . Oh. . . .
(*Pause—then she becomes the* KATRIN *of today.*) And that was
how it was born . . . suddenly in a flash . . . the story of
"Mama and the Hospital" . . . the first of all the stories. I
wrote it . . . oh, quite soon after that. I didn't tell Mama or
any of them. But I sent it to Miss Moorhead's agent. It was
a long time before I heard anything . . . and then one
evening the letter came. (*She takes an envelope from the desk in
front of her.*) For a moment I couldn't believe it. Then I went
rushing into the kitchen, shouting. . . . (*She rises from the
desk, taking some papers with her, and rushes upstage, crying,
"Mama, Mama." The curtains have parted on the kitchen—and
the family tableau—*MAMA, PAPA, CHRISTINE, *and* NELS.
DAGMAR *is not present.* KATRIN *comes rushing in, up the steps.
The* R. *turntable revolves out as soon as she has left it.*) Mama
. . . Mama . . . I've sold a story!

MAMA (R. *of table*). A story?

KATRIN. Yes, I've got a letter from the agent . . . with a check
for . . . (*Gasping.*) five hundred dollars!

NELS (*on the chest*). No kidding? (*He rises.*)

MAMA. Katrin . . . is true?

KATRIN. Here it is. Here's the letter. Maybe I haven't read it
right. (*She hands the letter.* PAPA *and* MAMA *huddle and gloat
over it.*)

CHRISTINE (*behind* MAMA'S *chair*). What will you *do* with five
hundred dollars?

KATRIN. I don't know. I'll buy Mama her warm coat. I know
that.

CHRISTINE. Coats don't cost five hundred dollars.

KATRIN. I know. We'll put the rest in the Bank.

NELS (*kidding,* C.). Quick. Before they change their mind, and
stop the check.

KATRIN. Will you, Mama? Will you take it to the Bank
downtown tomorrow. (MAMA *looks vague.*) What is it?

MAMA. I do not know how.

NELS. Just give it to the man and tell him to put it in your
account, like you always do.

(MAMA *looks up at* PAPA.)

PAPA. You tell them . . . now.

CHRISTINE. Tell us what?

MAMA (*desperately*). Is no bank account! (*She rises, feeling hemmed in by them—sits on bench.*) Never in my life have I been inside a bank.

CHRISTINE. But you always told us . . .

KATRIN. Mama, you've always said . . .

MAMA. I know. But was not true. I tell a lie.

KATRIN. But why, Mama? Why did you pretend?

MAMA. Is not good for little ones to be afraid . . . to not feel secure. (*Rising again and moving* L.) But now . . . with five hundred dollar . . . I think I can tell.

KATRIN (*going to her, emotionally*). Mama!

MAMA (*stopping her, quickly*). You read us the story. You have it there?

KATRIN. Yes.

MAMA. Then read.

KATRIN. Now?

MAMA. Yes. No——Wait. Dagmar must hear. (*She opens pantry door and calls.*) Dagmar.

DAGMAR (*off*). Yes, Mama?

MAMA (*calling*). Come here, I want you.

DAGMAR (*off*). What is it?

MAMA. I want you. No, you leave the rabbits! (*She comes back.*) What is it called . . . the story?

KATRIN (*seating herself in the chair that* MR. HYDE *took in the opening scene*). It's called "Mama and the Hospital."

PAPA (*delighted*). You write about Mama?

KATRIN. Yes.

MAMA. But I thought . . . I thought you say . . . I tell you . . . (*She gestures at* PAPA, *behind his back.*)

KATRIN. I know, Mama, but . . . well, that's how it came out.

(DAGMAR *comes in.*)

DAGMAR. What is it? What do you want?

MAMA. Katrin write story for magazine. They pay her five hundred dollar to print it.

DAGMAR (*completely uninterested*). Oh. (*She starts back for the pantry.*)

MAMA (*stopping her*). She read it to us. I want you should listen. (DAGMAR *sits on the floor at* MAMA'S *feet.*) You are ready, Katrin?

KATRIN. Sure.

MAMA. Then read.

(The group around the table is now a duplicate of the grouping around MR. HYDE *in the first scene, with* KATRIN *in his place.* CHRISTINE *is in* TRINA'S *chair.)*

KATRIN *(reading).* "For as long as I could remember, the house on Steiner Street had been home. All of us were born there. Nels, the oldest and the only boy . . ." (NELS *looks up, astonished to be in a story.)* "my sister, Christine . . ." *(*CHRISTINE *does likewise.)* "and the littlest sister, Dagmar. . . ."

DAGMAR. Am I in the story?

MAMA. Hush, Dagmar. We are all in the story.

KATRIN. "But first and foremost, I remember Mama." *(The lights begin to dim and the curtain slowly to fall. As it descends, we hear her voice continuing.)* "I remember that every Saturday night Mama would sit down by the kitchen table and count out the money Papa had brought home in the little envelope. . . ."

(By now, the curtain is down.)